national
STATISTICS

Agriculture in the United Kingdom 2006

Produced by:

Department for Environment, Food and Rural Affairs

Scottish Executive Environment and Rural Affairs Department

Department of Agriculture and Rural Development (Northern Ireland)

Welsh Assembly Government, The Department for Environment, Planning and Countryside

LONDON: TSO

TSO

Published by TSO (The Stationery Office) and available from:

Online
www.tsoshop.co.uk

Mail, Telephone, Fax & E-mail
TSO
PO Box 29, Norwich, NR3 1GN
Telephone orders/General enquiries: 0870 600 5522
Fax orders: 0870 600 5533
E-mail: customer.services@tso.co.uk
Textphone: 0870 240 3701

TSO Shops
123 Kingsway, London, WC2B 6PQ
020 7242 6393 Fax 020 7242 6394
16 Arthur Street, Belfast BT1 4GD
028 9023 8451 Fax 028 9023 5401
71 Lothian Road, Edinburgh EH3 9AZ
0870 606 5566 Fax 0870 606 5588

TSO@Blackwell and other Accredited Agents

First published 2007

ISBN 978-0-11243095-7

The paper on which this publication is printed uses pulp from managed forests only and is Total Chlorine Free (TCF)

Printed in the United Kingdom for The Stationery Office
N 5533610   C7   03/07   362782   19585

Contents

2006

Preface v

Legal basis; Changes; Structure of Tables; Source of data; Websites; 'Agriculture in the United Kingdom' Seminar 2007.

Chapter 1   Key Events in 2006   1

Total Income from Farming; Single Payment Scheme; Over Thirty Month Scheme/Older Cattle Disposal Scheme; Beef Exports; Sugar Reform; Rural Development Programmes 2007-2013; WTO negotiations; Secretary of State; 'One Planet Farming'.

Chapter 2   Farming Income   3

Summary; Long-term trends in farming income; Prospects for farming incomes; Summary measures; Summary measures by country; Comparison of income measures in EU Member States; Comparison of agriculture in EU Member States; Net farm incomes by farm type; Diversification.

Chapter 3   The Structure of the Industry   13

Summary; Introduction; Land use, crop areas and livestock numbers; Numbers and sizes of holdings and enterprises; Labour force in agriculture; Age of holders; Agricultural training; Fixed capital stock.

Chapter 4   Prices   27

Summary; Introduction; Price indices; Farm rents; Agricultural land prices.

Chapter 5   Commodities   31

Summary; Methodology note; Total cereals; Wheat; Barley; Oats; Oilseed rape; Linseed; Sugar beet and sugar; Peas and beans for stockfeed; Methodology note for fresh vegetables; Fresh vegetables; Plants and flowers; Potatoes; Fresh fruit; Methodology note for livestock tables; Cattle and calves: beef and veal; Pigs and pigmeat; Sheep and lambs: mutton and lamb; Poultry and poultrymeat; Milk; Milk products; Hen eggs.

Chapter 6   Intermediate Consumption   53

Summary; Introduction; Oil prices; Fuels; Electricity; Fertiliser; Pesticides; Veterinary expenses; Agricultural services; Animal feed; Seeds; Maintenance: materials; Maintenance: buildings.

Chapter 7   The Food Chain   59

Summary; Contribution of the agri-food sector to the national economy; The food chain; Food chain employees and self–employed farmers; Trade in food, feed and drink; Self-sufficiency; Consumers' expenditure on food, drink and catering; Farmers' share of consumers' expenditure; Changes in retail price indices.

Chapter 8   Overseas Trade   67

Summary; Introduction; Trade in food, feed and drink; Trading partners; Exports and imports; Trade in key commodities; Trade with EU 24 countries: Bacon and ham, Pork, Lamb and mutton, Beef and veal, Milk and cream, Unmilled wheat.

Chapter 9   Accounts   75

Summary; Introduction; Total Income from Farming; Production and income account at current prices; Balance sheets; Capital account; Revaluation account; Interest; Changes in volume of capital assets.

Chapter 10   Productivity   89

Summary; Introduction; Productivity; Productivity at the farm level; International comparison of productivity; Volume indices; Labour.

Chapter 11   Payments and Public Expenditure   95

Summary; Introduction; Payments and levies linked to agricultural production; Payments not linked to agricultural production; Public expenditure on agriculture.

Chapter 12   Rural Development Programme   99

Summary; Introduction; Rural Development Programme 2000-2006; Rural Development Programme 2007-2013; Payments made through key measures; Take-up of agri-environment schemes.

Chapter 13   Organic Farming   103

Summary; Introduction; Organic and in-conversion land; Regional analysis; Livestock statistics; Annex.

Chapter 14   Animal Health and Welfare   109

Summary; Introduction; Animal Health; Animal Welfare; On farm welfare.

Chapter 15   Environment   115

Summary; Introduction; Environmental impacts; Landscape; Habitats and species; Recreation; Water; Air; Soil; Other resources; Waste; Agricultural Change and Environment Observatory; Valuing environmental impacts of agriculture.

Chapter 16   Key Statistics for EU Member States   129

Summary; Introduction; Incomes: Indicator A of the income from agricultural activity; Agricultural products: Wheat, Cows' milk, Pigmeat, Beef and veal, Sheep and goat meat; Price indices: Crop products, Animal and animal products, Total means of agricultural production.

Preface

Legal basis

1 Agriculture in the United Kingdom 2006 fulfils the requirement under the Agriculture Act 1993 that Ministers publish an annual report on such matters relating to price support for agricultural produce as they consider relevant. The Government will draw on this information when considering policy issues, including proposals by the European Commission in respect of the Common Agricultural Policy (CAP) and the provision of agricultural support.

Changes

2 Some of the figures now given for past years may differ from those published in preceding issues. This is because of the use of later information, changes in the scope and nature of the available data and improvements in statistical methods.

Structure of Tables

3 Most of the data are on a calendar year basis. The data for 2006 are provisional because information for 2006 was still incomplete at the time of publication and therefore an element of forecasting was required.

4 The following points apply throughout.

(a) All figures relate to the United Kingdom unless otherwise stated.

(b) In the tables

- means 'nil' or 'negligible' (less than half the last digit shown).

. . means 'not available' or 'not applicable'.

(c) The figures for imports and exports include those from intervention stocks and the figures for exports include re-exports. Imports are based on country of consignment. Exports are based on country of reported final destination. The source of Overseas Trade Statistics is HM Revenue and Customs.

(d) Where statistics are shown for the European Union (EU) as a whole they represent the present Member States in all years regardless of when they became a member.

5 Where figures are presented in real terms the measure of inflation used is the all-items Retail Price Index.

Source of data

6 The source of data used in tables and charts is the Defra website at http://statistics.defra.gov.uk/esg/.

Websites

7 This publication and other Defra statistics can be found at http://statistics.defra.gov.uk/esg/. Further statistics of the Devolved Administrations can be found at:

- Scottish Executive - http://www.scotland.gov.uk/Topics/Statistics/Browse/Agriculture-Fisheries

- Department of Agriculture, Northern Ireland - http://www.dardni.gov.uk/index/dard-statistics/agricultural-statistics.htm

- Welsh Assembly Government - http://new.wales.gov.uk/topics/statistics/wales-figs/agriculture/?lang=en

'Agriculture in the United Kingdom' Seminar 2007

8   The fifth annual 'Agriculture in the United Kingdom' seminar takes place in York on 9 May 2007 and offers stakeholders the opportunity to discuss the prospects for farm incomes and the work of Defra statisticians.

9   The aims of the seminar are to:

- discuss the prospects for farm incomes in the medium term and the impact of CAP reform on individual farm sectors;

- present and discuss work currently being undertaken by Defra statisticians;

- update stakeholders on current priorities and plans for Defra statistics.

10   Further information will be placed on the Defra website at http://statistics.defra.gov.uk/esg/publications /auk/default.asp. Contact details and a reply form are below.

'Agriculture in the United Kingdom' Seminar 2007

Name _____   Organisation _____

Email or postal address   _____

_____

_____

I would like to attend the 'Agriculture in the United Kingdom' seminar on 9 May 2007. Please send me further details.

Return to:

Keith Seabridge, Defra, Room 137, Foss House, Kings Pool, 1-2 Peasholme Green, York YO1 7PX,

by post or

by fax (01904 455065) or

confirm by email (keith.seabridge@defra.gsi.gov.uk) or

by telephone to the Agriculture in the United Kingdom team on 01904 455407.

Chapter **1**   Key Events in 2006

Total Income from Farming

1 Total Income from Farming is estimated to have risen by 10 per cent at current prices to £2.7 billion, which equates to a rise of 6.9 per cent in real terms. Total Income from Farming per full-time person equivalent rose by 13 per cent at current prices, a rise of 9.4 per cent in real terms, to £13,840.

Single Payment Scheme

2 Following difficulties in implementing payments to which farmers in England were entitled under the Single Payment Scheme for 2005, the Secretary of State authorised in April, the making of partial payments to all customers who had not already received a payment. The Secretary of State also authorised the making of interest payments, calculated from 1 July, in respect of late payments.

3 Payments made by the Devolved Administrations to farmers in Scotland, Wales and Northern Ireland were unaffected and paid according to schedule.

Over Thirty Month Scheme/Older Cattle Disposal Scheme

4 The Over Thirty Month Scheme (OTMS) ended in January 2006 and was replaced by a voluntary compensation scheme, the Older Cattle Disposal Scheme. The OTMS was introduced in May 1996 as a market support measure to remove cattle from the market and pay compensation to producers for cattle over thirty months of age that could no longer enter the food chain as a result of the domestic OTM rule. The Older Cattle Disposal Scheme, which is part-funded by the EU, removes cattle born before 1 August 1996 and provides a safe mechanism for ensuring that these animals are disposed of safely and that farmers are adequately compensated. It will run for three years.

Beef Exports

5 The 10 year ban on the export of beef and cattle from the United Kingdom was lifted on 3 May 2006. This followed an unanimous approval at a meeting of the EU Standing Committee for "the Food Chain and Animal Health", of a Commission proposal to allow the United Kingdom to export cattle born on or after 1 August 1996, and beef and beef products derived from cattle slaughtered after 15 June 2005, on the same basis as other Member States.

Sugar Reform

6 In June 2006, the Government announced that additional support arising from reform of the sugar regime of the Common Agricultural Policy, agreed in November 2005, would be incorporated into the Single Payment Scheme by adding to entitlements held by sugar beet producers meeting certain criteria. Details of arrangements for 2007 will be announced in due course.

Rural Development Programme 2007-2013

7 The finalisation of rural development plans for England, Wales, Scotland and Northern Ireland was delayed as the EU regulation which would give legal basis to European Council agreement on modulation was blocked by the European Parliament. Defra and the Devolved Administrations have announced contingency arrangements to enable certain rural development schemes to continue until plans are agreed.

WTO negotiations

8 Following the Sixth WTO Ministerial Conference held in Hong Kong in December 2005, Doha Development Agenda (DDA) negotiations continued and draft modalities texts were circulated in June 2006. These texts formed the basis of discussion at Ministerial meetings with agreement on modalities scheduled for the end of July. However, the DDA negotiations were suspended indefinitely on 24 July 2006, following failure by WTO members to reach agreement.

Secretary of State

9 David Miliband was appointed Secretary of State for Environment, Food and Rural Affairs on 5 May 2006.

'One Planet Farming'

10 Speaking at the Royal Show on 3 July 2006, David Miliband said that farming must leave a lighter footprint on the planet as it restructures for the next decade and beyond, and a 'one planet' philosophy must be at the heart of a new partnership between farming and Government to tackle environmental challenges and deliver prosperity in the United Kingdom. He outlined four guiding principles for the new partnership:

* A long term view over the next 10 or more years in which the Government will provide a clear framework of funding and policy in return for clear commitments to change from the farming industry.

* Investment linked to reform. A sensible financial deal shared by Government and farmers.

* More streamlined regulation which is effective, transparent, proportionate and cost-effective.

* System-wide change, especially in the key areas of the food chain and animal health and welfare. The farming industry should share more of the responsibility and costs of controlling animal disease in exchange for a bigger say in how the risks of disease are controlled.

11 Mr Miliband hoped his speech would be the starting point for a debate about the way forward for a shared agenda to achieve shared goals for farming, creating a profitable, innovative and competitive industry which helps build sustainable rural communities, while at the same time making a positive net contribution to the environment and managing risks, especially of animal disease.

Chapter **2**   Farming Income

2006

Summary

In 2006:

- Total Income from Farming rose by 10 per cent, or 6.9 per cent in real terms, to £2.7 billion;

- Total Income from Farming per full-time person equivalent rose by 13 per cent in current prices, or 9.4 per cent in real terms, to £13,840;

- agriculture's share of national gross value added is expected to be about 0.5 per cent;

- agriculture's share of national employment declined by 0.1 percentage point to 1.7 per cent;

- Eurostat Indicator A (net value added at factor cost per full-time person equivalent) is estimated to have risen by 3.8 per cent for the United Kingdom compared to 2.6 per cent for the European Union as a whole;

- the United Kingdom ranked sixth out of EU Member States in terms of gross value added per full-time person equivalent with an average of 25,700 euros;

- in real terms, average net farm income for all types of farm in the United Kingdom is expected to be around £20,600 in 2006/07, about 20 per cent higher than 2005/06;

- in real terms, farm incomes for cereals and general cropping farm types are expected to have doubled in the 2006/07 while incomes for dairy and specialist poultry farms are expected to have fallen by about 20 per cent.

Long-term trends in farming income (chart 2.1)

1 In 2006, Total Income from Farming in the United Kingdom is estimated to have risen by 6.9 per cent in real terms. It is 41 per cent above the low point in 2000 and 61 per cent below the high point in 1995. The dramatic rise in farming's profitability in the early nineties followed the decline in the euro/sterling exchange rate after the United Kingdom left the Exchange Rate Mechanism. The equally rapid reverse in the second half of the decade was caused by increases in the exchange rate, lower world commodity prices and the impact of BSE.

Prospects for farming incomes (chart 2.2)

2 The future business prospects for farming will reflect the interaction of the key drivers (both long-term and short-term) which have shaped the present position. Chart 2.2 shows some projections of underlying trends; it should be emphasised that these types of projection have very broad margins of uncertainty and also that agriculture is an industry where specific events, such as disease outbreak or poor weather, can shift incomes from the underlying trend in individual years.

3 The latest projections suggest a possible fall of TIFF per person into 2007 and a return to near 2003 levels by 2011 as the impact of high oil prices is projected to ease.

4 A key driver of farming incomes is productivity. The high productivity scenario within this analysis has been chosen to broadly match the growth rate seen for the leading group of Member States of the European Union (France, Denmark, the Netherlands, Spain and Belgium).

Chart 2.1 Long-term trends in farming income in real terms at 2006 prices; United Kingdom

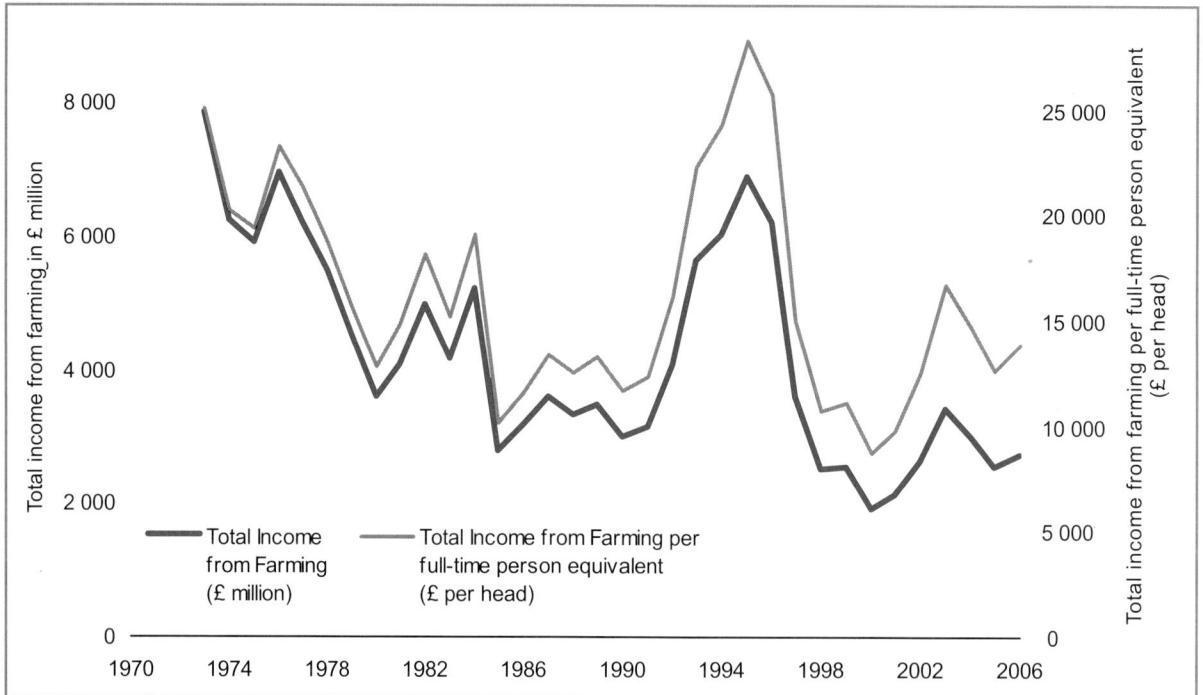

Chart 2.2 Prospects for farming incomes; Total Income from Farming in real terms at 2006 prices per full-time person equivalent up to 2011; United Kingdom

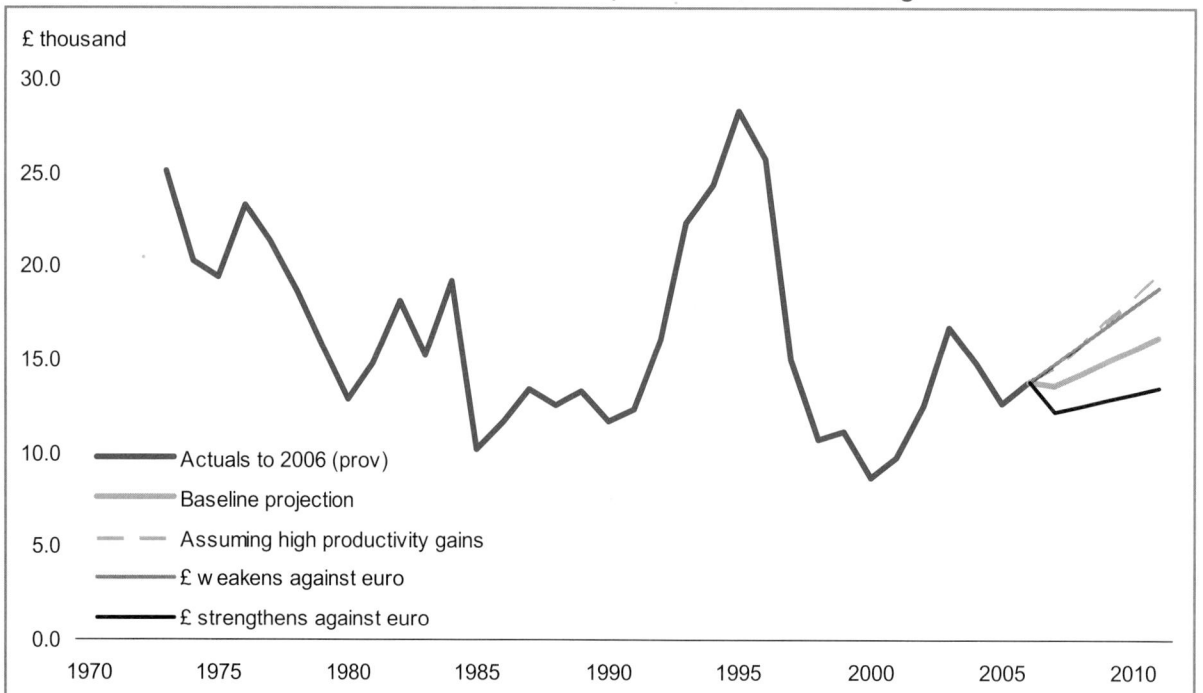

Summary measures including Total Income from Farming (tables 2.1, 2.2)

5 Net value added at factor cost includes all subsidies but makes no allowance for interest, rent or labour costs. In 2006, net value added at factor cost was £5.7 billion, 4.6 per cent higher than in 2005 (1.4 per cent in real terms).

6 Total Income from Farming in the United Kingdom in 2006 is estimated to have risen by 10 per cent at current prices, or by 6.9 per cent in real terms, to £2.7 billion. It is income generated by production within the agriculture industry, including subsidies, and represents business profits plus remuneration for work done by owners and other unpaid workers. It is calculated as: gross output at basic prices (market prices plus subsidies on product); plus other subsidies less taxes on production; less total intermediate consumption, total consumption of fixed capital (depreciation), paid labour, rent and interest.

7 Compensation of employees, or labour costs, fell by 0.8 per cent (3.8 per cent in real terms) in 2006 due to a continuing fall in the labour force. Income from agriculture of total labour input, which is the sum of 'Total Income from Farming' and 'compensation of employees', rose by 5.1 per cent, or 1.9 per cent in real terms. Total Income from Farming per full-time person equivalent ("Total income from farming per AWU of entrepreneurial labour" in table 2.1) is estimated to have risen by 13 per cent in current prices, or by 9.4 per cent in real terms, to £13,840.

Table 2.1 Summary measures from the aggregate agricultural account; United Kingdom

Enquiries: Christine Holleran on +44 (0)1904 455080   email: christine.holleran@defra.gsi.gov.uk

£ million (unless otherwise specified)   Calendar years

| Year | Net value added at factor cost | Income from farming | | | | Cash flow from farming |
		Total Income from Farming	Compensation of employees	Income from agriculture of total labour input	Total Income from Farming per AWU of entrepreneurial labour (a)	
Current prices		A	B	A + B	(£)	
1995	7 804	5 205	1 836	7 041	21 300	5 032
1996	7 450	4 786	1 881	6 667	19 900	4 801
1997	5 673	2 865	1 930	4 795	12 000	3 105
1998	4 997	2 083	1 975	4 058	8 800	2 792
1999	4 995	2 133	2 029	4 162	9 300	2 986
2000	4 409	1 656	1 901	3 556	7 500	2 724
2001	4 638	1 877	1 951	3 828	8 600	3 896
2002	5 053	2 348	1 966	4 315	11 100	2 689
2003	5 775	3 140	1 917	5 056	15 300	3 583
2004	5 583	2 824	2 009	4 833	13 900	2 801
2005	5 405	2 465	2 177	4 642	12 300	757
2006 (provisional)	5 654	2 718	2 161	4 879	13 800	4 854
In real terms, 2006 prices		A	B	A + B	(£)	
1995	10 365	6 913	2 439	9 352	28 300	6 683
1996	9 661	6 206	2 439	8 645	25 700	6 225
1997	7 132	3 602	2 426	6 028	15 100	3 904
1998	6 074	2 532	2 401	4 933	10 700	3 394
1999	5 980	2 553	2 429	4 982	11 200	3 575
2000	5 127	1 925	2 210	4 135	8 700	3 167
2001	5 296	2 144	2 228	4 371	9 800	4 449
2002	5 679	2 639	2 210	4 849	12 500	3 022
2003	6 307	3 429	2 093	5 522	16 800	3 913
2004	5 922	2 996	2 130	5 126	14 700	2 971
2005	5 575	2 542	2 246	4 788	12 700	781
2006 (provisional)	5 654	2 718	2 161	4 879	13 800	4 854

(a) An annual work unit (AWU) represents the equivalent of an average full-time person engaged in agriculture.

8   Cash flow from farming rose by £4.1 billion. Cash flow reflects sales and expenditure on gross fixed capital formation and includes capital transfers paid to the industry in exchange for assets. As cash flow reflects the income from receipts received during the year, the 2005 and 2006 estimates were affected by the majority of payments through the Single Payment Scheme in the United Kingdom being made in 2006.

9   Gross value added for the industry, which represents its contribution to national gross domestic product (GDP) rose by 4.8 per cent at basic prices or 7.3 per cent at market prices, compared to 2005. The smaller rise in gross value added at basic prices is a consequence of the ending of the Over Thirty Month Scheme in January 2006, which was not included in output at market price.

10   The agricultural industry is expected to account for around 0.5 per cent of the national economy in 2006, measured in terms of gross value added. Since 1973, when the share was almost 3.0 per cent, the overall trend has been downwards although there have been brief recoveries when prices for agricultural commodities improved. Gross value added at basic prices fell by 0.2 percentage points in 2005 due to the introduction of the Single Payment Scheme, which is not linked to production.

11   The industry's share of the workforce is now 1.7 per cent. Since the early 1980s, there has been a shift in the composition of the labour force with the proportion of part-time workers rising from 25 per cent to 57 per cent of the total.

Summary measures by country (table 2.2)

12   Table 2.2 shows the main indicators for the agricultural industries in England, Northern Ireland, Scotland and Wales in 2006. In 2006, England accounted for about 70 per cent of Total Income from Farming for the United Kingdom, Scotland accounted for about 20 per cent, Northern Ireland for 7.0 per cent and Wales for 3.9 per cent.

13   The measure 'Agriculture's share of total regional employment' gives an indication of the relative importance of the agricultural industry to each country. Agriculture's share of employment was greatest in Northern Ireland where it accounted for 6.0 per cent, and least in England where it accounted for 1.4 per cent.

Table 2.2 Summary measures by country in 2006

Enquiries: Sarah Tumber on +44 (0)1904 455084   email: sarah.tumber@defra.gsi.gov.uk

	Gross output at basic prices	Intermediate consumption	Gross value added at basic prices	Total Income from Farming	Agriculture's share of total regional gross value added at basic prices (a)	Agriculture's share of total regional employment (b) (c)	Agriculture's share of total gross fixed capital formation
	£ million	£ million	£ million	£ million	%	%	%
United Kingdom	14 822	9 242	5 580	2 718	0.5	1.7	1.2
England & Wales	10 894	6 471	4 423	1 844	..	1.4	..
Wales	937	771	166	106	..	4.0	..
Scotland	1 916	1 195	720	578	..	2.5	..
Northern Ireland	1 076	805	271	190	..	6.0	..

(a) Data on national and regional GVA for 2006 are not yet available. Data for 2005 are shown for illustration.

(b) The total workforce in employment consists of employees in employment, the self-employed and people in work-related government training schemes. For Northern Ireland, agriculture's percentage share is higher than that published by the Northern Ireland Department of Enterprise, Trade and Investment, which excludes part-time owners, partners, directors and spouses of farmers.

(c) The agriculture industry includes a high proportion of part-time workers. A comparison on the basis of full-time person equivalent would show lower percentages.

Comparison of income measures in EU Member States (chart 2.3, table 2.3)

14 Chart 2.3 shows estimated changes from 2005 to 2006 in income from agricultural activity across EU Member States as measured by Eurostat's Indicator A. The figures quoted are estimates published by Eurostat, based on data supplied by national authorities at the end of November 2006 except for the United Kingdom, which has been calculated from the latest data available.

Chart 2.3 Changes in income across the EU: Indicator A

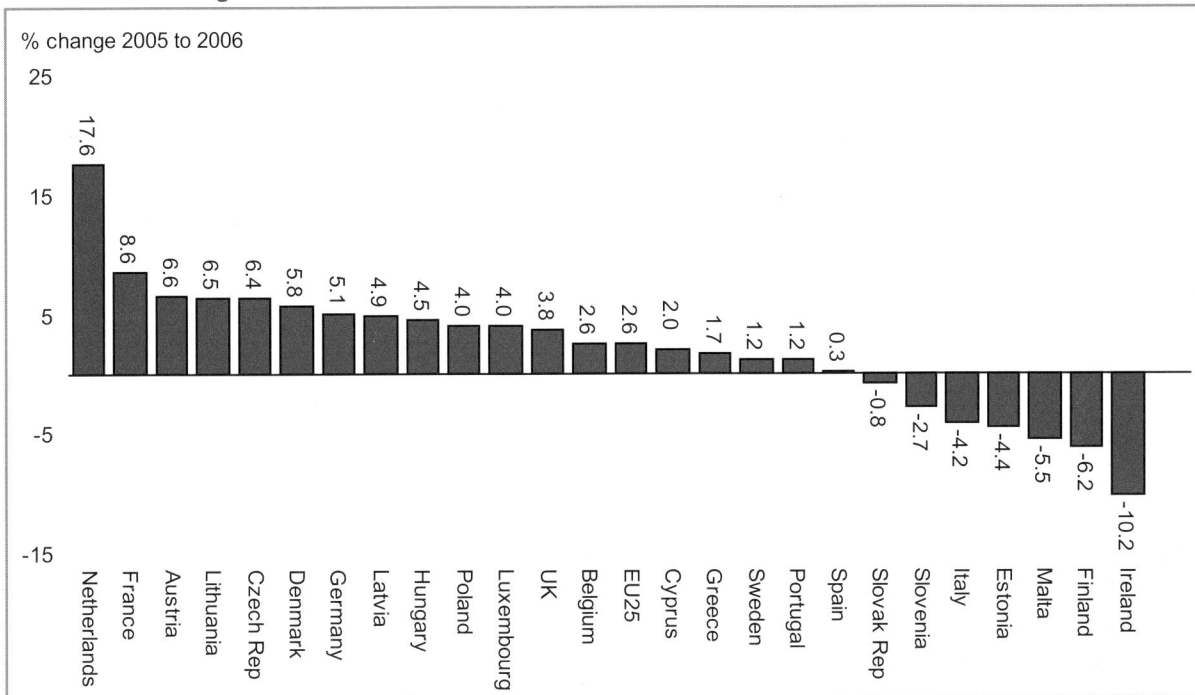

% change 2005 to 2006

Netherlands	17.6
France	8.6
Austria	6.6
Lithuania	6.5
Czech Rep	6.4
Denmark	5.8
Germany	5.1
Latvia	4.9
Hungary	4.5
Poland	4.0
Luxembourg	4.0
UK	3.8
Belgium	2.6
EU25	2.6
Cyprus	2.0
Greece	1.7
Sweden	1.2
Portugal	1.2
Spain	0.3
Slovak Rep	-0.8
Slovenia	-2.7
Italy	-4.2
Estonia	-4.4
Malta	-5.5
Finland	-6.2
Ireland	-10.2

Source: Eurostat News Release 169/2006; Defra

15 Net value added at factor cost (deflated by the GDP price index) per annual work unit (or full-time person equivalent), Indicator A, was forecast to have risen by 2.6 per cent in the EU as a whole in 2006, after decreasing by 7.3 per cent in 2005. This small growth is the result of agricultural output (at producer prices in real terms) remaining stable; slight increases in input costs (0.2 per cent) and depreciation (0.2 per cent) in real terms; and a rise in the real value of subsidies net of taxes (0.8 per cent). It was above the levels of 2005 in nineteen Member States. The strongest growth was observed in the Netherlands (18 per cent), France (8.6 per cent), Austria (6.6 per cent), Lithuania (6.5 per cent) and the Czech Republic (6.4 per cent). The largest falls were observed in Ireland (10 per cent), Finland (6.2 per cent) and Malta (5.5 per cent).

16 Table 2.3 compares Indicator A, Indicator B and Indicator C for the United Kingdom, EU15 and EU25 to 2006. Between 2002 and 2006, Indicator A rose by 4.8 per cent in the United Kingdom, by 16 per cent in the EU15 and by 9.8 per cent in the EU25. Indicator B rose by 4.1 per cent in the United Kingdom; it is not available for the EU as a whole but is available for most other Member States. Indicator C fell by 3.7 per cent in the United Kingdom, by 18 per cent in the EU15 and by 13 per cent in the EU25.

Table 2.3 Eurostat income indicators

Enquiries: Christine Holleran on +44 (0)1904 455080   email: christine.holleran@defra.gsi.gov.uk

Index 2000 = 100

	Average of 1995-97	2002	2003	2004	2005	2006
Net value added at factor cost of agriculture per total Annual Work Unit (Indicator A)						
United Kingdom	151.5	118.1	137.6	128.1	123.5	123.8
EU15	103.1	100.0	101.5	101.6	112.1	115.6
EU25	..	101.4	103.9	108.4	107.5	111.4
Net agricultural entrepreneurial income per unpaid Annual Work Unit (Indicator B)						
United Kingdom	245.9	143.3	186.8	165.6	154.0	149.2
EU15	..	..	..	..	..	..
EU25	..	..	..	..	..	..
Net entrepreneurial income from agriculture (Indicator C)						
United Kingdom	269.6	137.1	173.2	152.5	140.5	132.0
EU15	117.9	95.0	94.0	91.8	77.2	78.1
EU25	..	94.8	93.3	96.5	81.7	82.6

Source: Eurostat

Table 2.4 Comparison of agriculture in EU Member States in 2006

Enquiries: Christine Holleran on +44 (0)1904 455080   email: christine.holleran@defra.gsi.gov.uk

Country comparison at current prices and current exchange rates € million (except where otherwise stated)

	Total crop output	Total animal output	Total agricultural output	Gross Value Added at basic prices	Entrepreneurial income	Total labour input (a) '000 AWU	Gross Value Added per AWU €
Member States							
EU25	157 397	129 729	300 695	135 744	74 978	9 101	14 900
EU15	142 159	114 796	269 522	123 891	67 528	5 701	21 700
Austria	2 400	2 785	5 373	2 492	1 885	161	15 500
Belgium	3 016	3 649	6 712	2 262	1 167	67	33 700
Cyprus	283	288	568	335	65	22	15 400
Czech Republic	1 706	1 580	3 368	897	250	148	6 100
Denmark	2 399	5 018	7 831	2 612	207	63	41 500
Estonia	175	282	468	192	116	37	5 100
Finland	1 440	2 076	3 601	854	853	93	9 200
France	32 790	22 668	58 465	25 085	12 239	927	27 100
Germany	18 719	19 433	39 712	13 063	5 592	571	22 900
Greece	7 052	2 803	10 211	6 789	5 343	603	11 300
Hungary	3 468	2 249	6 071	2 429	1 327	495	4 900
Ireland	1 362	3 771	5 412	1 740	1 925	167	10 400
Italy	26 930	13 410	42 885	25 760	10 414	1 172	22 000
Latvia	351	339	715	277	284	133	2 100
Lithuania	751	772	1 543	602	346	139	4 300
Luxembourg	78	151	237	100	65	4	26 900
Malta	46	70	116	55	54	4	13 600
Netherlands	11 193	8 901	22 252	9 409	3 409	191	49 200
Poland	7 206	8 087	15 709	6 183	4 704	2 236	2 800
Portugal	3 639	2 486	6 355	2 629	1 762	368	7 200
Slovakia	736	736	1 550	420	13	96	4 400
Slovenia	517	529	1 065	463	290	90	5 100
Spain	21 996	14 147	36 571	22 538	17 738	950	23 700
Sweden	1 502	2 122	3 852	1 112	459	75	14 800
United Kingdom	7 641	11 376	20 052	7 446	4 468	290	25 700

source: Eurostat

(a) Differs from workforce in agriculture in tables 3.8 and 7.2 which is shown in thousand persons. In this table the basis is annual work units (AWU) (full-time equivalents) as opposed to persons employed.

Comparison of agriculture in EU Member States (table 2.4)

17 Table 2.4 shows the relative importance of agriculture in the 25 Member States in 2006. These are estimates based on forecast economic accounts for agriculture submitted to Eurostat by Member States at the end of November 2006.

18 France, Italy, Spain and Germany are estimated to account for almost two-thirds of the total value of crop output in the EU in 2006. France was also the main producer in the livestock sector and, together with Germany, Spain, Italy and the United Kingdom, was estimated to have accounted for over 50 per cent of the total value of livestock output in the European Union.

19 In terms of gross value added per annual work unit, the United Kingdom ranks sixth behind the Netherlands, Denmark, Belgium, France and Luxembourg, with an average of 25,700 euros per full-time person equivalent.

Net farm incomes by farm type (tables 2.5, 2.6, chart 2.4)

20 Estimates of net farm income and cash income include provision for Single Payment Scheme receipts which are recorded as due for the appropriate accounting year, e.g. receipts of the 2006 Single Payment Scheme are recorded in the 2006/07 accounting year. Estimates of Single Payment Scheme receipts by farm type are speculative. The level of payment will vary from farm to farm, even within the same farm type.

21 In real terms, average net farm income for all types of farm in the United Kingdom is expected to be around £20,600 in 2006/07, about 20 per cent higher than 2005/06. Incomes are forecast to have doubled for cereals and general cropping farms due to better prices for crops while lowland livestock farms and mixed farms also benefited from improved prices. Specialist poultry, specialist pigs and dairy farm incomes are expected to fall as are incomes for LFA grazing livestock farms.

Table 2.5 Net farm income by country and type of farm

Enquiries: Selina Matthews +44 (0)20 7238 3274   email: selina.matthews@defra.gsi.gov.uk

Average net farm income per farm (£ per farm)	2001/02 (a)	2002/03	2003/04	2004/05	2005/06	2006/07 (provisional)
At current prices						
England						
Cereals	5 900	13 200	36 400	15 600	14 100	31 000
General cropping	17 500	15 600	56 800	32 200	26 700	56 700
Dairy	30 900	16 400	23 600	26 400	27 100	20 100
Grazing livestock (lowland)	- 100	6 400	7 100	5 400	5 300	9 100
Grazing livestock (LFA)	7 400	17 700	15 000	13 400	11 800	11 600
Specialist pigs	21 600	25 300	34 400	25 100	29 000	24 500
Specialist poultry	26 700	97 100	53 200	89 700	97 500	77 200
Mixed	4 500	11 400	24 400	16 400	17 400	23 700
Wales						
Dairy	29 600	18 200	18 100	20 500	20 400	19 800
Grazing livestock (lowland)	2 200	9 400	8 900	3 900	1 100	6 700
Grazing livestock (LFA)	1 600	13 300	15 900	14 300	8 800	8 600
Scotland						
Cereals	1 100	500	17 000	1 400	3 100	. .
General cropping	2 600	-1 400	25 300	4 100	5 400	. .
Dairy	37 400	8 800	22 700	24 600	21 100	. .
Grazing livestock (LFA)	11 700	15 700	18 100	15 500	10 000	. .
Mixed	10 300	9 100	22 400	14 600	14 000	. .
Northern Ireland						
Dairy	17 500	6 500	15 500	17 100	20 700	18 500
Grazing livestock (LFA)	4 000	4 600	4 900	6 200	5 700	7 000

continued

Table 2.5 continued

Average net farm income per farm (£ per farm)				Accounting years ending on average in February		
	2001/02 (a)	2002/03	2003/04	2004/05	2005/06	2006/07 (provisional)
At current prices						
United Kingdom						
Cereals	5 000	11 000	33 500	13 600	12 700	27 900
General cropping	14 200	11 700	50 800	26 400	22 500	49 300
Dairy	28 200	14 200	21 100	23 700	24 500	19 700
Grazing livestock (lowland)	1 300	6 700	7 100	5 300	4 100	7 700
Grazing livestock (LFA)	5 800	13 000	14 300	13 000	9 300	9 300
Specialist pigs	20 000	23 500	32 100	25 100	29 000	24 500
Specialist poultry	22 100	83 500	49 900	89 700	97 500	77 200
Mixed	5 300	10 400	22 600	14 800	15 600	20 800
ALL TYPES (Including Horticulture)	13 000	13 700	23 900	17 900	17 100	21 300
In real terms (at 2005/06 prices)						
United Kingdom						
Cereals	5 500	12 000	35 500	14 000	12 700	27 000
General cropping	15 800	12 700	53 800	27 100	22 500	47 700
Dairy	31 300	15 500	22 300	24 300	24 500	19 100
Grazing livestock (lowland)	1 400	7 300	7 500	5 400	4 100	7 500
Grazing livestock (LFA)	6 400	14 200	15 100	13 400	9 300	9 000
Specialist pigs	22 200	25 600	34 000	25 800	29 000	23 700
Specialist poultry	24 500	90 900	52 800	92 100	97 500	74 700
Mixed	5 900	11 300	23 900	15 200	15 600	20 100
ALL TYPES (Including Horticulture)	14 400	14 900	25 300	18 400	17 100	20 600

(a) Excluding farms subjected to compulsory foot and mouth disease cull.

22   Table 2.6 shows there were wide variations in the level of income across farms in the United Kingdom in 2005/06. A quarter of farms had a net farm income of less than zero; a half had an income of less than £10,000. These proportions were reflected in each country with England being below the average and Wales, Scotland and Northern Ireland being above the average. Over 20 per cent of farms in England had an income of at least £30,000 but only 12 per cent in Northern Ireland.

23   The table compares three measures of farm income: net farm income, occupier's net income and cash income. Net farm income treats all farms, whether tenanted or owner-occupied, on the same basis so the profitability of farms with different tenure types can be compared. Occupier's net income differs because imputed rent is not deducted as a cost and land-type costs are included in inputs. This measure is therefore closer to the income position from the occupier's point of view. Cash income is defined as the cash return to the group (with an entrepreneurial interest in the business) for their labour and on all investment and is calculated as output less input.

Table 2.6 All farm types: distribution of farm incomes by country 2005/06

Enquiries: Selina Matthews +44 (0)20 7238 3274   email: selina.matthews@defra.gsi.gov.uk

Percentage of farms

	England	Wales	Scotland	Northern Ireland	United Kingdom
Net Farm Income					
Less than zero	23.5	29.2	30.0	26.4	25.4
0 to less than £5,000	11.7	14.4	11.7	16.0	12.5
£5,000 to less than £10,000	11.0	15.3	13.3	13.0	12.1
£10,000 to less than £20,000	19.2	15.2	18.5	23.4	19.0
£20,000 to less than £30,000	12.6	10.2	12.3	9.2	11.9
£30,000 to less than £50,000	10.8	9.7	9.0	7.7	10.0
£50,000 and over	11.3	6.1	5.2	4.3	9.0
Average (£ thousand per farm)	21.1	10.8	10.1	10.2	17.1

continued

Table 2.6 continued

Percentage of farms

	England	Wales	Scotland	Northern Ireland	United Kingdom
Occupier's Net Income					
Less than zero	20.8	21.4	28.8	24.9	22.4
0 to less than £5,000	10.8	10.4	10.3	13.0	10.9
£5,000 to less than £10,000	11.1	16.2	11.7	13.4	12.1
£10,000 to less than £20,000	17.9	21.5	19.4	26.5	19.5
£20,000 to less than £30,000	13.0	10.4	14.2	11.7	12.7
£30,000 to less than £50,000	13.3	12.6	8.8	7.2	11.9
£50,000 and over	13.1	7.5	6.7	3.3	10.4
Average (£ thousand per farm)	23.9	15.4	12.1	10.6	19.7
Cash Income					
Less than zero	7.2	5.2	5.9	3.1	6.3
0 to less than £5,000	6.4	7.3	10.8	8.7	7.4
£5,000 to less than £10,000	6.8	9.2	7.0	10.6	7.5
£10,000 to less than £20,000	17.0	21.4	15.1	21.8	17.8
£20,000 to less than £30,000	14.6	16.0	19.6	20.6	16.1
£30,000 to less than £50,000	21.1	21.6	23.4	18.8	21.2
£50,000 and over	27.0	19.5	18.3	16.3	23.7
Average (£ thousand per farm)	45.3	31.7	31.3	29.3	39.9

24 Chart 2.4 shows the differences in performance of farms in the United Kingdom for 2005/06. Performance is measured as £ of output per £100 of input, where input includes a charge for farmer and spouse manual labour, imputed or otherwise. The chart illustrates the significant variation in performance across all farms with over 55% of farms failing to recover their costs.

Chart 2.4 Distribution of performance across farms >0.5 SLR 2005/06; United Kingdom

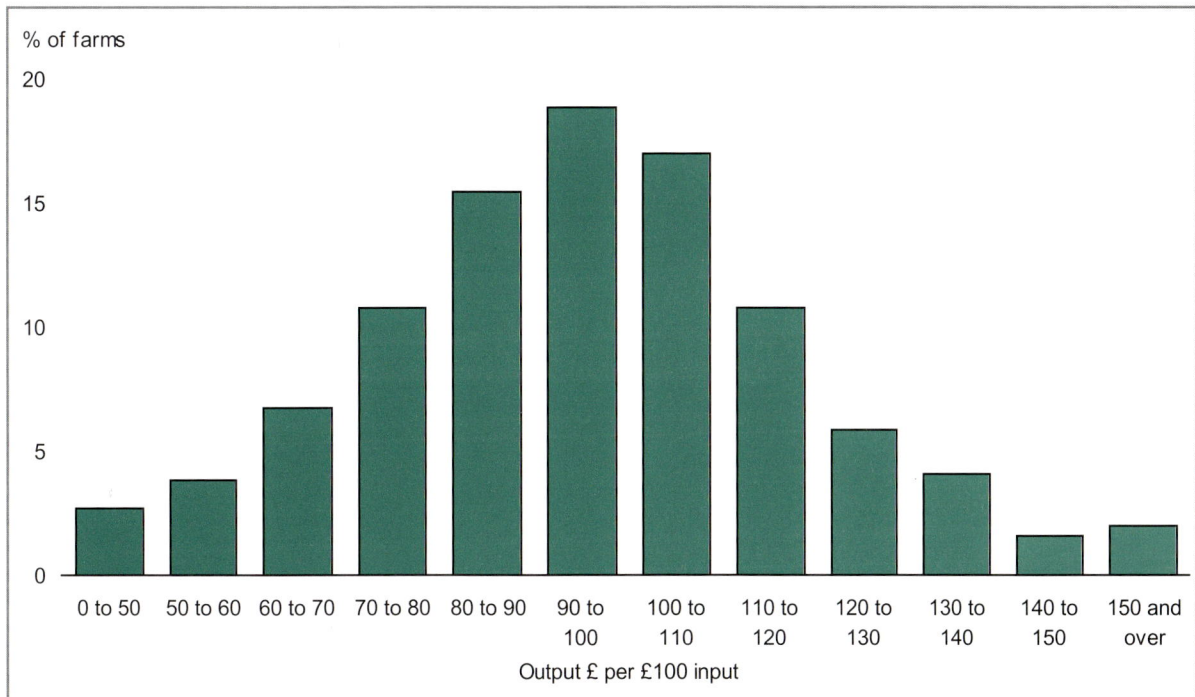

Diversification

25 Diversification is widely held to offer considerable scope for improving the economic viability of farm businesses. It can be thought of as "the entrepreneurial use of farm resources for a non-agricultural purpose for commercial gain". There are some obvious activities that are included as diversification such as tourism, sport, recreation and processing, and others that are not, such as the production of organic or novel crops, which while possibly reflecting a change in focus and entrepreneurial activity by the farmer, remain agricultural activities. Others such as off-farm employment or investment income are not regarded as diversified activities as they do not utilise farm resources.

26 Further information on diversification is available at:

http://statistics.defra.gov.uk/esg/publications/diversification.asp

http://www.ruralni.gov.uk/index/ruraldev/diversification.htm

http://www.scotland.gov.uk/Publications/2003/04/16927/21191

Chapter **3**   The Structure of the Industry

2006

Summary

In 2006:

- the total area of agricultural land was 18.7 million hectares, about 77 per cent of the total land area in the United Kingdom;

- the area of all crops grown fell by 2.2 per cent to 4.3 million hectares;

- the area for cereals fell by 2.0 per cent while other arable crops (excluding potatoes) fell by 3.2 per cent;

- the dairy herd rose slightly by 0.1 per cent while the beef breeding herd fell by 1.7 per cent;

- the size of the sheep flock fell by 2.0 per cent;

- the number of breeding pigs and gilts in pig fell by 0.3 per cent.

Introduction

1 The tables and charts in this chapter show the size and structure of the agricultural industry in the United Kingdom. They provide information on land use and livestock numbers, on the distribution of these between holdings, on the labour force, the age and training of holders and on the industry's fixed capital.

Land use, crop areas and livestock numbers (tables 3.1, 3.2, charts 3.1 to 3.4)

2 At June 2006, the total area of agricultural land was 19 million hectares, some 77 per cent of the total land area in the United Kingdom (excluding inland water).

Chart 3.1 Total area on agricultural holdings; United Kingdom

Chart 3.2 Total area of crops grown; United Kingdom

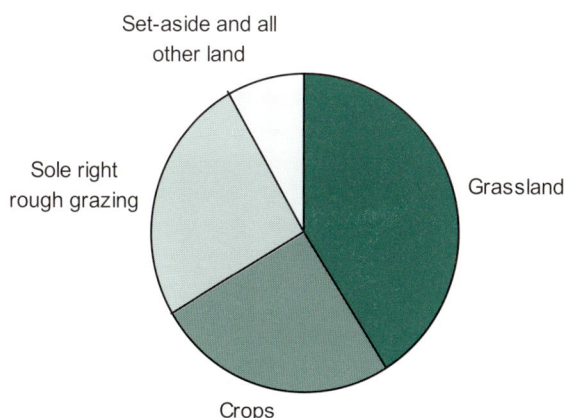

Chart 3.1: Set-aside and all other land; Sole right rough grazing; Crops; Grassland

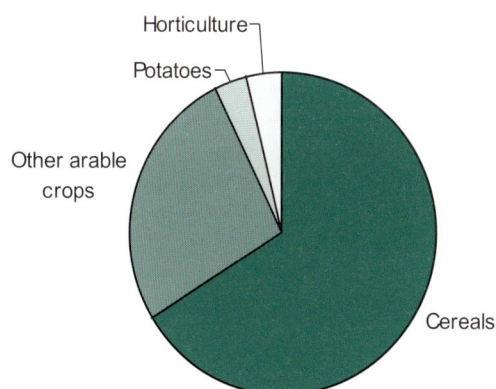

Chart 3.2: Horticulture; Potatoes; Other arable crops; Cereals

Table 3.1 Agricultural land use; United Kingdom

The data in this table cover all holdings (including minor holdings) in the United Kingdom (a)
Enquiries: Alison Wray on +44 (0)1904 455313   email: alison.wray@defra.gsi.gov.uk

Thousand hectares   At June

	Average of 1995-97	2002	2003	2004	2005	2006
Total agricultural area (b)	18 717	18 537	18 464	18 432	18 502	18 713
of which:						
crops	4 752	4 604	4 475	4 589	4 437	4 340
bare fallow	36	33	29	29	140	150
Total tillage	4 788	4 636	4 504	4 619	4 577	4 489
All grass under five years old	1 402	1 243	1 200	1 246	1 193	1 137
Total arable land	6 190	5 879	5 705	5 864	5 770	5 626
All grass five years old and over (excl. rough grazing)	5 337	5 519	5 683	5 620	5 711	5 967
Total tillage and grass (c)	11 527	11 397	11 388	11 485	11 481	11 594
Sole right rough grazing	4 734	4 488	4 329	4 326	4 354	4 491
Set-aside	483	612	689	559	559	513
All other land (d) and woodland	749	806	821	825	872	874
Total area on agricultural holdings	17 493	17 303	17 227	17 195	17 266	17 472
Common rough grazing (estimated)	1 223	1 234	1 236	1 237	1 236	1 241

(a) Before 2000 Scottish minor holdings were not included; data for earlier years are therefore not directly comparable.
(b) Total area on agricultural holdings plus common rough grazing.
(c) Includes bare fallow.
(d) In Great Britain other land comprises farm roads, yards, buildings (excluding glasshouses), ponds and derelict land.

3 The area of crops fell by 2.2 per cent to 4.4 million hectares, the lowest for 22 years. The total area of cereals fell by 2.0 per cent and the area of other arable crops fell by 3.2 per cent. The area planted with potatoes rose by 2.4 per cent to 140 thousand hectares and that used for horticulture fell by 1.9 per cent to 166 thousand hectares.

4 The cattle population fell by 1.2 per cent compared to June 2005. The long-term decline in the dairy herd paused in 2006 as the number of dairy cows rose slightly by 0.1 per cent to 2.1 million animals. The beef breeding herd fell by 1.7 per cent to 1.7 million animals while the number of heifers in calf rose by 1.0 per cent.

5 The population of sheep and lambs fell by 2.0 per cent to 35 million animals. The number of ewes and shearlings fell by 1.8 per cent and the number of lambs under one year old fell by 2.5 per cent.

6 The pig population rose by 1.5 per cent but the number of breeding sows and gilts in pig fell slightly by 0.3 per cent.

Chart 3.3 Changes in crop areas; United Kingdom

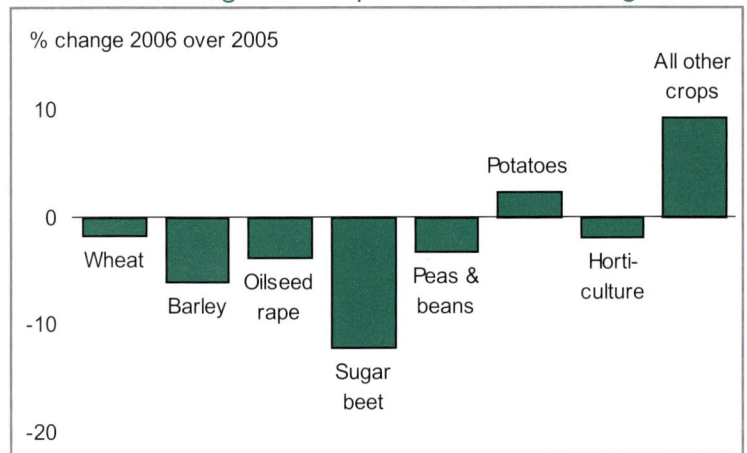

% change 2006 over 2005

Chart 3.4 Changes in livestock numbers; United Kingdom

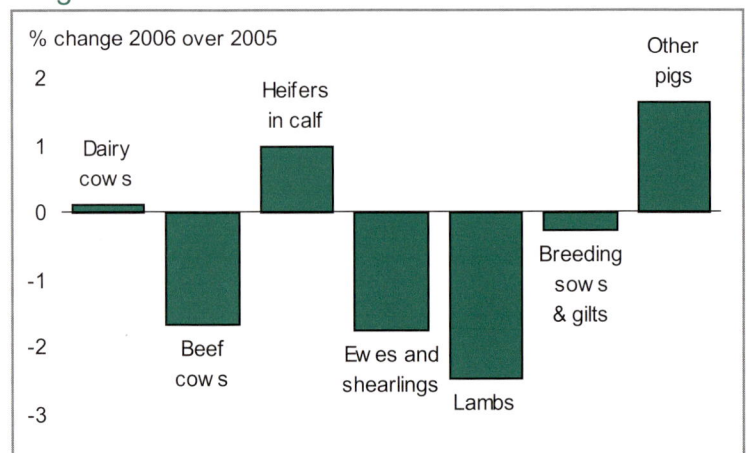

% change 2006 over 2005

Table 3.2 Crop areas and livestock numbers; United Kingdom

The data in this table cover all holdings (including minor holdings) in the United Kingdom. (a) (b)
Enquiries: Alison Wray on +44 (0)1904 455313   email: alison.wray@defra.gsi.gov.uk

	Average of 1995-97	2002	2003	2004	2005	At June 2006
Crop areas (thousand hectares)						
Total	4 752	4 604	4 475	4 589	4 437	4 340
of which:						
Total cereals	3 352	3 245	3 057	3 130	2 919	2 861
of which: wheat	1 957	1 996	1 836	1 990	1 867	1 833
barley	1 274	1 101	1 076	1 007	938	881
oats	103	126	121	108	90	121
rye and mixed corn	11	9	9	9	9	10
triticale	7	14	15	15	13	13
Other arable crops (excluding potatoes)	1 042	1 024	1 098	1 136	1 211	1 172
of which: oilseed rape	385	357	460	498	519	500
sugar beet not for stockfeeding	197	169	162	154	148	130
hops	3	2	2	2	1	1
peas for harvesting dry and field beans	190	249	235	242	239	231
linseed	58	12	32	30	45	33
other crops	207	204	201	203	252	278
Potatoes	172	158	145	148	137	140
Horticulture	187	176	176	175	170	166
of which: vegetables grown in the open	129	124	125	125	121	119
orchard fruit (c)	29	26	25	24	23	23
soft fruit (d)	12	9	9	9	9	10
plants and flowers (e)	14	15	14	15	14	12
glasshouse crops	2	2	2	2	2	2
Livestock numbers (thousand head)						
Total cattle and calves	11 844	10 345	10 508	10 588	10 392	10 270
of which: dairy cows	2 556	2 227	2 191	2 129	2 063	2 066
beef cows	1 855	1 657	1 698	1 736	1 762	1 733
heifers in calf	814	728	679	690	638	645
Total sheep and lambs	42 738	35 834	35 812	35 817	35 416	34 722
of which: ewes and shearlings	20 692	17 630	17 580	17 630	16 935	16 637
lambs under one year old	20 942	17 310	17 322	17 238	17 488	17 058
Total pigs	7 763	5 588	5 046	5 159	4 862	4 933
of which: sows in pig and other sows for breeding	662	483	442	449	403	401
gilts in pig	108	74	73	66	67	67
Total fowl (f)	139 786	168 996	178 800	181 759	173 909	173 081
of which: table fowl including broilers	88 268	105 137	116 738	119 888	111 475	110 672
laying fowl (g)	32 370	28 778	29 274	29 655	29 544	28 632
growing pullets	10 609	9 784	8 286	8 156	10 928	9 625

(a) For various reasons, the crop area figures and livestock numbers shown in this table may differ slightly from those shown in chapter 5.
(b) Before 2000 Scottish minor holdings were not included; data for earlier years are therefore not directly comparable.
(c) Includes non-commercial orchards.
(d) Includes wine grapes.
(e) Hardy nursery stock, bulbs and flowers.
(f) Improvements to the Census methodology were introduced in 1997 to account for poultry production on unregistered units; data for earlier years are therefore not directly comparable.
(g) Excludes fowls laying eggs for hatching.

Numbers and sizes of holdings and enterprises (tables 3.3 to 3.7)

7 Tables 3.3 to 3.6 show the relative sizes of all holdings in England, Wales, Scotland and Northern Ireland and of holdings in less favoured areas. The largest holdings in terms of European size units (ESU) are found in England while the largest in terms of area are found in Scotland. Table 3.7 shows agricultural holdings by farm type, size and country.

8 European size units measure the financial potential of the holding in terms of the margins which might be expected from crops and stock. The margins used are gross margins standardised at 1998-2002 values. The threshold of 8 ESU is judged to be the minimum for full-time holdings.

Table 3.3 Numbers and sizes of holdings (a); United Kingdom

Enquiries: Alison Wray on +44 (0)1904 455313   email: alison.wray@defra.gsi.gov.uk

At June

		2000		2005	
		Number of holdings (thousand)	Total ESU	Number of holdings (thousand)	Total ESU
Size of holding (ESU)	under 8 European Size Units (ESU)	154.6	201.2	197.5	225.5
	8 to under 40 ESU	61.0	1 043.3	55.4	926.1
	40 to under 100 ESU	38.0	2 248.0	33.1	1 928.8
	100 to under 200 ESU	15.9	2 093.1	16.1	2 096.7
	200 ESU and over	6.3	2 371.4	9.0	3 814.9
	Total	275.7	7 957.0	311.1	8 992.0
	Average size (ESUs):				
	All holdings		28.9		28.9
	Holdings 8 ESU and over		64.0		77.2
		Number of holdings (thousand)	Hectares (thousand)	Number of holdings (thousand)	Hectares (thousand)
Total area on holdings	under 20 hectares	144.4	920	183.3	909
	20 to under 50 hectares	52.8	1 740	49.3	1 625
	50 to under 100 hectares	37.9	2 701	36.8	2 628
	100 hectares and over	40.6	7 367	41.7	12 111
	Total	275.7	12 728	311.1	17 273
	Average area (hectares):				
	All holdings		46.2		55.5
	% of total area on holdings with 100 hectares and over		57.9		70.1
Tillage and grass area (b) (c)	0.1 to under 20 hectares	127.0	797	133.0	836
	20 to under 50 hectares	49.6	1 643	48.6	1 602
	50 to under 100 hectares	36.5	2 603	36.4	2 565
	100 hectares and over	31.7	6 218	33.2	6 484
	Total	244.9	11 262	251.2	11 488
	Average crops and grass area per holding (hectares) (d)		46.0		45.7
	% of total crops and grass area on holdings with 100 hectares and over		55.2		56.4

(a) Land in Great Britain let out under short term lets is attributed to the lessor, but land so let out in Northern Ireland (under the conacre system) is now attributed to the lessee. This difference affects both the number of holdings and their average size.

(b) The numbers of holdings shown in this part of the table are lower than those presented in the "total area" part of the table because holdings without crops and grass are excluded.

(c) The areas shown in this part of the table exclude set-aside land.

(d) Refers to holdings with crops and grass only.

Table 3.4 Numbers and sizes of enterprises; United Kingdom

Enquiries: Alison Wray on +44 (0)1904 455313   email: alison.wray@defra.gsi.gov.uk

Areas refer to the area of the specified crop and not to the area of the holding   At June of each year

		2000		2005	
		Number of holdings (thousand)	Hectares (thousand)	Number of holdings (thousand)	Hectares (thousand)
Cereals (excluding maize)	0.1 to under 15 hectares	23.8	167.5	19.9	150.2
	15 to under 30 hectares	12.5	267.2	10.4	240.6
	30 to under 50 hectares	9.0	351.3	8.4	349.4
	50 to under 100 hectares	11.3	800.6	10.2	753.0
	100 hectares and over	9.4	1 759.6	7.6	1 431.3
	Total	66.0	3 346.2	56.5	2 924.6
	Average area (hectares) (a)		50.7		51.7
	% of total cereals area on holdings with 100 hectares and over		52.6		48.9

continued

Table 3.4 continued

Areas refer to the area of the specified crop and not to the area of the holding · At June

2006

		2000		2005	
		Number of holdings (thousand)	Hectares (thousand)	Number of holdings (thousand)	Hectares (thousand)
Oilseed rape	0.1 to under 10 hectares	3.2	20.5	2.6	17.0
	10 to under 20 hectares	4.1	59.1	3.7	54.9
	20 to under 30 hectares	2.3	55.9	2.6	64.8
	30 to under 50 hectares	2.1	78.7	2.9	113.1
	50 hectares and over	1.4	118.1	3.0	269.3
	Total	13.1	332.3	14.8	519.0
	Average area (hectares) (a)		25.4		35.0
	% of total oilseed rape area on holdings with 50 hectares and over		35.5		51.9
Sugar beet (England and Wales only)	0.1 to under 10 hectares	3.4	19.1	2.3	14.9
	10 to under 20 hectares	2.4	34.4	1.9	28.7
	20 hectares and over	2.8	119.3	2.4	104.7
	Total	8.7	172.8	6.5	148.3
	Average area (hectares) (a)		20.0		22.7
	% of total sugar beet area on holdings with 20 hectares and over		69.1		70.6
Potatoes	0.1 to under 2 hectares	5.0	2.8	3.1	2.0
	2 to under 5 hectares	2.4	7.9	1.4	5.4
	5 to under 10 hectares	2.6	18.8	1.9	16.2
	10 to under 20 hectares	2.6	36.7	2.0	32.3
	20 hectares and over	2.3	99.8	1.7	81.5
	Total	14.9	166.0	10.2	137.4
	Average area (hectares) (a)		11.2		13.4
	% of total potato area on holdings with 20 hectares and over		60.2		59.3

		2000		2005	
		Number of holdings (thousand)	Number of livestock (thousand)	Number of holdings (thousand)	Number of livestock (thousand)
Dairy cows	1 to 49 dairy cows	13.0	316.3	9.6	263.9
	50 to 99	11.0	792.6	8.0	606.8
	100 and over	8.0	1 226.7	7.1	1 194.5
	Total	32.1	2 335.6	24.6	2 065.2
	Average size of herd (head)		73		84
	% of total dairy cows in herds of 100 and over		52.5		57.8
Beef cows	1 to 4 beef cows	13.5	32.2	11.0	29.1
	5 to 9	10.9	74.7	10.0	71.6
	10 to 19	14.2	197.4	13.3	190.8
	20 to 29	8.7	208.9	8.5	208.5
	30 to 49	9.4	355.9	8.9	341.5
	50 and over	10.5	969.6	9.8	925.5
	Total	67.2	1 838.7	61.5	1 767.0
	Average size of herd (head)		27		29
	% of total beef cows in herds of 50 and over		52.7		52.4
Sheep breeding flock	1 to 19 breeding sheep	13.9	129.5	15.9	157.9
	20 to 49	14.1	462.5	13.7	465.2
	50 to 124	18.6	1 517.4	17.9	1 504.7
	125 to 499	27.0	7 014.0	22.7	5 863.9
	500 and over	11.8	11 386.4	9.6	9 099.9
	Total	85.3	20 509.8	79.9	17 091.6
	Average size of flock (head)		240		214
	% of total breeding sheep in flocks of 500 and over		55.5		53.2

continued

Table 3.4 continued

		2000		2005	
		Number of holdings (thousand)	Number of livestock (thousand)	Number of holdings (thousand)	Number of livestock (thousand)
Pig breeding herd	1 to 4 breeding pigs	3.3	6.4	2.3	5.4
	5 to 24	1.7	18.5	1.6	18.1
	25 to 99	1.0	56.9	0.9	45.2
	100 and over	1.5	537.2	1.1	408.3
	Total	7.6	619.0	5.8	477.0
	Average size of herd (head)		82		82
	% of total breeding pigs in herds of 100 and over		86.8		85.6
Fattening pigs	1 to 9 fattening pigs	2.7	9.8	3.7	13.4
(Fattening pigs of over	10 to 49	1.6	36.2	1.6	32.0
20kg liveweight	50 to 299	1.5	216.7	1.2	155.4
excluding barren sows)	300 to 999	1.6	963.4	1.3	719.1
	1,000 and over	1.2	2 954.2	1.0	2 138.7
	Total	8.7	4 180.3	8.6	3 058.6
	Average size of herd (head)		480		355
	% of total fattening pigs in herds of 1,000 and over		70.7		69.9
Broilers	1 to 9,999 broilers	1.4	697.3	2.0	668.2
(Includes small	10,000 to 99,999	0.9	36 769.1	0.7	33 848.1
numbers of other table	100,000 and over	0.3	68 212.5	0.4	76 970.5
fowl in Scotland and	Total	2.6	105 678.9	3.1	111 486.8
Northern Ireland)	Average size of flock (head)		40 834		36 141
	% of total broilers in flock of 100,000 and over		64.5		69.0
Laying fowls	1 to 999 laying fowls	28.1	822.4	35.8	1 568.5
	1,000 to 4,999	0.5	1 360.6	0.7	1 665.1
	5,000 to 19,999	0.6	6 102.4	0.6	5 763.2
	20,000 and over	0.3	30 021.7	0.4	31 970.0
	Total	29.6	38 306.9	37.4	40 966.8
	Average size of flock (head)		1 295		1 095
	% of total laying fowls in flocks of 20,000 and over		78.4		78.0

(a) Average area refers to the average area of the specified crop on holdings that grow that crop. Holdings that do not grow the crop are excluded from the calculation.

Table 3.5 Agricultural holdings by size and country 2005 (a)

Enquiries: Alison Wray on +44 (0)1904 455313   email: alison.wray@defra.gsi.gov.uk

At June

	England		Wales		Scotland		Northern Ireland	
	Number of holdings (thousand)	Total ESU	Number of holdings (thousand)	Total ESU	Number of holdings (thousand)	Total ESU	Number of holdings (thousand)	Total ESU
Size of holding (ESU)								
under 8 ESU	122.8	168.4	24.5	26.8	37.5	30.3	12.7	45.8
8 to under 40 ESU	31.0	621.7	7.1	148.7	7.4	155.5	9.9	185.1
40 to under 100 ESU	21.9	1 424.7	3.7	230.8	4.3	273.1	3.3	205.8
100 to under 200 ESU	12.3	1 710.4	1.2	168.4	1.6	217.9	1.0	128.1
200 ESU and over	8.0	3 563.8	0.4	132.3	0.4	118.7	0.2	68.6
Total	195.9	7 489.0	37.0	707.0	51.1	795.4	27.1	633.4
Average size (ESU):								
All holdings		38.2		19.1		15.6		23.4
Holdings 8 ESU and over		100.1		54.6		56.3		40.9

continued

Table 3.5 continued

At June

2006

	England		Wales		Scotland		Northern Ireland	
	Number of holdings (thousand)	Hectares (thousand)	Number of holdings (thousand)	Hectares (thousand)	Number of holdings (thousand)	Hectares (thousand)	Number of holdings (thousand)	Hectares (thousand)
Total area on holdings								
Under 20 hectares	121.1	523.9	20.8	111.2	30.0	156.0	11.4	118.1
20 to under 50 hectares	26.5	875.8	7.2	240.7	6.3	207.1	9.3	301.8
50 to under 100 hectares	21.5	1 548.5	5.2	367.8	5.6	402.0	4.5	309.5
100 hectares and over	26.8	6 330.1	3.8	729.0	9.3	4 751.6	1.8	300.1
Total	195.9	9 278.4	37.0	1 448.7	51.1	5 516.7	27.1	1 029.5
Average area (hectares):								
All holdings		47.4		39.2		107.9		38.0
Holdings 8 ESU and over		112.7		78.4		275.8		57.8
% of total area on holdings								
with 100 hectares and over		68.2		50.3		86.1		29.2

(a) This table contains data for all holdings in Great Britain and all active farm businesses in Northern Ireland.

Table 3.6 Agricultural holdings wholly or mainly in Less Favoured Areas by size and country 2005 (a)

Enquiries: Alison Wray on +44 (0)1904 455313   email: alison.wray@defra.gsi.gov.uk

At June

	England		Wales		Scotland		Northern Ireland	
	Number of holdings (thousand)	Percent of total ESU	Number of holdings (thousand)	Percent of total ESU	Number of holdings (thousand)	Percent of total ESU	Number of holdings (thousand)	Percent of total ESU
Size of holding (ESU)								
under 8 ESU	16.0	5.2	16.5	4.1	27.1	5.9	9.3	9.6
8 to under 40 ESU	5.0	21.0	5.6	25.0	4.9	27.1	7.3	37.4
40 to under 100 ESU	2.9	37.2	2.8	36.7	2.3	39.2	2.0	33.1
100 to under 200 ESU	0.8	22.0	0.7	20.9	0.6	21.8	0.4	14.0
200 ESU and over	0.2	14.6	0.2	13.2	0.1	6.0	0.1	6.0
Total	24.9	100.0	25.9	100.0	35.1	100.0	19.0	100.0
Average size (ESU):								
All holdings		19.4		18.2		10.7		18.9
Holdings 8 ESU and over		51.4		48.5		44.5		32.2
% of total ESU on:								
LFA holdings		6.4		66.7		47.3		56.6
non-LFA holdings		93.6		33.3		52.7		43.4
	Number of holdings (thousand)	Hectares (thousand)	Number of holdings (thousand)	Hectares (thousand)	Number of holdings (thousand)	Hectares (thousand)	Number of holdings (thousand)	Hectares (thousand)
Total area on holdings								
Under 20 hectares	13.9	68.3	14.0	76.7	20.7	112.3	8.1	85.7
20 to under 50 hectares	4.2	136.9	5.0	166.7	4.4	146.9	6.7	216.9
50 to under 100 hectares	3.2	226.6	3.8	272.7	3.6	258.4	3.0	207.0
100 hectares and over	3.7	1 008.5	3.0	596.1	6.4	4 118.0	1.2	210.5
Total	24.9	1 440.3	25.9	1 112.2	35.1	4 635.7	19.0	720.2
Average area (hectares):								
All holdings		57.7		43.0		132.2		37.9
Holdings 8 ESU and over		140.8		83.4		377.3		58.4
% of total area on holdings								
with 100 hectares and over		70.0		53.6		88.8		29.2
% of total area on:								
LFA holdings		15.5		76.8		84.0		70.0
non-LFA holdings		84.5		23.2		16.0		30.0

(a) This table contains data for all holdings in Great Britain and all active farm businesses in Northern Ireland.

Table 3.7 Agricultural holdings by farm type, size and country 2004 (a)

This table will be updated on the Defra website when later data becomes available.
Enquiries: Alison Wray on +44 (0)1904 455313   email: alison.wray@defra.gsi.gov.uk

At June

| | England | | Wales | | Scotland | | Northern Ireland | |
	Number of holdings (thousand)	Percent of total ESU	Number of holdings (thousand)	Percent of total ESU	Number of holdings (thousand)	Percent of total ESU	Number of holdings (thousand)	Percent of total ESU
Dairy								
under 8 ESU	0.4	0.1	0.1	0.1	0.1	0.1	0.0	0.1
8 to under 40 ESU	1.2	2.4	0.4	4.0	0.1	2.0	1.3	12.8
40 to under 100 ESU	5.3	28.4	1.3	30.2	0.8	38.0	2.1	47.1
100 to under 200 ESU	3.8	41.3	0.8	38.5	0.5	47.2	0.7	32.4
200 ESU and over	1.3	27.7	0.3	27.1	0.1	12.7	0.1	7.6
Total	12.0	100.0	2.9	100.0	1.6	100.0	4.2	100.0
Cattle and sheep (LFA)								
under 8 ESU	5.6	7.6	5.2	5.8	8.2	7.5	8.7	18.3
8 to under 40 ESU	4.2	37.7	5.0	39.1	3.9	40.0	6.1	58.0
40 to under 100 ESU	1.5	39.8	1.9	40.8	1.4	39.6	0.6	19.7
100 to under 200 ESU	0.2	9.6	0.2	11.1	0.2	10.5	0.1	4.0
200 ESU and over	-	5.3	-	3.2	-	2.3		
Total	11.5	100.0	12.4	100.0	13.7	100.0	15.5	100.0
Cattle and sheep (lowland)								
under 8 ESU	23.8	13.6	2.1	12.6	1.9	15.1	2.8	19.4
8 to under 40 ESU	8.9	33.0	1.0	42.6	0.3	33.0	1.6	57.6
40 to under 100 ESU	1.6	21.8	0.2	26.6	0.1	31.9	0.2	18.6
100 to under 200 ESU	0.6	17.7	-	9.7	-	20.0	-	4.4
200 ESU and over	0.2	13.9	-	8.4	-	-		
Total	35.1	100.0	3.4	100.0	2.3	100.0	4.6	100.0
Cereals								
under 8 ESU	3.3	-	0.1	4.1	1.4	3.7	0.2	10.3
8 to under 40 ESU	7.4	9.1	0.1	18.1	1.6	26.8	0.2	34.0
40 to under 100 ESU	6.5	23.9	-	34.5	0.8	38.3	-	28.7
100 to under 200 ESU	3.8	29.6	-	43.3	0.2	22.5	-	27.1
200 ESU and over	2.0	36.6			-	8.8		
Total	22.9	100.0	0.3	100.0	4.0	100.0	0.5	100.0
General Cropping								
under 8 ESU	0.6	0.1	-	1.1	0.6	0.4	0.1	1.6
8 to under 40 ESU	1.5	2.0	-	9.5	0.4	7.2	-	17.0
40 to under 100 ESU	2.3	8.6	-	25.0	0.7	30.1	0.1	23.2
100 to under 200 ESU	2.3	17.8	-	28.5	0.4	35.2	0.1	26.8
200 ESU and over	2.6	71.5	-	35.9	0.1	27.1		31.4
Total	9.4	100.0	0.1	100.0	2.3	100.0	0.2	100.0
Pigs and poultry								
under 8 ESU	4.9	0.7	0.5	1.0	1.0	0.6	0.1	0.5
8 to under 40 ESU	1.0	3.4	-	3.1	0.1	3.3	0.2	11.9
40 to under 100 ESU	0.7	7.8	-	7.1	0.1	11.2	0.2	28.6
100 to under 200 ESU	0.6	14.5	-	16.2	0.1	27.3	0.1	17.7
200 ESU and over	0.8	73.6	-	72.6	-	57.6	-	41.3
Total	7.9	100.0	0.7	100.0	1.2	100.0	0.6	100.0
Horticulture								
under 8 ESU	3.3	1.1	0.3	3.7	0.7	9.0	0.1	1.1
8 to under 40 ESU	2.6	6.4	0.1	11.9	0.1	18.6	0.1	10.7
40 to under 100 ESU	1.8	13.2	0.1	15.7	-	14.8	0.1	17.8
100 to under 200 ESU	0.9	14.1	-	9.3	-	13.6	-	23.3
200 ESU and over	0.8	65.2	-	59.5			-	47.1
Total	9.5	100.0	0.5	100.0	0.9	100.0	0.3	100.0
Mixed								
under 8 ESU	3.5	1.2	0.4	3.1	0.8	1.6	0.2	2.5
8 to under 40 ESU	3.1	8.9	0.2	15.2	0.8	17.2	0.5	27.8
40 to under 100 ESU	2.0	17.2	0.1	29.0	0.6	33.7	0.2	34.3
100 to under 200 ESU	1.1	20.5	-	23.6	0.2	27.6	0.1	24.3
200 ESU and over	1.0	52.2	-	29.1	0.1	19.9	-	11.1
Total	10.7	100.0	0.7	100.0	2.5	100.0	1.0	100.0

continued

Table 3.7 continued

At June

	England Number of holdings (thousand)	Percent of total ESU	Wales Number of holdings (thousand)	Percent of total ESU	Scotland Number of holdings (thousand)	Percent of total ESU	Northern Ireland Number of holdings (thousand)	Percent of total ESU
Other								
under 8 ESU	72.6	29.8	14.8	68.4	22.3	83.1	0.6	2.7
8 to under 40 ESU	1.2	14.3	0.1	16.1	0.1	16.9	-	9.5
40 to under 100 ESU	-	2.4	}	}	-	-	0.1	62.5
100 to under 200 ESU	-	1.4	} -	} 15.5	-	-	}	}
200 ESU and over	-	52.0	}	}	-	-	} -	} 25.3
Total	73.9	100.0	14.9	100.0	22.4	100.0	0.7	100.0
Total								
under 8 ESU	118.1	1.9	23.7	4.8	36.9	3.7	12.8	7.0
8 to under 40 ESU	31.0	7.9	7.3	25.5	7.5	19.5	10.2	29.8
40 to under 100 ESU	21.7	18.1	3.6	37.0	4.4	34.5	3.5	33.7
100 to under 200 ESU	13.2	23.4	1.0	21.8	1.6	27.0	1.0	20.1
200 ESU and over	8.8	48.7	0.2	10.9	0.4	15.2	0.2	9.4
Total	192.8	100.0	35.9	100.0	50.8	100.0	27.6	100.0

(a) This table contains data for all holdings in Great Britain and all active farm businesses in Northern Ireland.

Labour force in agriculture (table 3.8)

9   The total labour force at June 2006 is estimated to have fallen by 1.2 per cent to 534,000 persons compared with June 2005. The total number of 'workers' fell by 3.2 per cent while the number of 'farmers, partners, directors and spouses' fell slightly by 0.1 per cent.

Table 3.8 Labour force in agriculture; United Kingdom
The data cover main and minor holdings in the United Kingdom.
Enquiries: Helen Hoult +44 (0)1904 455327

email: helen.hoult@defra.gsi.gov.uk

Thousand persons

At June

	Average of 1995-97	2002 (a)	2003	2004	2005	2006
Workers						
Regular whole-time:						
male	89	65	60	58	57	54
female	13	11	10	10	10	10
Regular part-time: (b)						
male	31	22	21	23	24	24
female	23	18	17	17	17	17
Seasonal or casual:						
male	56	46	45	50	46	44
female	26	18	18	19	19	20
Salaried managers	8	13	13	15	16	15
Total workers	246	194	184	192	190	184
Farmers, partners, directors and spouses						
whole-time	..	164	160	156	154	152
part-time (b)	..	193	190	198	196	198
Total farmers, partners, directors and spouses	370	356	349	354	351	350
Total labour force						
(including farmers and their spouses) (c)	616	550	533	546	541	534

(a) These results and those for following years include the effect of the register improvement in England and are NOT directly comparable with previous years.

(b) Part-time is defined as less than 39 hours per week in England and Wales, less than 38 hours per week in Scotland and less than 30 hours per week in Northern Ireland.

(c) Figures exclude schoolchildren and most trainees.

Age of holders (chart 3.5, tables 3.9, 3.10)

10 The holder is defined as the (natural or legal) person in whose name the holding is operated. The holder can either own or rent the holding, be a hereditary long-term leaseholder, or a usufructuary or a trustee. The data in chart 3.5, tables 3.9 and 3.10 relate to all holders whether or not the holder is also the manager of the holding. The exact definition of holder varies between countries of the United Kingdom. These data exclude holdings which are deemed not to have a single holder due to their legal status.

Chart 3.5 Age of holders; United Kingdom

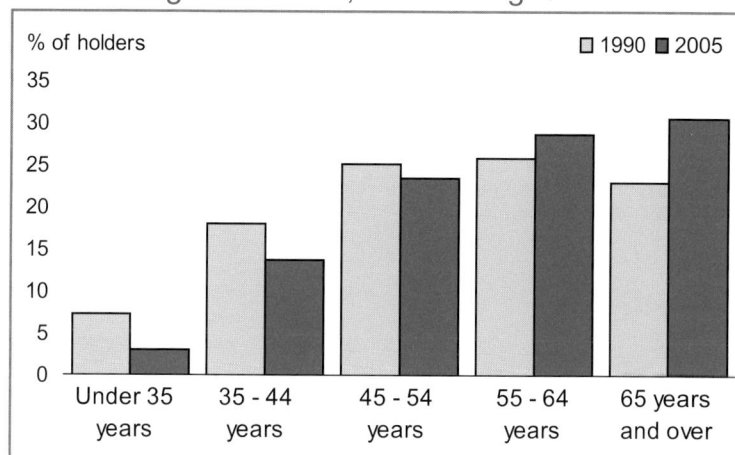

11 The average (median) age of holders increased from 55 years in 1990 to 58 years in 2005. The median age is the middle age when the ages of all holders are put in ascending order. The proportions of holders that are aged '55 to 64 years' and '65 years and over' have increased while those aged 'under 35 years', '35 to 44 years' and '45 to 54 years' have fallen. There is little variability across farm type but the concentration of holders aged '65 years and older' increases as holding size decreases.

Table 3.9 Holders age by farm type (a); United Kingdom

Enquiries: Robin Karfoot +44 (0)1904 456405   email: robin.karfoot@defra.gsi.gov.uk

Thousand persons

	Cereals	General	Horti-culture	Pigs & Poultry	Dairy	Cattle & Sheep (LFA and lowland)	Mixed	Other	All Types
				EU FARM TYPE					
1990									
Holders age									
Under 35 years	1.3	1.6	0.7	0.4	2.7	6.0	1.4	3.3	17.2
as a % of the total	8	7	6	7	8	8	8	6	7
35 - 44 years	3.0	4.5	2.0	1.1	7.0	13.0	3.3	8.7	42.6
as a % of the total	18	20	18	18	21	17	20	17	18
45 - 54 years	4.2	6.0	3.0	1.7	9.6	18.4	4.5	12.2	59.6
as a % of the total	26	26	27	30	28	24	27	24	25
55 - 64 years	4.3	6.3	3.2	1.5	9.5	20.4	4.4	11.7	61.3
as a % of the total	26	28	29	25	28	26	26	23	26
65 years and over	3.7	4.3	2.2	1.2	4.9	20.0	3.2	15.0	54.5
as a % of the total	22	19	20	20	15	26	19	30	23
Total	16.6	22.7	11.0	5.8	33.6	77.9	16.8	50.9	235.3
2005									
Holders age									
Under 35 years	0.6	0.4	0.1	0.3	0.7	3.4	0.5	2.5	8.6
as a % of the total	3	3	1	3	4	5	4	2	3
35 - 44 years	3.4	1.9	1.2	1.8	3.9	11.9	2.5	11.3	37.7
as a % of the total	17	17	14	16	21	16	16	11	15
45 - 54 years	6.0	3.0	2.2	2.9	5.9	19.0	4.0	21.3	64.3
as a % of the total	24	26	25	24	28	23	27	23	24
55 - 64 years	7.5	3.6	2.9	3.3	6.2	22.8	4.9	28.0	79.1
as a % of the total	29	29	35	33	28	28	32	29	29
65 years and over	7.5	3.6	2.3	2.9	4.2	25.4	3.7	34.6	84.2
as a % of the total	27	25	25	24	18	29	21	34	29
Total	27.3	12.6	8.3	6.2	24.4	75.4	14.3	53.8	222.2

Table 3.10 Holders age by farm size (a); United Kingdom

Enquiries: Robin Karfoot +44 (0)1904 456405

email: robin.karfoot@defra.gsi.gov.uk

2006

Thousand persons

	<8 ESU	8:<40 ESU	40: < 100 ESU	100: <200 ESU	200 and over ESU	All holdings
1990						
Holders age						
Under 35 years	6.9	5.8	3.4	0.9	0.3	17.2
as a % of the total	6	8	8	8	8	7
35 - 44 years	17.4	12.8	9.0	2.7	0.7	42.6
as a % of the total	16	18	22	23	22	18
45 - 54 years	24.4	18.7	11.8	3.6	1.1	59.6
as a % of the total	23	26	29	31	32	25
55 - 64 years	26.1	20.4	11.1	2.9	0.8	61.3
as a % of the total	24	29	27	25	26	26
65 years and over	33.4	13.6	5.6	1.5	0.4	54.5
as a % of the total	31	19	14	13	12	23
Total	108.3	71.3	40.9	11.5	3.3	235.3
2005						
Holders age						
Under 35 years	4.8	1.9	1.0	0.6	0.3	8.6
as a % of the total	3	3	3	3	3	3
35 - 44 years	19.5	7.7	5.9	3.1	1.6	37.7
as a % of the total	12	14	18	18	18	14
45 - 54 years	35.6	12.6	9.0	4.8	2.3	64.3
as a % of the total	22	23	27	27	27	24
55 - 64 years	46.5	15.8	9.7	4.8	2.3	79.1
as a % of the total	29	29	29	27	27	29
65 years and over	56.6	16.2	7.3	2.9	1.2	84.2
as a % of the total	35	30	22	17	14	31
Total	163.0	54.1	32.8	17.6	8.8	270.5

(a) European size units (ESU) measure the financial potential of the holding in terms of the margins which might be expected from crops and stock. The threshold of 8 ESU is judged to be the minimum for full-time holdings.

Agricultural training (chart 3.6, tables 3.11, 3.12)

12 The data in chart 3.6, tables 3.11 and 3.12 relate to managers of holdings whether or not the manager is the owner of the holding. 'Basic training' is defined as formal training lasting for less than two years and 'full agricultural training' is defined as formal training lasting for a minimum of two years.

Chart 3.6 Agricultural training; United Kingdom

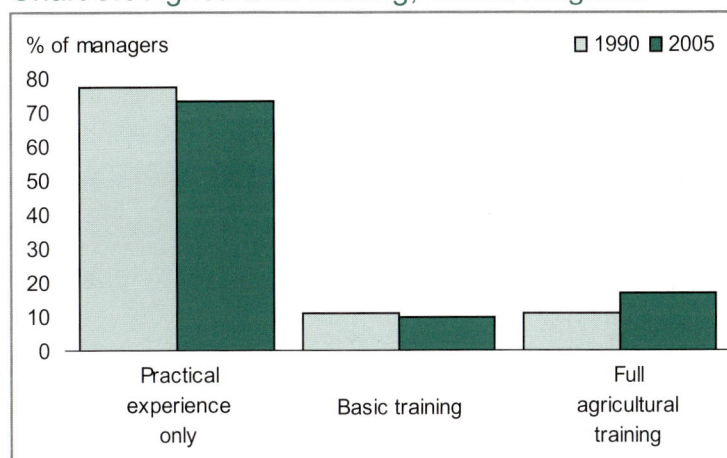

13 Between 1990 and 2005, there has been a increase in the proportion of managers in the United Kingdom who have received 'full agricultural training' from 11 per cent to 17 per cent. However, the proportion of those with 'practical experience only' at 73 per cent in 2005 remains far greater than that with 'full agricultural training'.

14 The proportion of managers who have received 'full agricultural training' has increased across all farm types and is highest among 'cereals' and 'general cropping' farm types. Similarly, the proportion of managers with 'full agricultural training' increased across all farm sizes between 1990 and 2005. The

2005 data show that the proportion of managers with 'full agricultural training' rises with farm size, with 54 per cent of managers on the largest farms having 'full agricultural training'.

Table 3.11 Agricultural training of managers by farm type; United Kingdom

Enquiries: Robin Karfoot +44 (0)1904 456405   email: robin.karfoot@defra.gsi.gov.uk

Thousand persons

	Cereals	General	Horti-culture	Pigs & Poultry	Dairy	Cattle & Sheep (LFA and lowland)	Mixed	Other	All Types
1990									
Agricultural training									
Practical experience only	10.2	13.2	7.1	3.8	21.6	57.6	10.6	37.3	161.4
as a % of the total	69	66	73	74	73	84	72	83	78
Basic training	2.3	3.2	1.1	0.6	4.6	5.5	2.2	3.9	23.3
as a % of the total	15	16	12	11	16	8	15	9	11
Full agricultural training	2.3	3.6	1.6	0.8	3.5	5.9	2.0	3.7	23.3
as a % of the total	16	18	16	15	12	9	14	8	11
Total	14.7	19.9	9.7	5.2	29.6	69.0	14.8	44.9	208.0
2005									
Agricultural training									
Practical experience only	14.3	7.6	6.5	8.9	12.9	66.2	10.6	83.1	210.2
as a % of the total	52	55	67	75	60	79	65	81	73
Basic training	4.2	1.8	0.9	1.0	3.7	8.1	2.2	6.1	28.1
as a % of the total	15	13	9	9	17	10	14	6	10
Full agricultural training	9.2	4.4	2.4	2.0	4.7	9.4	3.3	13.0	48.4
as a % of the total	33	32	24	16	22	11	21	13	17
Total	27.7	13.8	9.8	11.9	21.3	83.7	16.2	102.2	286.7

EU FARM TYPE spans Cereals through Other.

Table 3.12 Agricultural training of managers by farm size; United Kingdom (a)

Enquiries: Robin Karfoot +44 (0)1904 456405   email: robin.karfoot@defra.gsi.gov.uk

Thousand persons

	<8 ESU	8:<40 ESU	40: < 100 ESU	100: <200 ESU	200 and over ESU	All holdings
1990						
Agricultural training						
Practical experience only	80.9	49.8	23.9	5.7	1.2	161.4
as a % of the total	84	78	67	57	45	78
Basic training	7.2	7.2	6.4	2.0	0.5	23.3
as a % of the total	7	11	18	20	20	11
Full agricultural training	7.9	6.7	5.5	2.3	0.9	23.3
as a % of the total	8	10	15	23	35	11
Total	96.0	63.7	35.8	9.9	2.6	208.0
2005						
Agricultural training						
Practical experience only	139.4	39.9	19.7	8.0	3.2	210.2
as a % of the total	83	71	57	45	31	73
Basic training	10.5	6.9	5.9	3.4	1.5	28.1
as a % of the total	6	12	17	19	15	10
Full agricultural training	18.5	9.2	8.9	6.4	5.5	48.4
as a % of the total	11	16	26	36	54	17
Total	168.4	56.0	34.4	17.8	10.2	286.7

(a) European size units (ESU) measure the financial potential of the holding in terms of the margins which might be expected from crops and stock. The threshold of 8 ESU is judged to be the minimum for full-time holdings.

Fixed capital stock (table 3.13)

15 Agriculture's total volume of fixed capital stock is estimated to have been 1.5 per cent lower at the end of 2006 compared to the end of 2005, a fall of 15 per cent on the average for 1995 to 1997. In recent years, the capital stock of 'buildings and works', 'plant and machinery' and 'vehicles' have all declined.

16 Table 3.13 provides information on the volume of gross stock of fixed capital (excluding land and livestock) available to the agricultural industry. The figures are shown before allowing for consumption of fixed capital and give a broad indication of how this aspect of the industry's productive capacity has changed over the years.

Table 3.13 Fixed capital stock of agriculture; United Kingdom

Enquiries: Sarah Tumber on +44 (0)1904 455084   email: sarah.tumber@defra.gsi.gov.uk

Indices 2000 = 100				At year end	
	Average of 1995-97	2002	2003	2004	2005	2006 (provisional)
Gross capital stock (excludes livestock capital assets)						
Buildings and works	106.5	96.0	94.2	92.7	91.8	90.6
Plant and machinery	109.5	96.0	94.9	94.3	92.6	90.7
Vehicles	99.9	101.1	101.4	101.2	99.1	97.8
Total	107.2	96.3	94.8	93.8	92.5	91.1

2006

Chapter 4 Prices

Summary

In 2006:

- the average producer price of agricultural products rose by 4.4 per cent;

- the average price of crop products rose by 9.3 per cent;

- the average price of livestock and livestock products rose by 1.1 per cent;

- the average price of agricultural inputs rose by 3.5 per cent;

- provisional results for Great Britain suggest a fall of 0.5 per cent in average farm rents.

Introduction

1 This chapter presents price indices for agricultural products and inputs, indices for average farm rents and average prices for sales of agricultural land.

2 The price indices for agricultural products and inputs are constructed using fixed annual weights relating to 2000. They reflect observed market prices and do not take account of subsidy payments coupled to production. The price changes presented in table 9.2 are based on current production and may differ from the price movements presented here.

3 The surveys on which the indices for average farm rents are based are conducted in October. No survey was available for England and Wales in 2006 and estimates for this year are based on trends for previous years. No data has been available for Wales since 2000 and estimates have been made. Due to the duration of periods for rent settings, the values applying to the calendar year are deemed to be mainly (approximately 75 per cent) carried over from those recorded in the preceding October. The derivation of the changes are driven primarily by developments in 2005 and only to a lesser extent (approximately 25 per cent) by conditions in 2004.

4 The average prices for sales of agricultural land are obtained from data on land transfers collected by the Valuation Office Agency in Great Britain and the Valuation and Lands Agency in Northern Ireland. Only a very small proportion of the total area of farmland in the United Kingdom is sold in any particular year. The average price of land sold can therefore be subject to considerable variation from year to year and, in the case of unweighted averages shown here, may vary with size and type of lot sold in the year concerned. Recent data on land prices in Scotland should be treated with caution given difficulties with collecting accurate statistics and substantial time lags in gathering data; land price data for Scotland are not currently being collected.

Price indices (table 4.1, chart 4.1)

5 The average producer price of agricultural products in the United Kingdom rose by 4.4 per cent in 2006. It is 18 per cent below the peak in 1995 but 14 per cent above the low point in 2000. In 2006, the average price for crop products rose by 9.3 per cent. The average price for cereals rose by 12 per cent,

that for fresh vegetables rose by 8.8 per cent and that for potatoes rose by 30 per cent. The average price for livestock and livestock products rose by 1.1 per cent.

.6 The average price of agricultural inputs rose by 3.5 per cent in 2006 and is 15 per cent higher than in 1995. The average price of inputs that are currently consumed in agriculture rose by 3.6 per cent and for those inputs which contribute to agricultural investment, the average price rose by 2.8 per cent. All inputs increased in price, in particular the average price of energy and lubricants rose by 8.8 per cent in 2006 following a 26 per cent increase in the previous year.

Chart 4.1 Price indices for agricultural products and inputs; United Kingdom

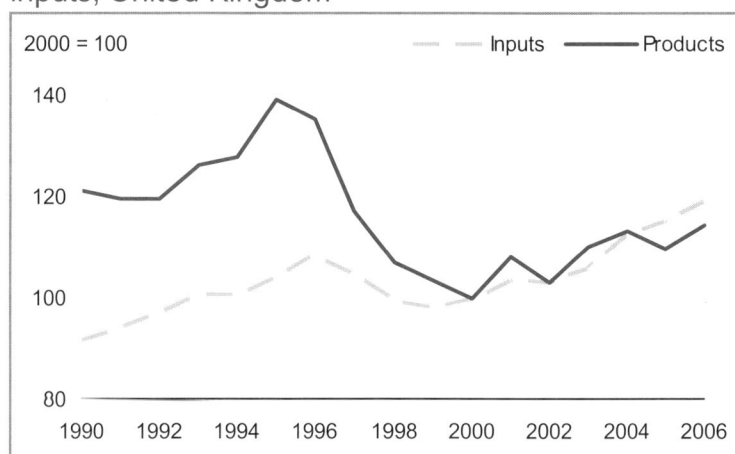

Table 4.1 Price indices for products and inputs; United Kingdom
Enquiries: Clare Burgon on +44 (0)1904 456583   email: clare.f.burgon@defra.gsi.gov.uk

Indices (a) 2000 = 100	Average of 1995-97	2002	2003	2004	2005	Calendar years 2006 (provisional)
Producer prices for agricultural products (b)	130.5	103.3	109.9	113.3	109.6	114.4
of which:						
Crop products:	128.9	104.0	110.7	115.1	108.5	118.6
Cereals	155.0	95.0	105.2	114.2	99.1	111.0
Industrial Crops	143.4	114.4	120.3	121.6	113.9	117.0
Forage Crops	82.9	125.5	75.9	88.1	110.4	104.2
Fresh vegetables	103.4	112.7	125.5	113.7	120.1	130.7
Potatoes	148.7	90.0	105.6	140.3	109.2	141.7
Fresh fruit	105.5	113.9	124.2	112.4	120.1	120.8
Seeds	144.7	95.7	113.6	112.9	114.1	113.1
Flowers and plants	99.9	106.8	107.9	105.3	105.6	108.3
Other crop products	132.6	98.9	108.6	109.7	110.8	110.6
Livestock and livestock products:	131.5	102.7	109.4	112.0	110.4	111.6
Livestock (for slaughter and export)	125.5	103.2	109.3	111.7	110.3	113.7
Milk	141.9	101.0	106.4	109.0	109.0	106.0
Eggs	130.2	109.5	130.7	135.1	121.1	126.0
Other livestock products	140.4	100.0	107.4	110.4	109.3	106.2
Prices of agricultural inputs:	105.7	103.2	105.9	112.5	115.0	119.0
of which:						
Currently consumed in agriculture:	107.3	103.7	106.5	113.7	115.9	120.1
Livestock feedingstuffs	132.2	103.5	104.9	111.6	102.9	107.4
Seeds	130.7	105.5	116.0	110.3	108.1	108.6
Fertilisers and soil improvers	106.4	110.3	119.0	130.5	143.3	151.4
Plant protection products	113.7	95.8	95.7	100.6	102.9	103.4
Maintenance and repair of plant and machinery	87.3	109.4	116.0	122.5	130.3	137.8
Energy, lubricants	81.3	92.4	100.5	108.8	137.4	149.5
Maintenance and repair of buildings	96.3	105.1	108.3	113.4	118.1	125.1
Veterinary services	99.0	97.8	101.6	104.6	103.9	110.3
Other Goods and Services	96.4	105.5	105.2	114.0	114.5	114.9
Contributing to agricultural investment (c):	95.1	100.0	101.5	104.4	108.7	111.7
Machinery and other equipment	91.9	95.7	95.1	96.1	103.8	108.2
Transport Equipment	100.8	97.8	99.1	101.5	103.2	103.4
Buildings	90.6	107.8	112.1	118.1	123.7	130.9
Engineering and Soil Improvement operations	87.6	107.4	110.7	114.0	118.3	120.8

(a) Indices covering an aggregation of commodities are weighted annual averages with weights based on the values of output of the respective commodities in 2000.
(b) These indices reflect prices received by producers but exclude direct subsidies.
(c) Covers the purchase and maintenance of capital items, but excludes stocks.

Farm rents (table 4.2)

7 Provisional results for Great Britain suggest a fall of 0.5 per cent in average farm rents in 2006. In England, average rents are estimated to have fallen by 0.7 per cent while rents for full agricultural tenancies are estimated to have fallen by 1.5 per cent.

Table 4.2 Farm rents
Enquiries: Dave Rimmer on +44 (0)1904 456406   email: david.j.rimmer@defra.gsi.gov.uk

Average per hectare: indices 2000 = 100

		Average of 1995-97	2002	2003	2004	2005	2006 (provisional)
England:	full agricultural tenancies (a)	93.3	93.4	93.3	93.2	90.4	89.0
	average (b)	89.4	100.4	98.4	96.5	96.9	96.3
Wales (c):	full agricultural tenancies (a)	97.9	100.1	100.4	100.6	100.8	101.0
	average (b)	83.4	105.6	107.4	109.2	111.0	112.8
Scotland (d)		85.0	99.3	101.4	103.4	96.0	96.0
Great Britain		88.6	100.8	99.3	97.8	97.9	97.4
Northern Ireland (e)		113.9	95.6	91.2	90.7	86.8	86.8

(a) Average rent estimates for full agricultural tenancies up to 1995 were sourced from the rent enquiry. For 1995 to 1997, a weighted average of rent enquiry and annual survey of tenanted land data was used. From 1998, estimates were sourced from the Tenanted Land Survey. From 2002, the Tenanted Land Survey has been run every two years with estimates for intervening years being based on the trend.

(b) A new series for England and Wales has been introduced giving a weighted average rent in £ per hectare for all agreements over a year in length.

(c) No data is available for Wales after 2000. Estimates for 2001 onwards have been made based on trends.

(d) Scottish estimates prior to 1998 relate to crops and grassland only. From 1998 onwards crops and grass were replaced by a non-less favoured area classification.

(e) In Northern Ireland, virtually all land is let in 'conacre', i.e. nominally short-term lettings (for 11 months or 364 days), although in practice some can be extended beyond this. The estimates are based on results from the Northern Ireland Farm Business Survey.

Agricultural land prices (table 4.3, chart 4.2)

8 Prices for agricultural land in 2005 are currently unavailable except for Northern Ireland and no data are available for Scotland from 2003. The average price of agricultural land in England increased by 8.9 per cent in 2004 but fell in Wales by 6.0 per cent. The average price is expected to have increased in Northern Ireland by 22 per cent in 2005.

Chart 4.2 Prices of agricultural land (all sales) at 2005 prices

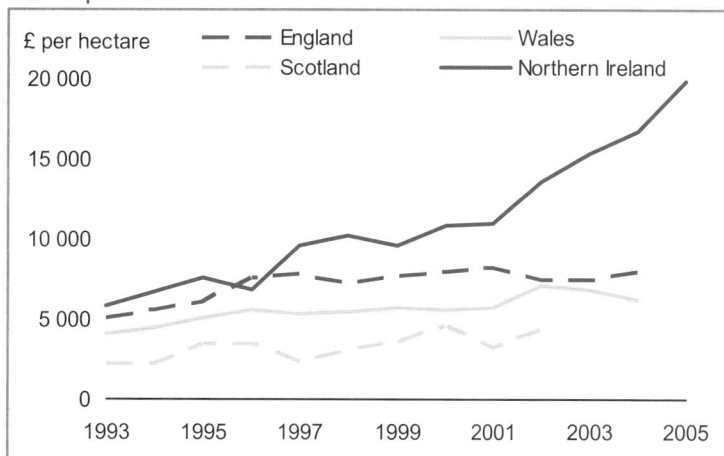

9 In Northern Ireland most land sales involve relatively small areas and the number of recorded sales has been declining in recent years. These factors, coupled with difficulties with data collection, means that figures for 2005 have been estimated.

10 Over the longer term, all of the four countries of the United Kingdom have shown upward trends since 1993. The average price of agricultural land in Northern Ireland has shown the most significant increase.

Table 4.3 Agricultural land prices

Enquiries: Joanne Gardiner on +44 (0)1904 455681   email: joanne.gardiner@defra.gsi.gov.uk

£ per hectare of all sales (a)   Calendar years

	Average of 1995-97	2001	2002	2003	2004	2005 (c)
England	5 765	7 406	6 915	7 172	7 654	..
Wales	4 283	5 192	6 513	6 498	6 107	..
Scotland	2 493	2 894	3 984	..	..	..
Northern Ireland (b)	6 409	9 961	12 456	14 475	16 286	19 837

(a) These series, based on HM Revenue & Customs data, exclude land sold for non-agricultural purposes. Also excluded are: sales of less than 5 hectares in England, Wales and Scotland and sales of less than two hectares in Northern Ireland.

(b) For Northern Ireland there is a delay, thought to average about 3 months, between the date on which a sale is agreed and the date on which it is included in the analysis.

(c) Data for 2005 is currently unavailable.

Chapter **5**   Commodities

Summary

In 2006, the value of production at market prices for:

- wheat rose by 16 per cent to £1.2 billion;

- barley rose by 9.8 per cent to £412 million;

- oilseed rape rose by 17 per cent to £307 million;

- sugar beet fell by 37 per cent to £168 million;

- fresh vegetables rose by 9.1 per cent to £986 million;

- plants and flowers fell by 4.4 per cent to £744 million;

- potatoes rose by 24 per cent to £625 million;

- fresh fruit fell by 1.2 per cent to £377million;

- beef and veal rose by 13 per cent to £1.6 billion;

- pigmeat rose by 1.3 per cent to £687 million;

- mutton and lamb rose by 2.7 per cent to £702 million;

- poultrymeat rose by 1.0 per cent to £1.3 billion;

- milk fell by 3.6 per cent to £2.5 billion;

- eggs rose by 2.0 per cent to £357 million.

Methodology note

1 In 2005, eleven subsidy schemes directly linked to production of commodities were replaced with one single payment, the Single Payment Scheme. The Single Payment Scheme is decoupled from production and it is inappropriate to include it in the value of production of commodities. To enable comparison with previous years, all comments in the text on value of production have been made on a 'value of production at market prices' basis, excluding all subsidies and levies where applicable. An additional line showing value of production at market prices has been incorporated into the statistical tables where appropriate.

Total cereals (table 5.1)

2 The area of cereals planted fell by 2.0 per cent in 2006, although overall production was down by just 0.9 per cent due to an increase in yields. Prices were higher in 2006, closer to the prices in late 2003 and early 2004, which followed the drought affected 2003 harvest in the European Union. The total value of production at market prices was £1.6 billion, 14 per cent higher than in 2005.

Table 5.1 Total cereals; United Kingdom

Enquiries: Heather Wheeler on +44 (0)1904 455592   email: heather.wheeler@defra.gsi.gov.uk

Thousand tonnes (unless otherwise specified)   Calendar years

	Average of 1995-97	2002	2003	2004	2005	2006 (provisional)
Production						
Area (thousand hectares)	3 352	3 245	3 056	3 130	2 920	2 861
Volume of harvested production	23 331	22 965	21 494	22 005	21 005	20 822
Value of production (£ million) (a)	3 262	2 175	2 335	2 401	1 415	1 614
Value of production at market prices (£ million) (b)	2 429	1 455	1 608	1 692	1 415	1 614
Supply and use						
Production	23 331	22 965	21 494	22 005	21 005	20 822
Imports from: the EU	1 930	2 239	1 954	1 948	2 051	1 954
the rest of the world	632	772	646	463	578	599
Exports to: the EU	4 056	2 478	4 240	2 933	3 103	2 744
the rest of the world	1 399	254	827	-80	208	18
Total new supply	20 438	23 244	19 027	21 402	20 325	20 612
Change in farm and other stocks	474	2 083	-2 054	489	- 388	- 2
Total domestic uses	19 964	21 161	21 081	20 914	20 712	20 615
Production as % of total new supply for use in UK	114	99	113	103	103	101

(a) Includes arable area payments, but excludes set-aside payments and farm saved seed. Taxes, where applicable, are deducted.
(b) Excluding subsidies and taxes.

Wheat (table 5.2)

3   The area of wheat planted fell by 1.8 per cent but production fell by just 0.9 per cent due to an increase in yield. Grain quality was generally better than in 2005, in particular for milling wheat harvested before the arrival of rain in mid-August. Prices at the start of the year averaged £75 per tonne for milling wheat and £68 per tonne for feed wheat from the 2005 crop. Prices rose steadily through the year with very substantial increases in October when prices peaked at £102 per tonne for milling wheat and £92 per tonne for feed wheat in response to the lower world harvest (which was down around 30 million tonnes on 2005), quality problems in parts of Europe and the generally good quality of the crop in the United Kingdom. These prices are similar but not quite as high as those seen in late 2003 and early 2004 following the drought affected 2003 harvest in the European Union.

4   The overall annual price in 2006 was £83 per tonne for milling wheat, up £10 per tonne or 14 per cent and for feed wheat this was £78 per tonne, up £12 per tonne or 19 per cent on 2005. The overall value of production of wheat in 2006 increased by 16 per cent to £1.2 billion.

5   Imports fell by 1.1 per cent as millers sourced a higher proportion of their wheat from the improved quality crop in the United Kingdom, whereas exports fell more significantly, by 12 per cent, as a result of lower production and availability. The volume of wheat grain available for domestic use was down 1.0 per cent on 2005.

Barley (table 5.3)

6   There was a 6.1 per cent fall in the area of barley grown, mainly spring barley. With a slight increase in yields, this resulted in a 4.7 per cent reduction in production. The lower areas of barley reflected the better market outlook of other crops such as oilseed rape and the reduction in capacity of the malting industry in the United Kingdom. The winter barley harvest was completed before the arrival of the unsettled weather in mid-August and was generally of good quality with good yields. Harvest of the spring barley was affected by wet weather resulting in lower yields and quality.

7   Prices for premium malting barley started the year at £78 per tonne and for feed barley at £68 per tonne, both very similar to 2005 prices. They remained reasonably steady around these prices through to

Table 5.2 Wheat; United Kingdom

Enquiries: Heather Wheeler on +44 (0)1904 455592   email: heather.wheeler@defra.gsi.gov.uk

Thousand tonnes (unless otherwise specified)   Calendar years

	Average of 1995-97	2002	2003	2004	2005	2006 (provisional)
Production						
Area (thousand hectares)	1 957	1 996	1 837	1 990	1 867	1 833
Yield (tonnes per hectare)	7.7	8.0	7.8	7.8	8.0	8.0
Volume of harvested production	15 143	15 973	14 288	15 473	14 863	14 735
Value of production (£ million) (a)	2 082	1 479	1 534	1 664	1 001	1 158
of which: sales	1 457	836	1 150	1 025	927	1 105
subsidies (b)	493	446	440	447	..	..
on farm use	67	39	79	103	87	90
change in stocks	65	159	- 136	89	- 13	- 37
Value of production at market prices (£ million) (c)	1 588	1 033	1 094	1 217	1 001	1 158
Prices (average prices weighted by volumes of sales (£ per tonne))						
Milling wheat	114.4	70.9	83.2	85.8	72.9	83.4
Feed wheat	103.2	62.6	75.1	76.1	66.2	78.5
Supply and use						
Production	15 143	15 973	14 288	15 473	14 863	14 735
Imports from: the EU	607	826	633	432	688	662
the rest of the world	312	542	352	352	487	500
Exports to: the EU	2 767	1 429	3 121	2 250	2 444	2 161
the rest of the world	777	195	657	43	22	11
Total new supply	12 519	15 717	11 495	13 964	13 572	13 725
Change in farm and other stocks	385	2 522	-1 909	680	- 128	166
Total domestic uses	12 134	13 195	13 404	13 284	13 700	13 559
of which: flour milling	5 458	5 616	5 592	5 576	5 613	5 578
animal feed	5 504	6 478	6 712	6 637	7 019	6 890
seed	363	281	281	273	254	254
other uses and waste	808	820	819	798	815	837
Production as % of total new supply for use in UK	121	102	124	111	110	107
% of home grown wheat in milling grist	86	83	85	86	82	82

Wheat (Crop Years: July-June); United Kingdom

Thousand tonnes (unless otherwise specified)   Crop years: July-June

	2001/02	2002/03	2003/04	2004/05	2005/06
Production and output					
Volume of harvested production	11 580	15 973	14 288	15 473	14 863
Value of production (£ million) (a)	1 287	1 453	1 712	1 490	1 040
of which: sales	829	986	1 158	956	951
subsidies (b)	350	446	440	447	..
on farm use	44	39	120	86	90
change in stocks	64	- 17	- 6	2	-
Value of production at market prices (£ million)	937	1 007	1 272	1 043	1 040

(a) Excludes farm saved seed
(b) Includes arable area payments but excludes set-aside payments and is net of taxes.
(c) Excluding subsidies and taxes.

September when prices increased substantially and continued to increase for the rest of the year to over £110 per tonne for premium malting barley and £90 per tonne for feed barley. The average annual price in 2006 for malting barley was £92 per tonne, up £15 per tonne or 20 per cent compared to 2005, and for feed barley the price was £74 per tonne, up £9 per tonne or 13 per cent.

8   The price increase for malting barley was driven by lower production and quality issues in the United Kingdom and the European Union. Feed barley prices were supported by strong feed grain markets in the United Kingdom and the European Union and a very substantial fall in the Australian crop due to severe drought. The overall value of barley production increased by 9.8 per cent to £412 million.

Table 5.3 Barley; United Kingdom

Enquiries: Heather Wheeler +44 (0)1904 455592   email: heather.wheeler@defra.gsi.gov.uk

Thousand tonnes (unless otherwise specified)   Calendar years

	Average of 1995-97	2002	2003	2004	2005	2006 (provisional)
Production						
Area (thousand hectares)	1 274	1 101	1 078	1 010	938	881
Yield (tonnes per hectare)	5.9	5.6	5.9	5.8	5.9	5.9
Volume of harvested production	7 487	6 128	6 370	5 816	5 495	5 239
Value of production (£ million) (a)	1 090	624	720	657	375	412
of which: sales	537	261	323	273	250	294
subsidies (b)	310	242	253	232	..	..
on farm use	199	143	159	149	138	167
change in stocks	43	- 21	- 15	3	- 13	- 49
Value of production at market prices (£ million) (c)	780	382	467	425	375	412
Prices (average prices weighted by volumes of sales (£ per tonne))						
Malting barley	122.4	72.4	82.1	79.6	76.4	91.5
Feed barley	95.4	58.2	70.7	69.9	65.3	73.8
Supply and use						
Production	7 487	6 128	6 370	5 816	5 495	5 239
Imports from: the EU	89	51	51	75	84	83
the rest of the world	23	31	7	4	-	6
Exports to: the EU	1 132	893	947	583	612	535
the rest of the world	622	58	170	37	186	1
Total new supply	5 845	5 259	5 311	5 275	4 782	4 792
Change in farm and other stocks	114	- 515	- 129	- 154	- 211	- 284
Total domestic uses	5 731	5 774	5 440	5 429	4 993	5 076
of which: brewing/distilling	1 891	1 917	1 949	1 850	1 729	1 681
animal feed	3 570	3 651	3 296	3 406	3 082	3 214
seed	220	162	151	132	143	143
other uses and waste	49	43	44	41	39	38
Production as % of total new supply for use in UK	129	117	120	110	115	109

Barley (Crop Years: July-June); United Kingdom

Thousand tonnes (unless otherwise specified)   Crop years : July-June

	2001/02	2002/03	2003/04	2004/05	2005/06
Production and output					
Volume of harvested production	6 660	6 128	6 370	5 816	5 495
Value of production (£ million) (a)	706	644	740	621	384
of which: sales	292	254	336	257	235
subsidies (b)	259	242	253	232	..
on farm use	150	145	170	129	149
change in stocks	5	3	- 19	4	-
Value of production at market prices (£ million)	447	402	487	389	384

(a) Excludes farm saved seed
(b) Includes arable area payments but excludes set-aside payments and is net of taxes.
(c) Excluding subsidies and taxes.

9   Imports of barley increased by 6.0 per cent, but the absolute level of imports was low. Exports declined more significantly, by 33 per cent as a result of lower availability. The volume available for domestic use rose by 1.7 per cent with use for animal feed rising by 4.3 per cent while use by the malting sector fell by 2.8 per cent.

Oats (table 5.4)

10   Following a fall in crop area in 2005, the area of oats grown in 2006 increased by 33 per cent back to the levels seen in 2002 and 2003 as a result of the improved market outlook and high prices in late summer of 2005. Yields were also slightly better. Together these resulted in a 37 per cent increase in production. The value of production of oats increased by 7.3 per cent to £40 million.

Table 5.4 Oats; United Kingdom
Enquiries: Heather Wheeler on +44 (0)1904 455592   email: heather.wheeler@defra.gsi.gov.uk

Thousand tonnes (unless otherwise specified)   Calendar years

	Average of 1995-97	2002	2003	2004	2005	2006 (provisional)
Production						
Area (thousand hectares)	103	126	122	108	91	121
Yield (tonnes per hectare)	5.8	6.0	6.2	5.8	5.8	6.0
Volume of harvested production	595	753	749	627	532	728
Value of production (£ million) (a)	82	65	73	73	37	42
of which: sales:	42	27	33	30	27	34
subsidies (b)	25	28	29	25	..	..
on farm use	15	10	11	12	10	12
change in stocks	-	-	-	6	-	- 4
Value of production at market prices (£ million) (c)	57	37	45	47	37	42
Prices (average prices weighted by volumes of sales (£ per tonne))						
Milling oats	97.0	57.3	63.2	63.6	69.9	79.3
Feed oats	92.9	53.7	60.9	63.3	68.1	80.7
Supply and use						
Production	595	753	749	627	532	728
Imports from: the EU	7	18	11	31	32	41
the rest of the world	-	-	-	-	-	-
Exports to: the EU	142	144	157	80	35	36
the rest of the world	-	-	-	-	-	6
Total new supply	459	627	603	578	529	727
Change in farm and other stocks	- 25	75	- 16	- 37	- 48	115
Total domestic uses	485	552	619	615	577	612
of which: milling	242	312	322	321	343	373
animal feed	220	219	278	274	215	219
seed	20	17	15	17	17	17
other uses and waste	3	4	4	3	3	4
Production as % of total new supply for use in UK	131	120	124	108	101	100

(a) Excludes farm saved seed
(b) Includes arable area payments but excludes set-aside payments and is net of taxes.
(c) Excluding subsidies and taxes.

11   The tight supply situation from the low 2005 harvest and increased demand, especially for milling oats resulted in continued increases in prices. The average price for milling oats was up by £9 per tonne to £79 per tonne while feed oats was up by £13 per tonne to £81 per tonne. The volume of oats available for domestic use was up 7.1 per cent mainly as a consequence of increased use by the milling sector.

Oilseed rape (table 5.5)

12   The total area planted fell by 3.0 per cent in 2006 while yields rose by 1.4 per cent. The volume of harvested production fell by 1.7 per cent from that in 2005, which was the highest level of production recorded in the United Kingdom. Market prices in 2006 were on average 17 per cent higher than in 2005 and the value of production was up 17 per cent at £307 million.

13   The increase in prices reflected global demand for both food and non-food uses, including a growing biodiesel industry. Both imports and exports of oilseed rape were significantly higher in 2006; imports more than doubled to 123 thousand tonnes while exports rose by 20 per cent to 207 thousand tonnes. Most exports were to Germany, France and Belgium with imports sourced from France.

Linseed (table 5.6)

14   The area of linseed fell significantly in 2006, by 12 thousand hectares compared with 2005 to a more typical 36 thousand hectares. The majority of linseed is grown under contract. In 2005 plantings rose in response to higher prices following a poor harvest in Canada in 2004. A fall in yields contributed to a fall

Table 5.5 Oilseed rape; United Kingdom

Enquiries: Lindsay Holmes on +44 (0)1904 455563   email: lindsay.holmes@defra.gsi.gov.uk

Thousand tonnes (unless otherwise specified)   Calendar years

	Average of 1995-97	2002	2003	2004	2005	2006 (provisional)
Production						
Area (thousand hectares)	442	432	542	557	592	575
Yield (tonnes per hectare)	3.2	3.4	3.3	2.9	3.2	3.3
Volume of harvested production	1 392	1 468	1 771	1 608	1 901	1 870
of which:						
Production not on set-aside land:						
Area (thousand hectares)	385	357	460	498	519	499
Yield (tonnes per hectare) (a)	3.2	3.5	3.4	3.0	3.3	3.4
Production (a)	1 240	1 246	1 548	1 471	1 706	1 674
Production on set-aside land:						
Area (thousand hectares)	57	75	82	59	74	75
Yield (tonnes per hectare)	2.8	2.9	2.7	2.3	2.7	2.6
Production	152	221	223	138	196	196
Value of production (£ million) (b)	409	298	417	375	262	307
of which: sales	236	205	283	262	249	309
subsidies (c)	164	80	113	118	. .	. .
change in stocks	9	12	21	- 5	13	- 2
Value of production at market prices (£ million) (d)	245	217	304	257	262	307
Supply and use						
Production	1 392	1 468	1 771	1 608	1 901	1 870
Imports from: the EU	255	265	136	198	47	123
the rest of the world	97	62	-	-	-	-
Exports to: the EU	114	162	271	101	168	191
the rest of the world	21	45	1	3	4	16
Total new supply	1 609	1 587	1 634	1 703	1 776	1 786
Production as % of total new supply for use in UK	87	92	108	94	107	105

(a) These figures are on the basis of a standard (9%) moisture content.

(b) Value of production is calculated taking into account the price for oilseed rape produced not on set-aside with an average oil content of 43%

(c) Includes arable area payments but excludes set-aside payments.

(d) Excluding subsidies and taxes.

in production to 49 thousand tonnes, nearly half the level of production in 2005. Exports to the European Union fell by 69 per cent as a consequence of reduced availability. The value of sales was £8 million in 2006, down from £17 million in 2005.

Sugar beet and sugar (table 5.7)

15 A 12 per cent fall in the area of contracted sugar beet and lower average yields compared to 2005 led to a fall in production of 18 per cent to 7.2 million tonnes. Average sugar content was lower and the average market price fell by 24 per cent. Consequently, the value of production in 2006 was 37 per cent lower than 2005 at £168 million. Production as a percentage of total new supply for use in the United Kingdom was 70 per cent, only very slightly down on 2005.

16 Agreement was reached on major reform of the sugar regime in November 2005 and the new European Union sugar regime came into effect on 1 July 2006. Sugar prices in the European Union are to be cut by 36 per cent over four years alongside a voluntary restructuring scheme aimed at reducing production by around 6 million tonnes in the same period. Against this background the fall in area in 2006 was not unexpected and reflected that British Sugar bought 160 thousand tonnes of quota from growers in 2005, removing sugar beet production in the South West, Lancashire and Cheshire.

Table 5.6 Linseed; United Kingdom

Enquiries: Lindsay Holmes on +44 (0)1904 455563   email: lindsay.holmes@defra.gsi.gov.uk

Thousand tonnes (unless otherwise specified)   Calendar years

	Average of 1995-97	2002	2003	2004	2005	2006 (provisional)
Production						
Area (thousand hectares)	64	13	34	31	48	36
Yield (tonnes per hectare)	1.4	1.4	1.7	1.7	1.9	1.4
Volume of harvested production	91	18	59	52	89	49
of which:						
Production not on set-aside land:						
Area (thousand hectares)	58	12	32	30	45	32
Yield (tonnes per hectare) (a)	1.4	1.3	1.7	1.7	1.9	1.4
Production (a)	83	16	56	50	84	44
Production not on set-aside land:						
Area (thousand hectares)	5	1	2	1	3	4
Yield (tonnes per hectare) (a)	1.5	2.9	1.5	1.5	1.6	1.4
Production (a)	8	2	3	1	5	5
Value of production (£ million)	44	6	18	16	17	8
of which: sales	14	3	10	9	16	8
subsidies (b)	30	3	8	7	. .	. .
change in stocks	-	-	1	-	1	- 1
Value of production at market prices (£ million) (c)	14	3	10	9	17	8
Supply and use						
Production	91	18	59	52	89	49
Imports from: the EU	1	1	1	2	3	4
the rest of the world	45	21	10	3	-	2
Exports to: the EU	17	9	22	36	63	19
the rest of the world	1	-	-	1	-	-
Total new supply	119	32	48	21	30	35
Production as % of total new supply for use in UK	76	58	122	251	300	139

(a) These figures are based on a standard (9%) moisture content.
(b) Includes arable area payments but excludes set-aside payments.
(c) Excluding subsidies and taxes.

Table 5.7 Sugar beet and sugar; United Kingdom

Enquiries: Lindsay Holmes on +44 (0)1904 455563   email: lindsay.holmes@defra.gsi.gov.uk

Thousand tonnes (unless otherwise specified)   Calendar years

	Average of 1995-97	2002	2003	2004	2005	2006 (provisional)
Sugar beet						
Area (thousand hectares)	197	169	162	154	148	131
Yield (adjusted tonnes per hectare)	50.6	56.5	56.6	58.7	58.5	54.7
Volume of harvested production	9 978	9 557	9 168	9 042	8 687	7 150
Value of production (£ million)	347	283	280	278	269	168
Sugar content %	17.23	17.38	18.74	17.20	17.40	17.00
Prices (average market price (£ per adjusted tonne) (a)	35.4	29.6	30.5	30.8	30.9	23.5
Sugar (refined basis)						
Production (b)	1 430	1 430	1 368	1 390	1 341	1 100
Imports from: the EU	97	118	122	131	221	246
the rest of the world	1 124	1 104	1 008	1 140	1 104	1 080
Exports to: the EU	99	127	132	159	120	156
the rest of the world	377	329	565	628	668	709
Total new supply	2 175	2 197	1 800	1 874	1 879	1 561
Production as % of total new supply for use in UK	66	65	76	74	71	70

(a) Average price for all sugar beet, including transport allowance and bonuses.
(b) Sugar coming out of the factory in the early part of the new year is regarded as being part of the previous calendar year's production.

Peas and beans for stockfeed (table 5.8)

17 The value of production of peas and beans for stockfeed fell by 14 per cent to £61 million in 2006. The area of dried peas grown for stockfeed fell by 17 per cent and with a fall in yield of 13 per cent led to a 28 per cent fall in production. The area of field beans grown for stockfeed fell by 0.7 per cent in 2006 and with a fall in yield of 13 per cent led to a 13 per cent fall in production.

Table 5.8 Peas and beans harvested dry; United Kingdom
Enquiries: John Close on +44 (0)1904 455059   email: john.close@defra.gsi.gov.uk

Thousand tonnes (unless otherwise specified)

	Average of 1995-97	2002	2003	2004	2005	2006 (provisional)
Peas for harvesting dry (a)						
Area (thousand hectares)	67	77	65	51	41	34
Yield (tonnes per hectare)	3.8	3.4	3.9	3.5	3.8	3.3
Volume of harvested production	255	262	254	176	156	113
Value of production (£ million)	53	39	41	30	15	11
of which: sales	28	20	24	15	13	9
subsidies (b)	25	19	17	15	2	1
Value of production at market prices (£ million) (c)	28	20	24	15	13	9
Field beans						
Area (thousand hectares)	106	164	165	178	184	183
Yield (tonnes per hectare)	3.2	3.9	3.9	3.7	3.8	3.4
Volume of harvested production (a)	338	632	639	661	705	613
Value of production (£ million)	78	88	106	103	65	59
of which: sales	38	46	59	54	58	52
subsidies (b)	40	42	48	49	7	7
Value of production at market prices (£ million) (c)	38	46	59	54	58	52

(a) The figures presented here cover only that part of the crop which is harvested dry (about 80% to 90% of total production) and largely used for stockfeed. The remainder is included in fresh vegetables, table 5.9.
(b) Includes arable area payments but excludes set-aside payments; includes protein crop premium from 2004.
(c) Excluding subsidies and taxes.

Methodology note for fresh vegetables (table 5.9)

18 Valuations for the fresh vegetables sector have been subject to major changes during 2006. In particular, the methodology that calculates quantities and prices of output marketed through various distribution outlets (e.g. supermarkets, processors) was re-examined. This has led to a significant reduction in the overall value of production for a number of high value crops in comparison to data published in 2005. Revisions for these high value crops, e.g. carrots, have been phased back to 2000 to ensure that any adjustments project a more realistic trend and an accurate reflection of the industry.

Fresh vegetables (table 5.9)

19 The area of field vegetables grown in the open rose slightly in 2006, while the value of production rose by 10 per cent to £729 million. The value of production of cabbages rose by 13 per cent to £66 million due to increased yields and prices for summer, autumn and winter varieties. The value of production of carrots fell by 7.0 per cent to £88 million due to a fall in output and updates to methodology (see note above). The exceptional hot weather in July resulted in reduced demand for brassicas and irrigation was a concern prior to August. Production costs rose for some growers due to drought conditions in June and July. The value of production of mushrooms fell by 4.9 per cent to £99 million; the industry continued to face strong competition from imports, especially from Poland, and there were some further farm closures. Overall production levels were maintained as some continental producers were more adversely affected by the hot summer weather.

20 The area of protected vegetables fell by 9.0 per cent while the value of production rose by 6.2 per cent to £257 million. An increase in the value of production for field lettuces contributed to an increase in the overall value of production for lettuces of 22 per cent to £103 million. The value of production of tomatoes rose by 20 per cent to £83 million. Growers experienced relatively low spring light levels followed by an extremely hot July and then poor weather in August. Generally, there was good demand for salad produce particularly tomatoes, coinciding with higher production levels for some speciality tomatoes and higher prices.

Table 5.9 Fresh vegetables; United Kingdom

Enquiries: Lisa Szydlowska +44 (0)1904 455070   email: lisa.szydlowska@defra.gsi.gov.uk

Thousand tonnes (unless otherwise specified)

	Average of 1995-97	2002	2003	2004	2005	2006 (provisional)
Production						
Area (thousand hectares):	160	120	124	117	122	123
of which: grown in the open (a) (b)	158	119	124	117	122	122
protected (c)	2	1	1	1	1	1
Value of production (£ million):	1 032	845	905	827	904	986
of which: grown in the open	692	558	625	593	662	729
protected	340	287	280	234	242	257
of which: subsidies (d)	6	4	4	3	. .	. .
Selected crops: cabbages	70	52	56	53	58	66
carrots	88	83	72	75	95	88
cauliflowers	57	38	42	50	45	48
lettuces	124	86	105	87	84	103
mushrooms	167	137	119	106	104	99
peas	62	55	53	46	40	38
tomatoes	71	80	79	59	69	83
Value of production at market prices (£ million) (e)	1 025	841	901	824	904	986
Prices (farm gate price (£ per tonne))						
Selected crops: cauliflowers	251.8	329.6	331.7	296.3	344.6	363.1
tomatoes	624.8	793.7	1 042.3	751.2	871.4	993.1
Supply and use (f)						
Total production	2 945	2 573	2 543	2 556	2 686	2 564
Supplies from the Channel Islands	18	12	12	11	8	8
Imports from: the EU	1 402	1 365	1 415	1 498	1 736	1 495
the rest of the world	221	201	197	203	204	202
Exports to: the EU	235	105	97	74	57	66
the rest of the world	46	7	6	18	31	5
Total new supply	4 305	4 039	4 064	4 175	4 547	4 198
Production as % of total new supply for use in the UK	68	64	63	61	59	61

(a) Includes peas harvested dry for human consumption.
(b) Areas relate to field areas multiplied by the number of crops in the year and hence differ from those shown in table 3.2
(c) Excludes area of mushrooms.
(d) Arable area payments for peas harvested dry.
(e) Excluding subsidies and taxes.
(f) Trade figures relate to fresh produce where distinguishable.

Plants and flowers (table 5.10)

21 The area used for production of plants and flowers fell by 8.2 per cent in 2006 to 19 thousand hectares. The value of production fell by 4.4 per cent to £744 million. The value of production of the relatively small flowers and bulbs sector remained unchanged at £33 million. Daffodils remained the major volume flower crop in the United Kingdom although significant quantities of other flowers were grown especially gladioli and lilies. However, strong competition from imports kept prices static.

22 The value of production of ornamental hardy nursery stock fell by 3.5 per cent to £457 million. It was a challenging year for nursery stock sales with competition from imports. Sales of container plants began slowly with poor spring weather and fell away during the dry mid-summer. Autumn sales rose although prices remained largely static. Many growers rationalised their production to reduce costs and wastage.

23 The value of production of protected plants and flowers fell by 6.4 per cent to £254 million. Sales of bedding plants started well in May but poor weather conditions over bank holiday periods led to a fall in sales. Late season products (larger pots, tubs and baskets) increased slightly. Demand in the south-east was affected by water restrictions.

Table 5.10 Plants and flowers; United Kingdom

Enquiries: Lisa Szydlowska +44 (0)1904 455070   email: lisa.szydlowska@defra.gsi.gov.uk

Thousand tonnes (unless otherwise specified)   Calendar years

	Average of 1995-97	2002	2003	2004	2005	2006 (provisional)
Production						
Area (thousand hectares) (a):	20	22	21	21	20	19
Value of production (£ million)	660	750	772	787	778	744
of which: flowers and bulbs in the open (b)	51	32	33	33	33	33
hardy plants and flowers nursery stock	343	441	456	474	473	457
protected crops	266	277	283	279	272	254
Trade (£ million)						
Imports						
Bulbs	37	43	43	48	53	45
Cut flowers	269	549	552	528	522	496
Foliage	17	27	27	26	25	21
Indoor plants	75	112	100	102	105	95
Outdoor plants	28	42	55	53	69	68
Trees	17	47	52	57	64	57
Other	18	29	33	32	31	35
Total Imports (exc. Channel Islands)	461	849	862	846	869	817
Exports						
Bulbs	8	6	8	8	7	9
Cut flowers	14	18	23	19	22	25
Foliage	3	2	1	2	2	2
Indoor plants	2	1	-	1	2	-
Outdoor plants	3	3	4	4	4	4
Trees	1	1	2	2	2	2
Other	2	3	3	5	5	5
Total Exports	34	33	41	40	44	47

(a) Areas relate to field areas multiplied by the number of crops in the year and hence differ from those shown in table 3.2.
(b) Including forced flower bulbs.

Potatoes (table 5.11)

24 The area used for potatoes increased by 2.8 per cent in 2006. The yield for early potatoes was 8.7 per cent higher than in 2005, while yields for the main crop were 8.4 per cent lower. An overall fall in yield offset the higher crop area and production of potatoes fell by 4.6 per cent to 5.7 million tonnes. Lower yields and reduced imports helped prices to recover from the low levels seen in 2005 and increase by 25 per cent. Despite lower production, the higher prices resulted in an increase of 24 per cent in the value of production to £625 million in 2006.

Table 5.11 Potatoes; United Kingdom
Enquiries: Alex Clothier +44 (0)1904 455068

email: alex.clothier@defra.gsi.gov.uk

Thousand tonnes (unless otherwise specified)

Calendar years

2006

	Average of 1995-97	2002	2003	2004	2005	2006 (provisional)
Production						
Area (thousand hectares)	172	158	145	149	137	141
of which: early	16	14	14	15	12	11
maincrop	156	144	132	134	124	129
Yield (tonnes per hectare):						
early	22.7	16.4	20.0	17.4	15.2	16.5
maincrop	42.1	46.7	42.9	45.2	46.4	42.5
overall	40.3	44.0	40.7	42.5	43.5	40.4
Volume of harvested production	6 920	6 966	5 918	6 316	5 961	5 684
of which: early	362	235	271	257	189	187
maincrop	6 559	6 732	5 647	6 060	5 771	5 498
End year stocks	3 636	3 386	2 915	3 006	2 885	2 743
Value of production (£ million)	707	480	517	654	503	625
of which: sales	653	469	559	629	503	619
on farm seed use	28	15	6	13	12	23
change in stocks	26	- 4	- 48	11	- 12	- 17
Prices (average price paid to registered producers (£ per tonne)) (a)						
early potatoes	109.2	110.3	132.3	178.5	140.8	193.6
maincrop potatoes	117.0	75.5	99.1	111.3	93.6	121.1
all potatoes	118.2	81.1	102.8	117.0	98.9	123.7
Supply and use						
Total production	6 920	6 966	5 918	6 316	5 961	5 684
Supplies from the Channel Islands	49	39	31	31	38	30
Imports	1 086	1 788	1 709	1 777	1 702	1 571
of which:						
early from:						
the EU	64	96	68	97	71	63
the rest of the world	150	68	75	95	127	103
maincrop from:						
the EU	135	152	124	154	245	178
the rest of the world	5	10	7	12	7	1
processed (raw equivalent) from:						
the EU	663	1 425	1 390	1 371	1 225	1 201
the rest of the world	37	10	11	12	11	14
seed from:						
the EU	32	28	34	36	17	11
the rest of the world	-	-	-	-	-	-
Exports	328	461	444	386	410	416
of which:						
raw to:						
the EU	120	176	175	97	118	149
the rest of the world	42	4	7	5	5	8
processed (raw equivalent) to:						
the EU	65	155	166	192	163	134
the rest of the world	26	21	20	22	27	20
seed to:						
the EU	34	49	14	19	46	44
the rest of the world	40	56	62	50	50	61
Total new supply	7 727	8 334	7 213	7 739	7 291	6 869
Change in stocks	176	- 49	- 471	91	- 121	- 142
Total domestic uses	7 552	8 383	7 684	7 649	7 412	7 012
of which: used for human consumption	6 129	6 892	6 446	6 542	6 169	5 956
seed for home crops (including seed imports)	484	416	369	369	389	387
chats, waste and retained stockfeed	939	1 076	868	738	854	668
Production as % of total new supply for use in the UK	90%	84%	82%	82%	82%	83%

continued

Table 5.11 continued

Potatoes (Crop Years: June-May); United Kingdom

Thousand tonnes (unless otherwise specified)   Crop years: June-May

	2001/02	2002/03	2003/04	2004/05	2005/06 (provisional)
Production					
Volume of harvested production	6 649	6 966	5 918	6 316	5 961
Value of production (£ million)	561	422	699	541	557
of which: sales	532	413	691	513	543
on farm seed use	18	7	8	20	17
change in stocks	12	2	1	7	- 2
Prices (average realised return (£ per tonne) (a)	98.8	71.9	131.4	99.6	106.3

(a) Takes account of support buying, seed sales and sacks where appropriate.

Table 5.12 Fresh fruit; United Kingdom

Enquiries: Lisa Szydlowska +44 (0)1904 455070   email: lisa.szydlowska@defra.gsi.gov.uk

Thousand tonnes (unless otherwise specified)   Calendar years

	Average of 1995-97	2002	2003	2004	2005	2006 (provisional)
Production						
Area (thousand hectares):	39	28	27	26	27	28
of which: orchard fruit (a)	27	20	19	18	18	19
soft fruit (b)	12	8	8	8	9	9
End year stocks (c)	82	62	61	81	90	123
Value of production (£ million) (d):	249	251	310	316	382	377
of which: orchard fruit	111	85	102	105	115	144
soft fruit	132	143	175	173	235	201
of which: sales	261	260	309	307	378	366
change in stocks (c)	- 11	- 8	1	9	4	12
Selected crops: dessert apples	55	32	32	36	47	57
culinary apples	32	27	35	28	32	38
pears	15	14	10	8	8	11
raspberries	31	31	40	41	73	65
strawberries	71	94	109	100	134	111
Prices (farm gate price (£ per tonne)						
Selected crops: dessert apples	490.7	385.2	460.3	348.9	401.9	607.5
culinary apples	281.4	285.7	471.7	259.1	350.8	355.9
pears	446.9	402.9	344.0	354.9	341.3	363.7
Supply and use (e)						
Total production	351	294	269	293	360	384
Imports from: the EU	1 246	1 362	1 244	1 258	1 312	1 190
the rest of the world	1 306	1 640	1 752	1 935	1 992	2 004
Exports to: the EU	79	69	78	105	119	138
the rest of the world	2	1	1	1	1	1
Total new supply	2 825	3 226	3 186	3 380	3 543	3 438
Change in stocks	- 23	- 19	- 1	20	8	33
Total domestic uses	2 848	3 246	3 187	3 360	3 534	3 405
Production as % of total new supply for use in the UK	13	9	8	9	10	11

(a) Includes field area of commercial orchards only, and may therefore differ from the area in table 3.2, which also includes non-commercial orchards.
(b) Excludes area of wine grapes and may therefore differ from the area in table 3.2.
(c) Stocks relate to apples and pears.
(d) Includes glasshouse fruit.
(e) Trade figures relate to fresh produce where distinguishable.

Fresh fruit (table 5.12)

25 The area of orchard fruit increased by 3.1 per cent in 2006 and the value of production increased by 24 per cent to £144 million. Early apples sold well in 2006, although crop volumes were variable between orchards. An upturn in the demand for fruit for cider production led to an increase in the prices for cider and culinary fruit. The value of production for dessert apples increased by 22 per cent to £57 million with a strong demand for Gala varieties. Culinary apples increased by 20 per cent to £38 million.

26 The area of soft fruit fell slightly, by 0.9 per cent and the value of production decreased by 14 per cent to £201 million. The value of production of strawberries fell by 18 per cent to £111 million and raspberries fell by 11 per cent to £65 million. In general the hot summer brought about a rapid ripening of soft fruit and led to an over supply of fruit due to an expanded production base.

27 Prices for the summer strawberry crop were lower than expected due in part to a competitive market and hot weather conditions in June and July which adversely affected the fruit size and quality and led to some wastage. Imports in particular from the USA filled the gap in the market.

Methodology note for livestock tables (tables 5.13, 5.14 and 5.15)

28 Two measures of production are shown in tables 5.13, 5.14 and 5.15. Gross indigenous production is a measure of animal production commonly used in other European Union Member States and is therefore useful for making international comparisons. It is measured as total slaughterings plus all live exports minus all live imports of breeding and non-breeding livestock. Home-fed production includes imports and exports of non-breeding animals only, i.e. it is measured as total slaughterings plus live exports (non-breeding) minus live imports (non-breeding).

Cattle and calves: beef and veal (table 5.13)

29 The value of production at market prices of beef and veal rose by 13 per cent in 2006 to £1.6 billion. This was due to increased home production as well as strong finished cattle prices which rose by 8.2 per cent in 2006 to an average of 110.6 pence per kg liveweight. Home-fed production of beef and veal rose by 12 per cent in 2006. Prime cattle marketings fell by 3.0 per cent; the rise in production was due to cow and adult bulls born after 1 August 1996 now being allowed to enter the food chain following the ending of the Over Thirty Month Scheme. The ban on exports of cattle and beef from the United Kingdom was lifted in May 2006 and exports steadily increased throughout the year. Imports of beef and veal fell by 21 per cent as a result of increased home-fed production.

Pigs and pigmeat (table 5.14)

30 The value of production of pigmeat rose by 1.3 per cent to £687 million, the highest value seen since 2002. Prices strengthened in the last six months of 2006, resulting in an average clean pig price of 104.2 pence per kg deadweight, 2.1 pence higher than in 2005. Clean pig marketings fell only slightly in 2006, with the decline being less severe than in recent years. Average clean pig carcase weights remained stable at 75 kg per head. Home-fed production of pork rose slightly to 582 thousand tonnes while the quantity of pork available for domestic use fell slightly to 937 thousand tonnes. Home-cured production of bacon fell by 7.1 per cent to 199 thousand tonnes with the quantity available for domestic use also falling by 7.1 per cent to 453 thousand tonnes. Imports accounted for more than half of the domestic supplies of bacon and ham.

Table 5.13 Cattle and calves: beef and veal; United Kingdom

Enquiries: Sarah Thompson on +44 (0)1904 455097   email: sarah.thompson@defra.gsi.gov.uk

Thousand tonnes (unless otherwise stated)   Calendar years

	Average of 1995-97	2002	2003	2004	2005	2006 (provisional)
Population						
Total cattle and calves (thousand head at June)	11 844	10 345	10 508	10 588	10 392	10 270
of which: dairy cows	2 556	2 227	2 191	2 129	2 063	2 066
beef cows	1 855	1 657	1 698	1 736	1 762	1 733
heifers in calf	814	728	679	690	638	645
Production (a)						
Total home-fed marketings (thousand head)	2 833	2 289	2 286	2 355	2 421	2 750
of which: steers, heifers and young bulls	2 295	2 187	2 194	2 250	2 289	2 221
calves	203	98	87	101	111	138
cows and adult bulls	335	4	5	4	22	391
Average dressed carcase weight (kg) (b):						
steers, heifers and young bulls	305	315	319	319	334	335
calves	49	26	26	26	26	28
cows and adult bulls	280	243	237	264	344	316
Production (dressed carcase weight):						
home-fed production	803	694	703	722	776	869
gross indigenous production	799	682	690	707	755	854
Value of production (£ million)	2 467	2 125	2 188	2 331	1 585	1 639
value of home-fed production	1 560	1 113	1 174	1 281	1 374	1 588
subsidies (c)	980	979	960	1 053	196	71
change in work-in-progress (d)	- 67	36	55	- 2	17	- 19
less imported livestock	6	3	2	1	2	1
plus breeding animals exported	-	..	..	..	..	-
Value of production at market prices (£ million) (e)	1 487	1 146	1 227	1 278	1 389	1 568
Prices						
Store cattle (£ per head) (f):						
Hereford/cross bull calves (g)	148.4	84.9	112.7	113.7	81.5	76.3
Beef/cross yearling steers (h)	449.0	403.8	451.5	465.3	429.0	444.8
Finished cattle (pence per kg liveweight): All prime cattle	108.5	91.4	95.2	101.2	102.2	110.6
Over Thirty Month Scheme and Older Cattle Disposal Scheme (i)						
Over Thirty Month Scheme:						
prime cattle throughput (thousand head)	221	65	43	36	27	1
cull cattle throughput (thousand head)	770	766	679	761	683	49
receipts (£ million)	443.0	236.7	198.9	204.2	177.5	16.7
Older Cattle Disposal Scheme:						
throughput (thousand head)	..	..	..	..	..	150
receipts (£ million)	..	..	..	..	..	36.8
Supply and use (dressed carcase weight) (j)						
Home-fed production (a)	803	694	703	722	776	869
Imports from: the EU (k) (l)	127	211	222	235	237	187
the rest of the world	72	88	85	88	86	68
Exports to: the EU (l)	113	10	10	11	14	44
the rest of the world	29	-	-	-	-	-
Total new supply	860	983	1 000	1 034	1 084	1 079
Change in stocks	30	- 6	2	8	- 10	2
Total domestic uses	831	989	998	1 026	1 094	1 077
Home-fed production as % of total new supply for use in the UK	93%	71%	70%	70%	72%	81%
Closing stocks	113	33	35	42	33	35

(a) Measures of marketings, production and value exclude all cattle removed from the food chain by the Over Thirty Month Scheme and the Older Cattle Disposal Scheme. Payments to producers through these schemes are included as subsidies in the value of production.
(b) Average dressed carcase weight of animals fed and slaughtered in the United Kingdom.
(c) Comprising hill livestock compensatory allowances, suckler cow premium, beef special premium, deseasonalisation premium, extensification payments, slaughter premium and Scottish Beef Calf Scheme. Includes payments made under the Over Thirty Month Scheme and the Calf Processing Aid Scheme.
(d) A valuation of the change in work in progress of animals to be slaughtered.
(e) Excluding subsidies and taxes.
(f) Average prices at representative markets in England and Wales.
(g) Category changes: Prior to January 2002, 1st quality Hereford/cross bull calves. From January 2002, Hereford/cross bull calves.
(h) Category changes: Prior to January 2002, Hereford/cross, Charolais/cross, Limousin/cross, Simmental/cross, Belgian blue/cross, other continental/cross, other beef/dairy cross, other beef/beef cross. From January 2002, Hereford/cross, Continental/cross, others.

continued

Table 5.13 continued

(i) Cattle slaughtered under the Over Thirty Month Scheme and Older Cattle Disposal Scheme are not included within the volume of production. Receipts for these scheme are included in the value of production as subsidies.
(j) Does not include meat offals or trade in preserved or manufactured meat products. Boneless meat has been converted to bone-in weights.
(k) Includes meat from finished animals imported from the Irish Republic.
(l) Adjusted, as necessary, for unrecorded trade in live animals.

Table 5.14 Pigs and pigmeat; United Kingdom
Enquiries: Sarah Thompson on +44 (0)1904 455097   email: sarah.thompson@defra.gsi.gov.uk

Thousand tonnes (unless otherwise specified)

	Average of 1995-97	2002	2003	2004	2005	2006 (provisional)
Population						
Total pigs (thousand head at June)	7 763	5 588	5 046	5 159	4 862	4 933
of which: sows in pig and other sows for breeding	662	483	442	449	403	401
gilts in pig	108	74	73	66	67	67
Production						
Total home-fed marketings (thousand head)	14 828	10 282	9 007	8 827	8 777	8 746
of which: clean pigs	14 460	9 966	8 760	8 582	8 561	8 538
sows and boars	368	316	247	245	216	208
Average dressed carcase weight (kg) (a):						
clean pigs	68	73	74	75	75	75
sows and boars	140	156	161	158	156	153
Production (dressed carcase weight):						
home-fed production	1 032	774	688	678	675	670
gross indigenous production	1 031	774	689	678	676	671
Value of production (£ million)	1 245	687	672	679	678	687
of which: value of home-fed production	1 237	694	682	677	671	681
change in work in progress (b)	1	- 10	- 14	- 1	-	- 1
less imported livestock	..	..	..	..	..	..
plus breeding animals exported	7	2	3	3	6	7
Prices (pence per kg deadweight)						
Clean pigs	122.5	93.3	102.6	102.9	102.1	104.2
Supply and use of pork (dressed carcase weight) (c) (d)						
Home-fed production	820	613	569	576	577	582
Imports from: the EU (e)	181	310	421	420	467	454
the rest of the world	1	6	3	8	4	8
Exports to: the EU (f)	185	80	67	79	92	90
the rest of the world	26	15	7	15	10	16
Total new supply	791	834	919	910	947	938
Change in stocks	2	- 2	- 2	- 1	2	1
Total domestic uses	790	836	921	911	945	937
Home-fed production as % of total new supply for use in the UK	104%	73%	62%	63%	61%	62%
Closing stocks	14	10	8	8	9	11
Supply and use of bacon and ham (product weight) (c)						
Home-cured production	244	215	214	211	214	199
Imports from: the EU	243	292	301	302	283	264
the rest of the world	-	-	-	-	-	-
Exports to: the EU	6	10	14	12	10	9
the rest of the world	-	1	-	1	-	1
Total new supply	481	496	502	499	487	454
Change in stocks	-	- 2	2	1	- 1	1
Total domestic uses	481	498	500	498	488	453
Home-cured production as % of total new supply for use in UK	51%	43%	43%	42%	44%	44%
Closing stocks	3	3	5	7	6	6

(a) Average dressed carcase weight of animals fed and slaughtered in the United Kingdom.
(b) A valuation of the change in work in progress of animals to be slaughtered.
(c) Does not include meat offals or trade in preserved or manufactured meat products.
(d) Boneless meat has been converted to bone-in weights.
(e) Includes meat from finished animals imported from the Irish Republic.
(f) Adjusted, as necessary, for unrecorded trade in live animals.

Sheep and lambs: mutton and lamb (table 5.15)

31 The value of production of sheepmeat rose by 2.7 per cent in 2006 to £702 million, primarily due to increases in prices of about 4.5 per cent. Clean sheep marketings remained fairly static in 2006 with an average carcase weight of about 19 kg per head, just slightly down on the previous year. As a result, home-fed production dropped a little, to 333 thousand tonnes, with 375 thousand tonnes of sheepmeat available for domestic use.

Table 5.15 Sheep and lambs: mutton and lamb; United Kingdom

Enquiries: Sarah Thompson on +44 (0)1904 455097   email: sarah.thompson@defra.gsi.gov.uk

Thousand tonnes (unless otherwise specified)   Calendar years

	Average of 1995-97	2002	2003	2004	2005	2006 (provisional)
Population						
Total sheep and lambs (thousand head at June)	42 738	35 834	35 812	35 817	35 416	34 722
of which: ewes and shearlings	20 692	17 630	17 580	17 630	16 935	16 637
lambs under one year old	20 942	17 310	17 322	17 238	17 488	17 058
Production						
Total home-fed marketings (thousand head)	19 356	15 342	15 436	15 493	16 539	16 541
of which: clean sheep and lambs	17 018	13 417	13 493	13 530	14 300	14 296
ewes and rams	2 338	1 925	1 943	1 963	2 238	2 245
Average dressed carcase weight (kg) (a):						
clean sheep and lambs	18	19	19	19	19	19
ewes and rams	28	29	28	29	28	28
Production (dressed carcase weight):						
home-fed production	369	307	310	319	336	333
gross indigenous production	369	307	310	319	336	333
Value of production (£ million)	1 252	888	984	1 048	683	702
of which: value of home-fed production	827	623	701	708	688	711
subsidies (b)	425	275	286	322	..	..
change in work in progress (c)	7	- 10	- 4	17	- 5	- 1
less imported livestock	6	-	-	-	-	8
plus breeding animals exported	-	-	-	-	-	-
Value of production at market prices (£ million) (d)	827	613	698	726	683	702
Prices						
Store sheep (£ per head): (e)						
Lambs, hoggets and tegs	48.2	..	37.7	..	30.5	31.2
Finished sheep (pence per kg estimated dressed carcase weight) (f):						
Great Britain	252.9	233.4	271.1	262.6	250.0	262.2
Northern Ireland	234.4	222.8	239.9	227.8	223.8	233.3
Supply and use (dressed carcase weight) (g)						
Home-fed production	369	307	310	319	336	333
Imports from: the EU (h)	20	14	19	22	20	21
the rest of the world	132	109	117	120	113	119
Exports to: the EU (i)	154	69	83	85	93	98
the rest of the world	2	1	1	1	1	1
Total new supply	365	360	362	375	375	374
Change in stocks	2	- 1	-	- 2	1	- 1
Total domestic uses	363	361	362	377	373	375
Home-fed production as % of total new supply for use in the UK	101%	85%	86%	85%	90%	89%
Closing stocks	14	8	8	6	8	7

(a) Average dressed carcase weight of animals fed and slaughtered in the United Kingdom.

(b) Comprising hill livestock compensatory allowances and sheep annual premium.

(c) A valuation of the change in work in progress of animals to be slaughtered.

(d) Excluding subsidies and taxes.

(e) Average prices at representative markets in England and Wales, excluding prices at autumn hill sheep sales. Category changes: Prior to January 2002, 1st quality lambs, hoggets and tegs. From January 2002, lambs, hoggets and tegs.

(f) Unweighted average of weekly prices at representative markets as reported to the European Commission.

(g) Does not include meat offals or trade in preserved or manufactured meat products. Boneless meat has been converted to bone-in weights.

(h) Includes meat from finished animals imported from the Irish Republic.

(i) Adjusted, as necessary, for unrecorded trade in live animals.

Poultry and poultrymeat (table 5.16)

32 The value of production of poultrymeat rose by 1.0 per cent to £1.3 billion with higher prices offsetting a 2.4 per cent fall in the quantity of poultrymeat produced. About 75 per cent of the value of poultrymeat comes from the production of chicken, other table fowls and boiling fowls.

Table 5.16 Poultry and poultrymeat; United Kingdom

Enquiries: Michael Chatten on +44 (0)1904 455098   email: michael.j.chatten@defra.gsi.gov.uk

Thousand tonnes (unless otherwise specified)   Calendar years

	Average of 1995-97	2002	2003	2004	2005	2006 (provisional)
Population						
Number (thousand head at June) (b):	156 888	168 996	178 800	181 759	173 909	173 081
of which: chickens and other table fowls	88 268	105 137	116 738	119 888	111 475	110 672
birds in the laying flock (c)	32 370	28 778	29 274	29 655	29 544	28 632
growing pullets	10 609	9 784	8 286	8 156	10 928	9 625
fowls for breeding	8 539	11 307	10 988	10 125	8 561	9 273
turkeys, ducks, geese & all other poultry (d)	17 101	13 991	13 514	13 935	13 400	14 879
Production						
Slaughterings (millions) (c):	819	862	882	882	903	880
of which: fowls	765	819	840	843	864	844
turkeys	38	23	21	21	19	17
ducks & geese	16	20	20	18	19	19
Production (carcase weight) (f):	1 478	1 557	1 570	1 564	1 582	1 544
of which: chickens and other table fowls	1 092	1 222	1 245	1 246	1 281	1 265
boiling fowls (culled hens)	54	51	50	48	51	50
turkeys	294	238	229	228	206	185
ducks & geese	37	46	46	41	45	44
Value of production (£ million):	1 466	1 261	1 343	1 332	1 302	1 315
of which: fowls	971	845	899	922	943	973
change in work in progress in fowls (g)	4	- 22	3	11	- 25	- 16
turkeys, ducks, geese	442	356	370	322	307	284
exports of live poultry	45	70	69	74	76	73
hatching eggs for export	14	24	19	23	20	15
less live poultry imported	6	5	5	6	6	5
less hatching eggs imported	4	7	11	14	13	10
Prices (average producer prices (pence per kg carcase weight)):						
chickens and other table fowls	87.2	68.8	71.9	73.6	73.2	76.5
boiling fowls (culled hens)	34.7	9.8	9.6	9.5	9.6	10.2
turkeys	130.3	113.8	124.1	109.7	109.0	108.3
ducks	150.5	169.2	169.1	158.6	163.6	170.4
geese	210.3	396.2	450.7	441.8	491.1	468.1
Supply and use (carcase weight) (f)						
Production	1 478	1 557	1 570	1 564	1 582	1 544
Imports from: the EU	256	332	361	410	400	404
the rest of the world	14	34	50	67	85	51
Exports to: the EU	116	159	171	196	206	162
the rest of the world	67	54	89	72	55	67
Total new supply	1 565	1 709	1 721	1 773	1 805	1 769
Change in stocks	10	- 9	11	- 24	10	6
Total domestic uses	1 555	1 719	1 710	1 797	1 795	1 763
Production as % of total new supply for use in the UK	94%	91%	91%	88%	88%	87%

(a) For comparability with other years, the figures for 1992, 1998 and 2004 have been adjusted from a 53-week to a 52-week basis where appropriate.
(b) Improvements to the Census methodology were introduced in 1997 onwards to account for poultry production on unregistered units. Consequently the figures from 1997 onwards are not directly comparable with those for earlier years.
(c) Hens and pullets kept mainly for producing eggs for eating.
(d) Data prior to 1996 does not include figures for turkeys.
(e) Slaughtering figures include registered and un-registered slaughterhouses.
(f) Excludes offal.
(g) A valuation of the change in work-in-progress of birds to be slaughtered.

33 Average producer prices for broilers, boilers and ducks all rose while prices for turkeys and geese fell. The average producer price for broilers rose by 4.5 per cent to 76.5 pence per kg carcase weight, the price for boilers rose by 6.3 per cent to 10.2 pence per kg carcase weight and the price for ducks rose by 4.1 per cent to 170.4 pence per kg carcase weight. The average producer price for turkeys fell by 0.6 per cent to 108.3 pence per kg carcase weight and the price for geese fell by 4.7 per cent to 468.1 pence per kg carcase weight.

34 The 2.4 per cent fall in production and a 6.1 per cent fall in imports were offset by a 12 per cent fall in exports. The quantity of poultrymeat available for domestic use fell by 1.8 per cent to just under 1.8 million tonnes.

Table 5.17 Milk; United Kingdom
Enquiries: Lesly Lawton on +44 (0)1904 455095   email: lesly.lawton@defra.gsi.gov.uk

Million litres (unless otherwise specified)   Calendar years

	Average of 1995-97	2002	2003	2004	2005	2006 (provisional)
Population and yield						
Dairy herd (annual average, thousand head) (a)	2 567	2 224	2 203	2 151	2 083	2 045
Average yield per dairy cow (litres per annum)	5 577	6 494	6 618	6 571	6 749	6 815
Production						
Milk from the dairy herd (b)	14 305	14 441	14 580	14 132	14 058	13 938
Milk from the beef herd (b)	7	7	7	7	7	7
less on farm waste and milk fed to stock	270	269	223	209	226	225
Volume for human consumption	14 042	14 178	14 364	13 930	13 839	13 720
Value of production (£ million)	3 382	2 466	2 629	2 711	2 592	2 501
of which: raw milk leaving farm (c)	3 310	2 391	2 556	2 538	2 524	2 433
raw milk processed on farm (d)	109	75	73	73	69	68
subsidies	..	..	..	108	..	..
less levies	37	..	..	8	1	..
Value of production at market prices (£ million) (e)	3 418	2 466	2 629	2 611	2 593	2 501
Prices (average price received by milk producers, net of delivery charges (pence per litre)) (f)						
Farmgate price of milk excluding bonus payments	23.8	17.1	18.0	18.5	18.5	17.9
Farmgate price of milk including bonus payments	24.0	17.1	18.0	18.5	18.5	18.0
Supply and use (g)						
Production	14 312	14 448	14 587	14 139	14 065	13 945
Imports	140	72	105	69	50	43
Exports	216	421	400	434	624	627
Total new supply	14 236	14 099	14 292	13 774	13 491	13 361
of which:						
for liquid consumption	6 865	6 824	6 754	6 694	6 655	6 726
for manufacture	6 945	6 884	7 139	6 725	6 490	6 287
of which: butter (h)	274	279	268	249	266	242
cheese	3 313	3 369	3 315	3 402	3 706	3 829
cream (h)	233	303	316	320	302	316
condensed milk (i)	691	491	375	359	351	303
milk powder	1 964	1 798	2 267	1 774	1 294	1 165
other	471	644	598	620	571	431
dairy wastage and stock change	101	85	134	109	90	94
other uses (j)	325	306	266	245	256	254

(a) Dairy herd is defined as cows and heifers in milk plus cows in calf but not in milk, kept mainly for producing milk or rearing calves for the dairy herd.
(b) Excludes suckled milk.
(c) Value of raw milk sold to other businesses for processing.
(d) Value of milk and milk products processed on farm and sold direct to the consumer.
(e) Excluding subsidies and taxes/levies.
(f) No deduction is made for superlevy. In the current year, estimated bonuses for April to December have been included.
(g) Aggregated data from surveys run by Defra, SEERAD and DARD, NI, on the utilisation of milk by dairies.
(h) Includes the utilisation of the residual fat of low fat liquid milk production.
(i) Includes condensed milk used in the production of chocolate crumb and in the production of machine skimmed milk.
(j) Includes farmhouse consumption, milk fed to stock and on farm waste. Excludes suckled milk.

Milk (table 5.17)

35 The total value at market prices of milk produced for human consumption fell by 3.6 per cent in 2006 to £2.5 billion. The value of raw milk sold from farms to dairy companies for processing into pasteurised drinking milk, cheese, butter and other milk products, accounted for over 97 per cent of the total value in 2006. A 3.6 per cent fall in the value of milk sold to dairy companies was due to a 2.8 per cent fall in the average farmgate price of milk to 18.0 pence per litre and a 0.9 per cent fall in the volume milk sold to dairies. The value of milk processed on farm for sale direct to consumers fell by 2.3 per cent and accounted for 2.7 per cent of the total value of milk produced for human consumption in 2006. There was no superlevy charge in 2006 as the United Kingdom was under the national quota level in the 2005/06 quota year.

Milk products (table 5.18)

36 Production of butter fell by 9.2 per cent in 2006, imports rose by 9.9 per cent and exports, particularly to non-European Union countries, fell. There was little change in the quantity of butter available for domestic use. Stocks of butter in intervention remain low with the few purchases in 2006 being followed by sales out of intervention. As a result of CAP reform, intervention prices for butter have been reduced each year since 2004. By the end of 2006 market prices were about 10 per cent above the new intervention price.

37 Production of cheese rose by 3.3 per cent and imports rose by 6.5 per cent in 2006. This was only partly offset by increased exports leading to a 3.6 per cent increase in the quantity of cheese available for domestic use to 680 thousand tonnes.

38 Production of skimmed milk powder (SMP) fell by 1.6 per cent to 68 thousand tonnes in 2006. Imports fell by over 40 per cent while exports rose by 5.9 per cent leading to a 29 per cent reduction in the quantity of SMP available for domestic use. As a result of CAP reform, intervention prices for SMP have been reduced each year since 2004. By the end of 2006 market prices were about 30 per cent above the new intervention price and there were no stocks of SMP in intervention in the United Kingdom.

Table 5.18 Milk products; United Kingdom

These tables show production and supplies of milk products manufactured by both dairy companies and on farm. The figures are quoted in thousand tonnes and are not directly comparable with the figures shown in table 5.17, which are quoted in million litres.
Enquiries: Lesly Lawton on +44 (0)1904 455095   email: lesly.lawton@defra.gsi.gov.uk

Thousand tonnes (unless otherwise specified)		Average of 1995-97	2002	2003	2004	2005	Calendar years 2006 (provisional)
Butter (a)							
Production (b)(c)		134	136	131	122	130	118
Imports from: (d)	the EU	55	97	118	114	128	141
	the rest of the world	58	19	-	-	-	-
Exports to:	the EU (e)	47	35	33	22	26	26
	the rest of the world	13	4	11	12	19	9
Total new supply (e)		187	213	205	201	213	224
Change in stocks (f)		- 4	1	- 2	- 8	- 6	1
Total domestic uses (e)(f)		191	212	207	209	220	223
Production as % of total new supply for use in the UK		72%	64%	64%	61%	61%	53%
Closing stocks (f)		11	19	17	9	3	4

continued

Table 5.18 continued

Thousand tonnes (unless otherwise specified)	Average of 1995-97	2002	2003	2004	2005	2006 (provisional)
Cheese						
Production (c)	374	371	352	359	391	404
Imports (g) from: the EU	204	255	288	310	333	353
the rest of the world	25	31	28	25	20	23
Exports (g) to: the EU	41	64	73	78	83	90
the rest of the world	15	19	17	16	13	12
Total new supply	547	574	577	600	648	679
Change in stocks	- 1	- 3	- 5	4	- 8	- 1
Total domestic uses	548	576	583	596	656	680
Production as % of total new supply for use in the UK	68%	65%	61%	60%	60%	60%
Closing stocks (h)	17	12	7	11	3	3
Cream - fresh, frozen, sterilized						
Production (b) (c)	236	308	321	325	306	321
Imports from: the EU	7	15	15	15	30	39
the rest of the world	-	-	-	-	-	-
Exports to: the EU	87	91	112	81	92	96
the rest of the world	2	-	1	-	-	-
Total new supply	153	232	222	259	244	264
Change in stocks	..	..	..	..	..	..
Total domestic uses	153	232	222	259	244	264
Production as % of total new supply for use in the UK	154%	133%	144%	126%	125%	122%
Closing stocks	..	..	..	..	..	..
Condensed milk (h)						
Production	201	174	158	161	143	116
Imports from: the EU	12	12	20	25	33	43
the rest of the world	-	-	-	-	-	-
Exports to: the EU	26	28	20	18	4	5
the rest of the world	36	1	-	-	-	-
Total new supply	150	156	157	169	172	153
Change in stocks	- 2	- 1	- 2	-	- 3	- 3
Total domestic uses	152	157	159	168	175	157
Production as % of total new supply for use in the UK	134%	112%	101%	96%	83%	75%
Closing stocks	9	9	7	8	5	1
Skimmed milk powder						
Production	111	87	115	88	69	68
Imports from: the EU	13	17	32	52	51	30
the rest of the world	-	-	-	-	-	-
Exports to: the EU (d)	21	21	30	53	20	35
the rest of the world	19	9	26	25	16	3
Total new supply (d)	84	75	91	61	84	60
Change in stocks	12	16	22	- 30	- 11	- 8
Total domestic uses (d)	72	59	69	91	95	67
Production as % of total new supply for use in the UK	135%	115%	126%	144%	82%	114%
Closing stocks	34	28	51	21	10	2

(a) Includes butterfat and oil, dehydrated butter and ghee.

(b) Includes production from the residual fat of low fat milk products.

(c) Includes farmhouse manufacture.

(d) In 2001, New Zealand Milk entered a partnership with Arla Foods and manufacturing operations were switched from the United Kingdom to Denmark. Consequently, New Zealand butter is entering the United Kingdom via Denmark and is included in Danish butter imports statistics.

(e) Includes the use for animal feed.

(f) Until 2005 stocks include both public cold store stocks surveyed by Defra and all intervention stocks in private cold stores. From March 2006 stocks are just those in intervention stores. Total domestic uses does not equate exactly with consumption since changes in unrecorded stocks are not included in the calculation.

(g) Includes processed cheese

(h) Cheese stocks held in public cold stores. Public coldstores make their storage space available to the public or to the Rural Payments Agency, formerly the Intervention Board. The ownership of the store whether public or private is irrelevant. From March 2006 stocks are no longer available.

(i) Includes condensed milk used in the production of chocolate crumb and in the production of sweetened and unsweetened machine skimmed milk.

Hen eggs (table 5.19)

39 The value of production of eggs produced for human consumption in 2006 rose by 2.0 per cent to £357 million while the quantity of eggs produced for human consumption fell by 4.4 per cent to 738 million dozen. Production of processed eggs accounted for 25 per cent of total production and eggs sold in shell accounted for 75 per cent. The weighted average price of eggs graded in the United Kingdom rose by 6.7 per cent to 48.3 pence per dozen.

Table 5.19 Hen eggs; United Kingdom

Enquiries: Lesly Lawton on +44 (0)1904 455095

email: lesly.lawton@defra.gsi.gov.uk

Million dozen (unless otherwise specified)   Calendar years

	Average of 1995-97	2002	2003	2004	2005	2006 (provisional)
Population and yield						
Number of fowls laying eggs for eating (millions) (a)	33	30	30	31	31	30
Average yield per layer (number of eggs per bird per year)	283	297	298	301	304	298
Production						
Volume of production of eggs	884	856	843	892	884	855
of which: eggs for human consumption	781	746	733	778	772	738
eggs for hatching (b)	91	95	98	99	98	105
hatching eggs for export (c)	4	7	5	7	6	5
waste	8	7	7	8	8	7
Value of production of eggs for human consumption (£m) (d)	321	314	337	380	350	357
Prices (pence per dozen)						
Weighted average of eggs graded in the UK (e)	41.1	42.1	46.0	48.9	45.3	48.3
Supply and use						
UK production of eggs for human consumption	781	746	733	778	772	738
of which: eggs sold in shell	663	598	580	613	582	557
eggs processed	118	149	154	165	190	181
Imports from (f): the EU	68	124	156	148	135	102
the rest of the world	2	3	2	2	2	1
Exports to (f): the EU	17	14	15	13	13	12
the rest of the world	3	2	1	1	-	-
Total new supply	830	858	875	915	895	829
Production as % of total new supply for use in the UK	94%	87%	84%	85%	86%	89%

(a) Population is implied from gross production and average yield and hence differs from the census figures in table 3.2

(b) Eggs for hatching are not valued as they are included in the final value for poultry in table 5.16.

(c) Hatching eggs for exports are valued in table 5.16.

(d) Excludes the value of eggs for hatching.

(e) Represents the price paid by packers to producers in the United Kingdom, excluding bonus, and takes accounts of all egg systems - laying cages, free range and barn.

(f) Includes shell egg equivalent of whole (dried, frozen and liquid) egg, egg yolk and albumen.

Chapter **6** Intermediate Consumption

2006

Summary

- Crude oil prices reached a high point of over $70 per barrel during 2006;

- expenditure on fuels has risen by over 500 per cent since 1973 to over £500 million despite usage falling by 60 per cent;

- the cost of electricity has also risen by over 500 per cent to about £250 million;

- expenditure on fertiliser has levelled out at about £750-800 million while the volume has declined since 1997 to the lowest levels in over 30 years;

- expenditure on pesticides rose by over 25 times between 1973 and 1997 to about £550 million;

- veterinary expenses are estimated to be about £275 million and the cost of agriculture services is estimated to be about £650 million;

- expenditure on animal feed is estimated to be about £2.4 billion while the cost of seeds and planting stock is estimated to be about £325 million.

Introduction

1 In recent years, increases in crude oil prices have led to increased concerns for the impact of high oil prices on the margins and profitability of agricultural businesses, which are dependent on products derived from petroleum, notably fuels. This chapter presents long-term trends in crude oil prices and intermediate consumption as recorded in the production and income account (see chapter 9). Intermediate consumption represents the consumption of goods and services, e.g. fuels, feed, seeds, fertiliser, plant protection products. Some inputs, such as fuels, electricity and fertilisers, are closely linked to the oil price while others are not and trends for these are shaped by other factors.

Oil prices (chart 6.1)

2 Chart 6.1 shows the trend in prices for Brent crude oil, which is widely used to determine crude oil prices in Europe. The prices for 1979 to 1986 are as at the Friday that is closest to 1 January and those from 1987 are the average of daily spot prices.

3 Prices have risen from under $5 per barrel in the early 1970s to over $70 per barrel during 2006 before ending the year at about $60 per barrel. In real terms however, the price remains significantly lower than in the early 1980s.

Chart 6.1 Brent crude oil price

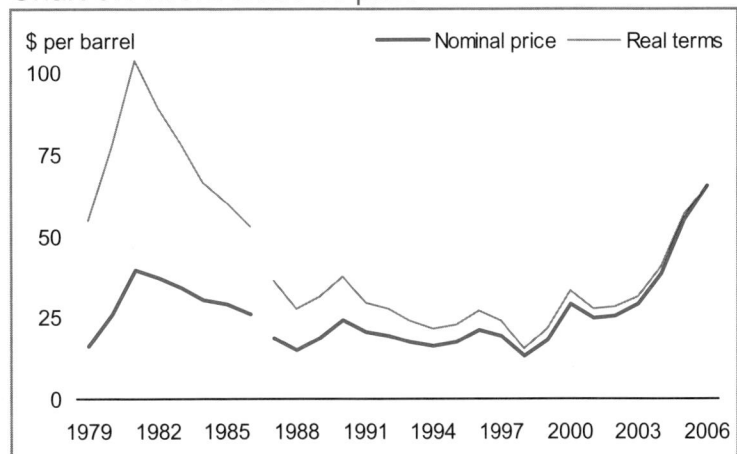

Source: Energy Information Administration, U.S. Department of Energy
(a) The annual average for 1987 is the average of daily spot prices from 20 May 1987 to 1 Jan 1988

Fuels (chart 6.2, 6.3)

4 As might be expected, the average unit price of fuel is influenced by the trend in oil prices, although the oil price is more volatile.

5 Expenditure on fuels has followed the trend in the unit price and has risen by over 500 per cent since 1973 with a notable peak in 1985, which reflects the trend in oil prices. Expenditure in 2006 is estimated to be over £500 million.

6 There has been a declining trend in the volume of fuels purchased, which has fallen by 60 per cent since 1973. The fall in usage has only partially offset the increase in the unit price.

7 Red diesel prices have been higher for most of 2006 than in 2005 and peaked at 43.92 pence per litre in August 2006. The price then fell to 36.86 pence per litre in November before rising to 38.69 pence per litre in December as a result of an increase in excise duty.

Chart 6.2 Fuels; United Kingdom

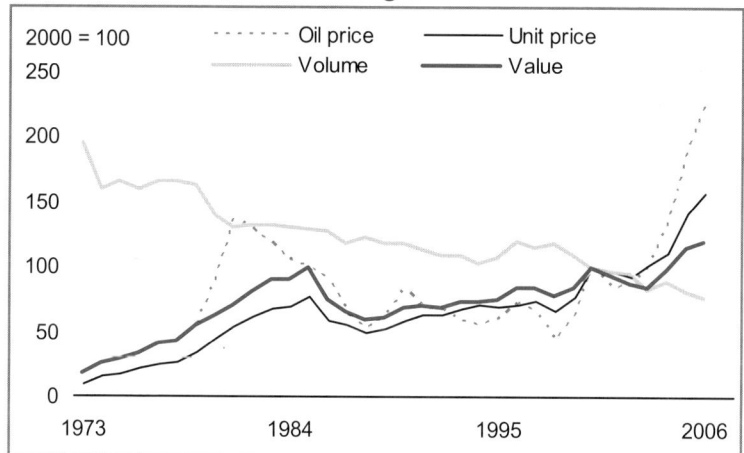

Chart 6.3 Red diesel prices; United Kingdom

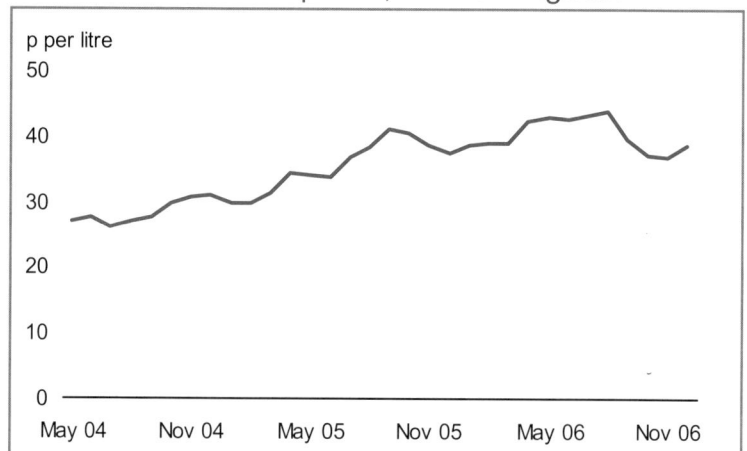

Source: DTi

Electricity (chart 6.4)

8 Electricity is also a significant source of energy, used primarily for stationary activities, such as facility operations and dairies. The volume of electricity used has remained fairly constant since 1973, only declining after 2002. Consequently, expenditure has closely followed the trend in the unit price and has risen over 500 per cent since 1973. Expenditure in 2006 is estimated to be about £250 million.

Chart 6.4 Electricity; United Kingdom

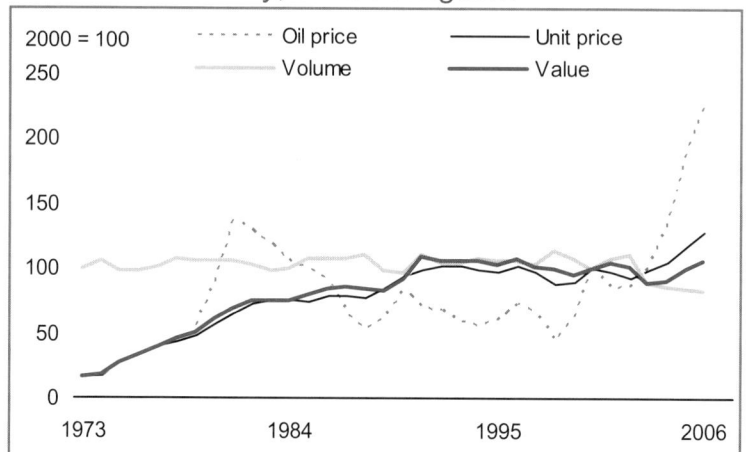

Fertiliser (chart 6.5, 6.6)

9 The price of oil not only affects the price of fuels, it also affects other input costs such as fertiliser, which has an energy intensive manufacturing process. The price of natural gas, used to synthesise atmospheric nitrogen, is a significant driver of the cost and is linked to the oil price.

10 The volume rose gradually from 1973 to the early 1990s. After declining slightly, it rose again to a peak in 1997 as the area of land under tillage increased. Since 1997, the volume has fallen by almost 50 per cent.

11 Expenditure has largely followed the trend in the unit price only diverging from it after 2000 since when it has remained fairly constant at around £750-800 million.

12 Gas prices were a significant driver underlying the increase in fertiliser prices between September 2004 and April 2006, when the price of nitrogen based fertiliser rose by 25 per cent. Gas prices fell in the second half of the year and, in December, the price of nitrogen based fertiliser was 4.7 per cent below the peak in April.

Chart 6.5 Fertiliser; United Kingdom

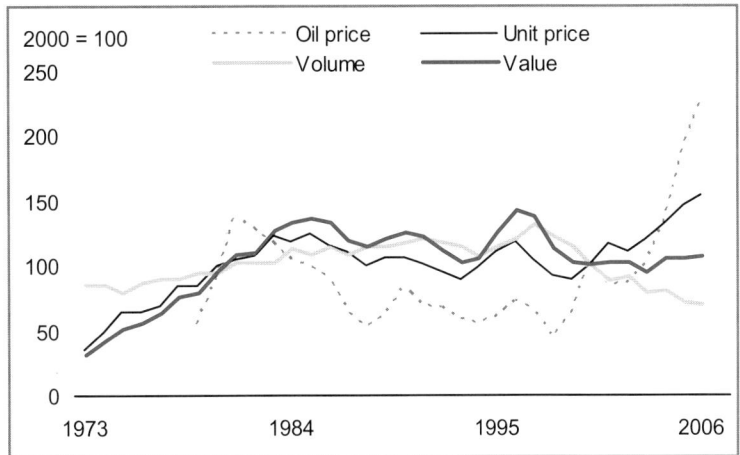

Source: Agricultural Price Index

Chart 6.6 Fertiliser prices; United Kingdom

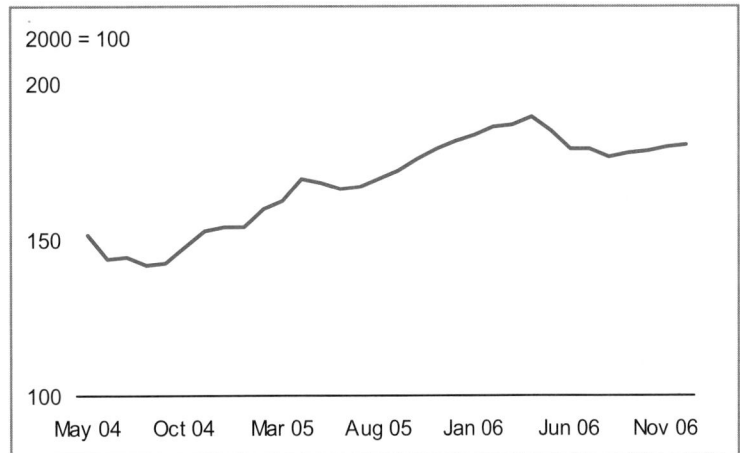

Pesticides (chart 6.7)

13 Oil and gas are also used in the production of many herbicides and pesticides as raw materials and energy although use is relatively small compared to that for the manufacture of fertiliser. Prices during the 1990s were in part shaped by exchange rate movements.

14 The volume shows an upward trend from 1973 to a peak in 1997 and then a decline of about 15 per cent. Expenditure has largely followed the trend in the volume and is now about £550 million.

Chart 6.7 Pesticides; United Kingdom

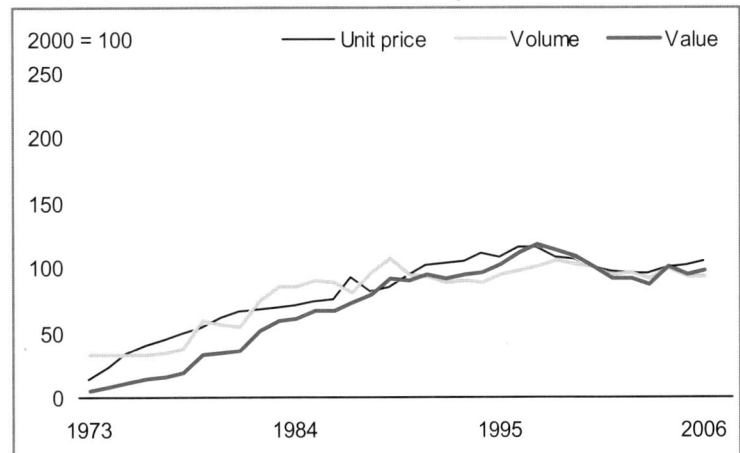

Veterinary expenses (chart 6.8)

15 The volume of veterinary expenses declined gradually from 1973 to 1988, rose to a peak in 1997 due in part to trends in profitability in the 1990s, declined to 2001 and then resumed a rising trend. Expenditure rose steadily from 1973 to 1997, then followed the trend for volume and is now about £275 million.

Chart 6.8 Veterinary expenses; United Kingdom

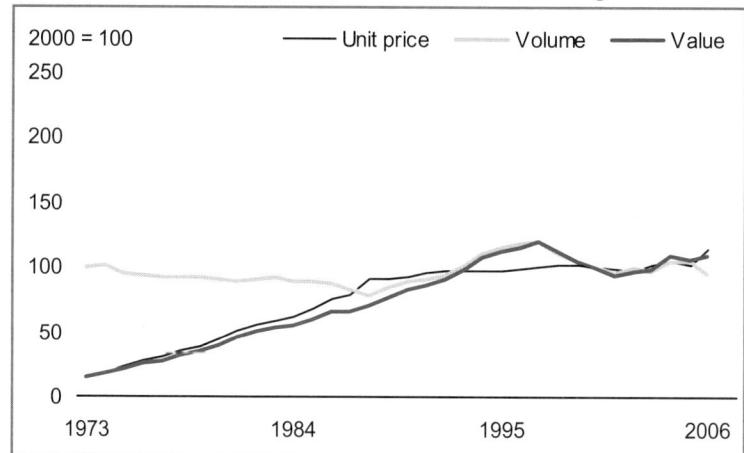

2000 = 100   —— Unit price —— Volume —— Value

Agricultural services (chart 6.9)

16 The volume of agricultural services, such as contract work and machinery rental, has risen on a gentle upward trend reflecting increasing use of contractors on farm for operations such as planting, tilling, chemical applications, discing and harvesting. Expenditure, which has followed a long term upward trend, is currently about £650 million.

Chart 6.9 Agricultural services; United Kingdom

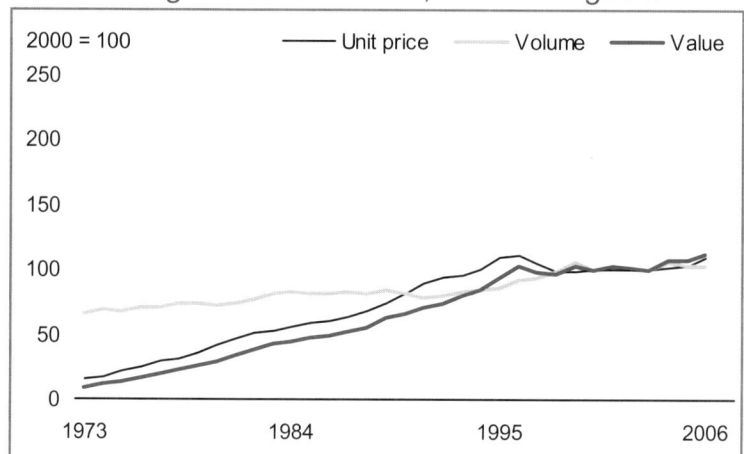

2000 = 100   —— Unit price —— Volume —— Value

Animal feed (chart 6.10, table 6.1)

17 The cost of animal feed is the largest item of expenditure recorded in the production and income account. Expenditure rose steeply from 1973 to 1984 but levelled out after the introduction of milk production quota in 1984. It fell sharply after 1996, largely as a result of the fall in commodity prices which were shaped by exchange rates and world prices, and a fall in the volume of feed for pigs which mirrored the decline in the pig herd, before levelling out from 2000 onwards at about £2.4 billion. Prices for feed wheat, barley and oats were higher in 2006 whereas compound feed prices in 2006 were similar to 2005.

Chart 6.10 Animal feed; United Kingdom

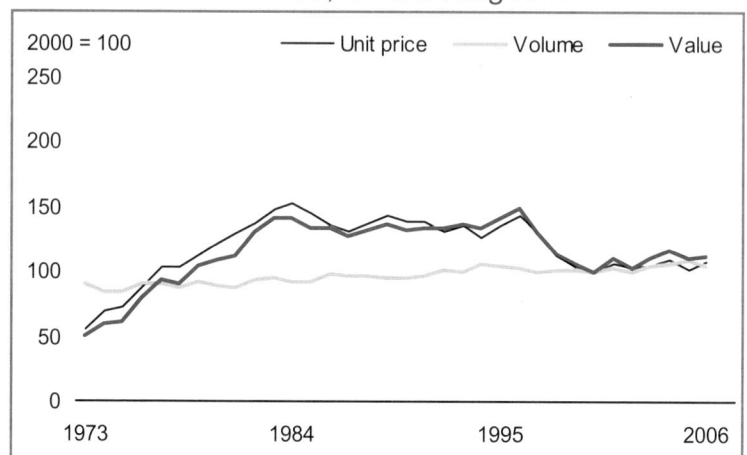

2000 = 100   —— Unit price —— Volume —— Value

18 The volume of feed shows an increasing trend between 1973 and 2006. In 2006, production increased by 6.2 per cent, particularly production of cattle compounds, which increased by 10 per cent, and sheep compounds, which increased by 20 per cent, as a result of wet weather during the spring and hot weather in the summer reducing availability of fodder and silage.

19 Poultry compound feed by retail compound feed manufacturers fell by 4.9 per cent mainly due to falling consumer demand for poultry in early 2006 following outbreaks of avian influenza outside the United Kingdom. The use of straight concentrates increased by 20 per cent compared to 2005. The straights concentrates figure also includes production of poultry compounds by integrated poultry units; this sector did not appear to be significantly affected by the avian influenza outbreaks. Inter/intra farm transfer of feed increased by 8.4 per cent.

Table 6.1 Animal feed; United Kingdom

Including direct inter-farm and intra-farm transfer
Enquiries: Karen Stark on +44 (0)1904 455076

email: karen.p.stark@defra.gsi.gov.uk

Thousand tonnes (unless otherwise specified)

Calendar years

	Average of 1995-97	2002	2003	2004	2005	2006 (provisional)
Compounds:						
cattle	4 160	4 124	4 406	4 384	4 181	4 609
calves	269	177	193	200	185	185
pigs	2 534	1 802	1 560	1 619	1 586	1 630
poultry (a)	3 234	3 456	3 337	3 373	3 267	3 107
other	743	627	692	722	704	845
Total (b)	10 868	10 077	10 083	10 197	9 825	10 433
Straight concentrates (c)	6 355	6 417	7 129	7 219	8 284	6 646
Non-concentrates (d)	535	525	525	525	525	525
Inter/intra farm transfer	2 845	3 170	3 351	3 454	3 241	3 514
Total all purchased animal feed	20 603	20 188	21 087	21 395	21 874	21 117
Value of purchased animal feed (£ million)	3 010	2 223	2 372	2 517	2 391	2 423
of which:						
compounds	1 846	1 377	1 348	1 450	1 321	1 436
straights	883	654	774	804	836	717
feed purchased from other farms	280	192	250	264	234	269

(a) Includes poultry feed produced by 'retail' compounders but excludes production from integrated poultry units which are included within the straight concentrates data.
(b) Includes imports less exports
(c) Cereals, cereal offals, proteins and other high energy feeds.
(d) Low-energy bulk feeds expressed as concentrate equivalent. Brewers and distillers grains, hay, milk by-products and other low-energy bulk feeds expressed in terms of equivalent tonnage of high energy feeds.

Seeds (chart 6.11)

20 The volume of seeds and planting stock purchased has remained fairly constant between 1973 and 2006. Expenditure rose from 1973 to a high point in the mid-1990s, then fell before resuming an upward trend after 2000 to the early 1990s, reflecting trends in commodity prices which were shaped by exchange rates and world prices. Expenditure is currently about £325 million.

Chart 6.11 Seeds; United Kingdom

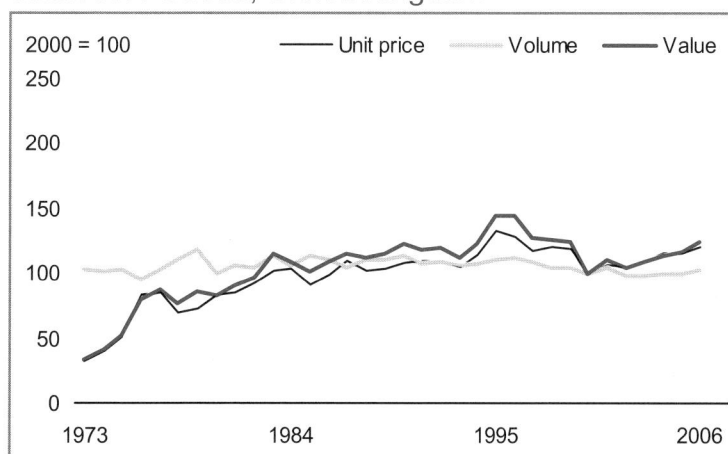

Maintenance: materials (chart 6.12)

21 The volume of materials purchased for maintenance use shows a long term declining trend from 1973 to 2006. The unit price on the other hand shows a long term rising trend. Expenditure followed the unit price trend until 2000 when it levelled out at about £650 million.

Chart 6.12 Maintenance: materials; United Kingdom

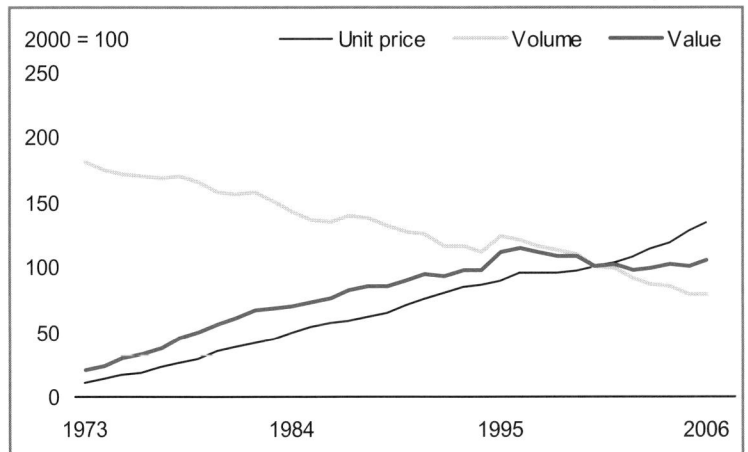

Maintenance: buildings (chart 6.13)

22 The volume of maintenance on buildings fluctuated between 1973 and 2006. It fell to a low point in 1981 before rising to a high point in the mid-1990s and then declined to about 25 per cent lower than in 1973. The unit price shows a long term rising trend. Expenditure followed a similar rising trend to a high point in 1997 then fell until 2000 before resuming an upward trend to a value of about £125 million in 2006.

Chart 6.13 Maintenance: buildings; United Kingdom

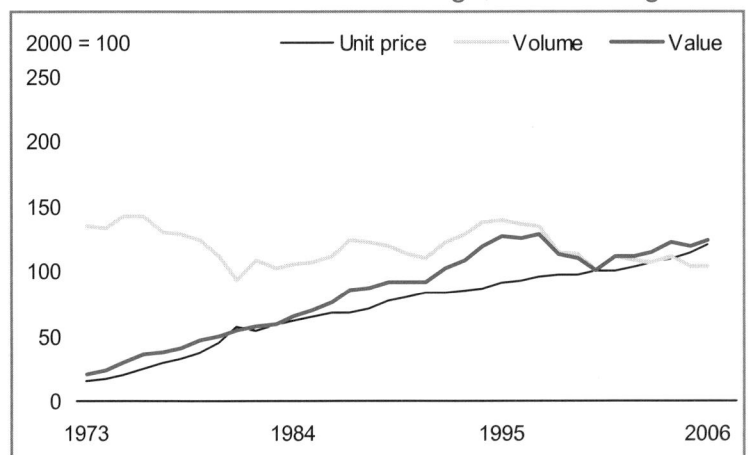

Chapter **7** The food chain

Summary

- The agri-food sector accounted for 6.9 per cent of the total economy in 2005.

- The food supply chain in the United Kingdom in 2006 received £149 billion from spending by consumers and the balance of revenue from exports less spending on imports.

- The agri-food sector provided a total of just over 3.6 million jobs in the third quarter of 2006, 14 per cent of all employees in Great Britain.

- The trade gap in food, feed and drink widened by 10 per cent to £13.5 billion.

- Self-sufficiency is estimated to be 58 per cent for all food in 2006 and 71 per cent for indigenous type food.

- Expenditure on food increased by 2.5 per cent in real terms over the year to the third quarter of 2006.

- Farmers' share of a basket of food staples is estimated to have fallen by 23 per cent between 1988 and 2006.

- In 2006 food prices increased in line with the Retail Price Index having previously risen more slowly.

- Since 1998 food prices have increased by 14 per cent while prices of all items have increased by 27 per cent.

Contribution of the agri-food sector to the national economy (chart 7.1, table 7.1)

1 The agri-food sector in the United Kingdom accounted for a total estimated gross value added of £74 billion in 2005, a 4.0 per cent fall on 2004. Food manufacturing, non-residential catering and food retailing are about the same size in terms of gross value added. Food and drink wholesaling and agriculture are the smallest sub-sectors, accounting for 10 per cent and 7.2 per cent of gross value added respectively. In 2005, gross value added for agriculture fell by over 30 per cent to £5.2 billion due to changes in the way subsidies are paid. The only sub-sector with an

Chart 7.1 Gross value added by the agri-food sector 2005; United Kingdom

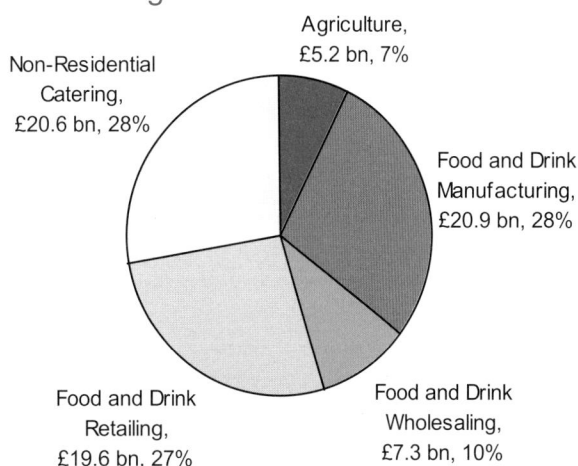

Non-Residential Catering, £20.6 bn, 28%

Agriculture, £5.2 bn, 7%

Food and Drink Manufacturing, £20.9 bn, 28%

Food and Drink Wholesaling, £7.3 bn, 10%

Food and Drink Retailing, £19.6 bn, 27%

Source: Annual Business Inquiry (ONS) and Defra

increase in gross value added in 2005 was the food retail sub-sector with a 4.2 per cent rise. Gross value added of non-residential catering fell by 2.5 per cent after rising by 38 per cent between 2000 and 2004. In 2005 the agri-food sector contributed 6.9 per cent of national gross value added, falling from 7.5 per cent in 2004; 0.2 percentage points of this fall is attributable to the fall in gross value added for agriculture.

Table 7.1 Agri-food sector contribution to the national economy; United Kingdom

Enquiries: Jim Holding on +44 (0)1904 455069   email: jim.holding@defra.gsi.gov.uk

£ million (unless otherwise specified)   Calendar years

	Average of 1995-97	2002	2003	2004	2005	2006 (provisional)
Agri-food sector's contribution to total economy gross value added						
at current prices Agriculture	9 453	7 151	7 881	7 613	5 325	5 580
Food Manufacturing (a)	..	19 561	20 679	21 457	20 934	..
Food Wholesaling (a)	..	7 106	6 633	7 821	7 275	..
Food Retailing (a)	..	17 316	17 947	18 833	19 619	..
Food Non-Residential Catering (a)	..	17 898	18 359	21 143	20 607	..
% of national gross value added (current prices)	..	7.6	7.4	7.5	6.9	..
Workforce in the food sector (thousand persons)						
Agriculture (b)	616	496	478	493	490	484
Food Manufacturing (c)	..	447	440	423	418	411
Food Wholesaling (c)	..	213	213	212	215	217
Food Retailing (c)	..	1 205	1 214	1 171	1 184	1 157
Food Non-Residential Catering (c)	..	1 355	1 360	1 401	1 394	1 373
% of total workforce in employment	..	14.7	14.6	14.5	14.3	13.9
Imports of food, feed and drink (d) (e)	16 904	19 091	20 944	21 942	23 429	..
% of total UK imports	9.5	8.4	8.9	8.7	8.6	..
Exports of food, feed and drink (d) (e)	9 903	8 915	9 881	9 702	9 942	..
% of total UK exports	6.1	4.8	5.2	5.1	4.7	..
Self-sufficiency						
% of all food	70.6	62.4	63.5	62.3	58.5	58.1
% of indigenous type food	83.8	75.5	76.6	75.0	72.0	71.5
Household final consumption expenditure on food and alcoholic drinks						
at current prices	105 872	139 355	144 040	150 571	156 262	162 412
of which: household food	52 171	61 310	63 174	65 521	67 101	70 047
food eaten out	24 838	39 771	42 010	44 721	48 232	49 583
alcoholic drinks	28 863	38 274	38 856	40 329	40 929	42 800
at constant 2003 prices (£ million)	123 253	142 117	144 040	148 794	150 977	153 386
of which: household food	56 012	62 143	63 174	65 181	65 806	67 662
food eaten out	32 278	41 060	42 010	43 507	45 516	45 538
alcoholic drinks	34 963	38 914	38 856	40 106	39 655	40 221
% of total household final consumption expenditure	22.5	21.0	20.7	20.6	20.6	20.5
of which: household food	11.1	9.2	9.1	8.9	8.8	8.8
food eaten out	5.3	6.0	6.0	6.1	6.3	6.3
alcoholic drinks	6.1	5.8	5.6	5.5	5.4	5.4
Producer prices for agricultural products (2003 = 100)	118.7	93.9	100.0	103.0	99.7	104.1
Retail price index (2003 = 100):						
food	84.4	97.2	100.0	103.0	105.9	109.3
alcoholic drinks	84.7	97.7	100.0	101.9	103.9	106.4
all items	92.6	98.7	100.0	100.6	101.8	104.0

(a) Results from the Annual Business Inquiry (ONS). 2005 data are provisional.

(b) Results from 1998 are not consistent with previous years, due to changes in the labour questions on the June Agricultural and Horticultural Census, and due to revisions made to English and Welsh results. This series now includes spouses of farmers, partners and directors, which were not previously available.

(c) Results are for the third quarter of the year and from Labour Force Survey (ONS) For GB.

(d) This aggregate covers Standard International Trade Classification divisions 01-09, 11, 22 and Section 4 (see table 8.1).

(e) The figures are Overseas Trade Statistics (OTS), based on data collected by HM Revenue and Customs. Data shown are quoted in real terms at 2005 prices.

The food chain (chart 7.2)

2 In 2006, the food supply chain in the United Kingdom as a whole received £149 billion from spending by consumers in the United Kingdom, plus exports less imports of agricultural commodities and processed food and drink products (assuming that imports and exports directly to and from consumers are negligible). Chart 7.2 shows the largest elements of the food chain from agriculture as a primary producer through food manufacturing and retail trade to consumers' expenditure.

Chart 7.2 The food chain; United Kingdom

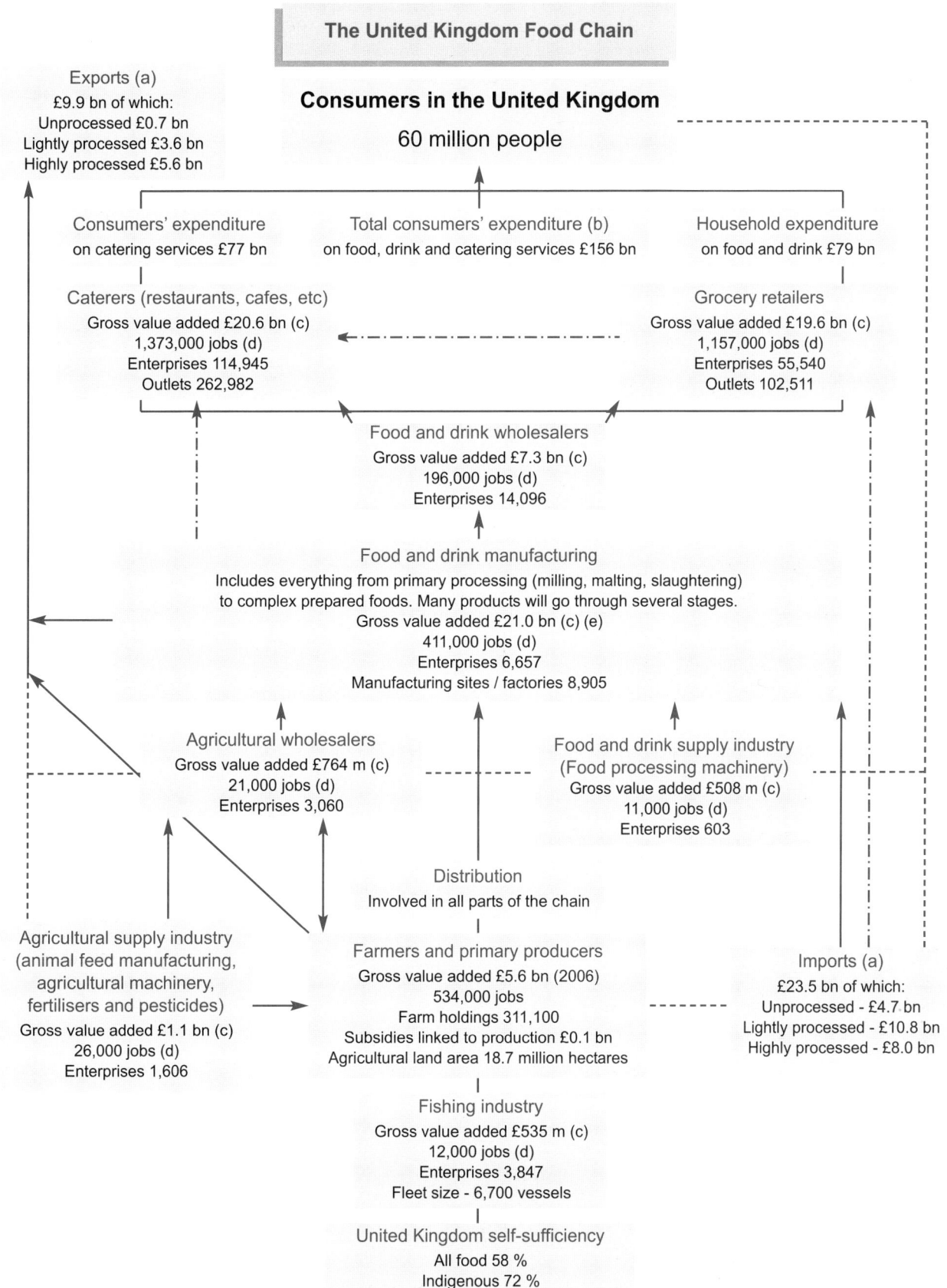

2006

The United Kingdom Food Chain

Exports (a)
£9.9 bn of which:
Unprocessed £0.7 bn
Lightly processed £3.6 bn
Highly processed £5.6 bn

Consumers in the United Kingdom
60 million people

Consumers' expenditure
on catering services £77 bn

Total consumers' expenditure (b)
on food, drink and catering services £156 bn

Household expenditure
on food and drink £79 bn

Caterers (restaurants, cafes, etc)
Gross value added £20.6 bn (c)
1,373,000 jobs (d)
Enterprises 114,945
Outlets 262,982

Grocery retailers
Gross value added £19.6 bn (c)
1,157,000 jobs (d)
Enterprises 55,540
Outlets 102,511

Food and drink wholesalers
Gross value added £7.3 bn (c)
196,000 jobs (d)
Enterprises 14,096

Food and drink manufacturing
Includes everything from primary processing (milling, malting, slaughtering)
to complex prepared foods. Many products will go through several stages.
Gross value added £21.0 bn (c) (e)
411,000 jobs (d)
Enterprises 6,657
Manufacturing sites / factories 8,905

Agricultural wholesalers
Gross value added £764 m (c)
21,000 jobs (d)
Enterprises 3,060

Food and drink supply industry
(Food processing machinery)
Gross value added £508 m (c)
11,000 jobs (d)
Enterprises 603

Distribution
Involved in all parts of the chain

Agricultural supply industry
(animal feed manufacturing,
agricultural machinery,
fertilisers and pesticides)
Gross value added £1.1 bn (c)
26,000 jobs (d)
Enterprises 1,606

Farmers and primary producers
Gross value added £5.6 bn (2006)
534,000 jobs
Farm holdings 311,100
Subsidies linked to production £0.1 bn
Agricultural land area 18.7 million hectares

Imports (a)
£23.5 bn of which:
Unprocessed - £4.7 bn
Lightly processed - £10.8 bn
Highly processed - £8.0 bn

Fishing industry
Gross value added £535 m (c)
12,000 jobs (d)
Enterprises 3,847
Fleet size - 6,700 vessels

United Kingdom self-sufficiency
All food 58 %
Indigenous 72 %

(a) Overseas Trade data are provisional for the full year 2006 from HM Revenue and Customs.
(b) Consumers' expenditure, properly known as household final consumption expenditure, is a provisional estimate by Defra for 2006 calculated at current prices.
(c) Gross value added figures are provisional data from the Office for National Statistics for 2005 calculated at basic prices (market prices less taxes plus subsidies).
(d) Employee data are for Q3 2006 from the Office for National Statistics.
(e) GVA for food manufacturing does not include farm animal feed, which is included in agricultural supply industry. This figure therefore does not match that shown in table 7.1.

Food chain employees and self–employed farmers (chart 7.3)

3 The agri-food sector provided a total of just over 3.6 million jobs in the third quarter of 2006, 14 per cent of all employees in Great Britain. Of these a little under half a million were employed in agriculture. Chart 7.3 shows how the different parts of the sector make up this total.

4 Employment in the agri-food sector as a whole fell by 1.6 per cent over the year to the third quarter of 2006 while employment for the whole economy grew by 0.6 per cent over the same period. Employment in agriculture fell by around 1.1 per cent while manufacturing saw employment fall by 1.6 per cent. The reduction of employment in manufacturing is in line with long term trends.

Chart 7.3 Employees in the agri-food sector Q3 2006; Great Britain

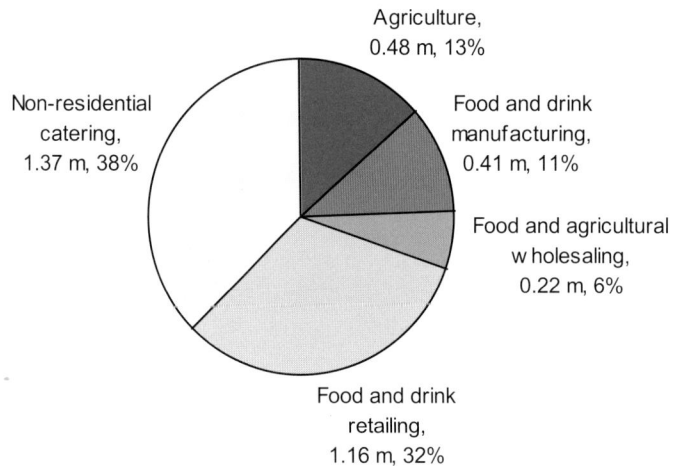

Agriculture, 0.48 m, 13%

Food and drink manufacturing, 0.41 m, 11%

Food and agricultural wholesaling, 0.22 m, 6%

Food and drink retailing, 1.16 m, 32%

Non-residential catering, 1.37 m, 38%

Source: Labour Force Survey (ONS); June Survey (Defra)

Trade in food, feed and drink

5 The value of imports of food, feed and drink into the United Kingdom was £23 billion in 2005, an increase of 6.8 per cent compared to 2004, while the value of exports of food, feed and drink rose by 2.5 per cent to £9.9 billion. This led to the trade gap in food, feed and drink widening by 10 per cent to £13 billion. More information on overseas trade can be found in Chapter 8.

Self-sufficiency (chart 7.4)

6 Self-sufficiency, which is calculated as the value of production of raw food divided by the value of raw food for human consumption is estimated to be 58 per cent for all food in 2006 and 71 per cent for indigenous type food. Self-sufficiency declined after 1995, shaped by the high level of the pound compared to the euro, the impact of outbreaks of disease and the beef export ban introduced in 1996.

Chart 7.4 Self sufficiency; United Kingdom

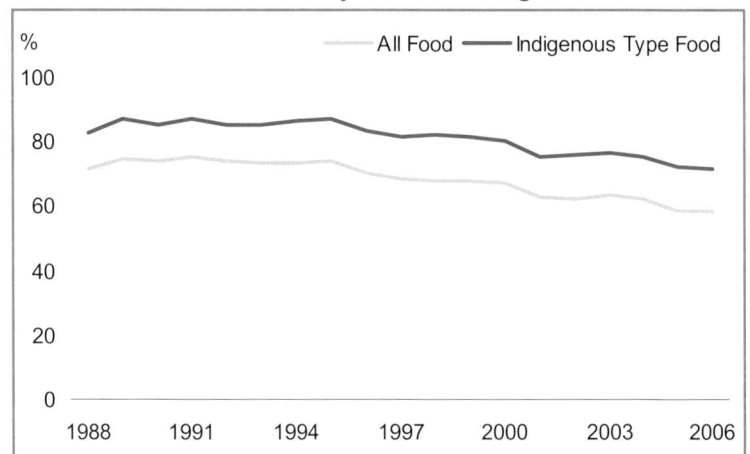

Consumers' expenditure on food, drink and catering (chart 7.5)

7 During the third quarter of 2006 consumers' expenditure on food, drink and catering totalled £40.9 billion. This represents 20 per cent of expenditure on all items, unchanged from the same quarter in the previous year.

8 | Expenditure on food increased by 2.5 per cent in real terms between quarter 3 in 2005 and quarter 3 in 2006 while expenditure on non-residential catering rose by 0.4 per cent. The largest increase was in expenditure on drink where expenditure rose by 4.2 per cent over the same period. In the calendar year 2006 consumers' expenditure on food and drink rose in real terms by 1.6 per cent. In real terms it has risen by 11 per cent since 2000 and by 26 per cent since 1990.

Chart 7.5 Consumer's expenditure Q3 2006; United Kingdom

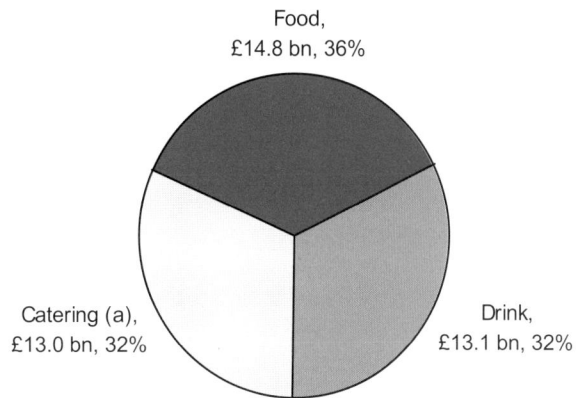

Food, £14.8 bn, 36%

Catering (a), £13.0 bn, 32%

Drink, £13.1 bn, 32%

Source: Consumer Trends (ONS)

(a) Catering excludes on-trade alcohol sales

Farmers' share of consumers' expenditure (table 7.2, charts 7.6, 7.7)

9 | Compared with 1988, farmers are estimated to have received 23 per cent less in 2006 (or 11 percentage points less) for their contribution to a basket of food items covering staples of agricultural production in the United Kingdom. However, since 1998 the farmers' share has remained relatively constant. The absolute level of the farmers' share is sensitive to precisely which retail products are chosen for the basket; some have a greater amount of added value beyond the farmgate and it would therefore be expected that the share accounted for by the farmer would be lower.

Chart 7.6 Farmgate share of retail prices for a basket of items; United Kingdom

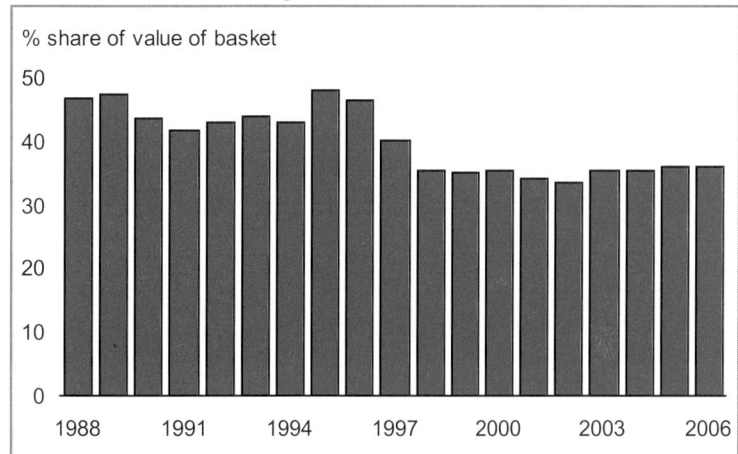

% share of value of basket

10 | Table 7.2 shows the items in the basket and how the farmers' share has changed for each. They are weighted according to their value to farmers in the United Kingdom. Most weight is given to milk and then other livestock products. The fruit and vegetables selected have a small impact on the overall value of the basket.

11 | The farmers' reducing share of the basket of food items corroborates evidence that farmgate prices are not keeping up with retail food prices. This can be explained partly by retail price rises accounted for by greater processing and packaging beyond the farmgate though the items in the basket have not changed substantially over this period. Another reason for retail food prices to rise ahead of farmgate prices is additional regulation beyond the farmgate to ensure food safety, notably in meat processing.

12 | Changes in exchange rates have a significant impact on farmgate prices. Farmgate prices increased up to 1995 but then reduced when sterling strengthened against the euro. CAP reform over the last 15 years, which cut commodity support prices and compensated with direct payments to farmers, has also

played a role. Retail food prices were less affected by these factors as the food chain contains a large cost component that reflects overall conditions in the economy.

Table 7.2 Farmers' share of the value of a basket of food items (a); United Kingdom

Enquiries: Jim Holding on +44 (0)1904 455069   email: jim.holding@defra.gsi.gov.uk

		Farmgate share in 1988 %	Farmgate share in 2006 %	Change in share %	Weight in basket 2006
Farmers' share of basket		47	36	- 23	
Farm gate product	**Retail product**				
apples	dessert apples per kg	55	42	- 23	6
beef	untrimmed beef (b) per kg	67	47	- 29	184
carrots	carrots per kg	30	45	48	12
cabbages	cabbage, hearts, per kg	38	42	10	8
chicken	oven ready roasting chicken, fresh or chilled per kg	47	42	- 12	127
eggs	size 2 eggs per dozen	28	30	8	47
lamb	untrimmed lamb (b) per kg	65	47	- 27	85
onions	onions per kg	25	24	- 7	5
pork	untrimmed pork (b) per kg	57	36	- 37	88
potatoes	old loose white potatoes per kg	24	21	- 11	68
tomatoes	tomatoes per kg	48	72	50	9
wheat	white loaf sliced, 800g	23	15	- 35	18
milk	whole milk (c)	38	29	- 22	342

(a) Farmgate prices from Defra, retail prices from the Office for National Statistics and the Meat and Livestock Commission (MLC).
(b) Retail prices for beef, lamb and pork are untrimmed MLC prices adjusted for drip loss.
(c) The average price of one pint of delivered milk and one pint of shop milk (the shop milk based on a two pint purchase).

13 Chart 7.7 shows a related analysis: the farmgate share of total household food sales. This analysis compares the estimates of the value of farmgate output with estimates of consumers' expenditure on all household food, including highly processed foods. This approach differs because it encompasses all purchased food and therefore incorporates changes due to consumers changing their types of purchase. In particular, it will over time include a higher share of food items incorporating greater processing or value added beyond the farmgate.

Chart 7.7 Farmgate share of total household sales; United Kingdom

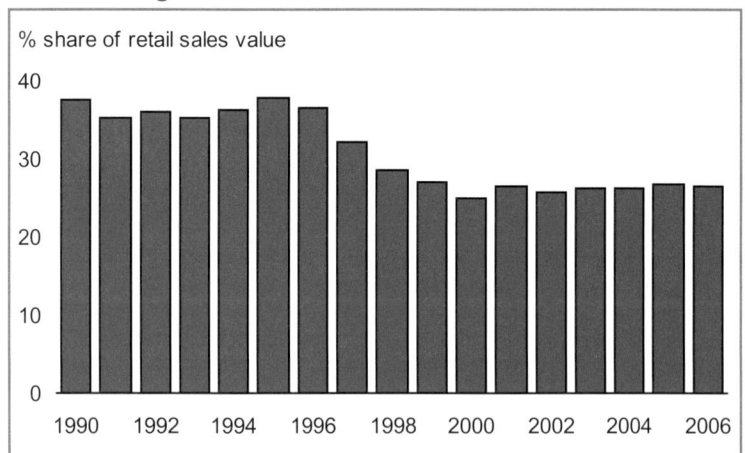

14 This explains why farmers receive a lower share of the total household food sales than of the basket of household food items. In the second half of the 1990s, farm incomes tumbled and the farmers' share dropped from 38 to 25 per cent. Since 2000 farmers have seen little change in their percentage share of the retail sales value; it is now at 28 per cent.

Changes in retail price indices (chart 7.8)

15 Retail food prices were 4.6 per cent higher in December 2006 than in the same month in the previous year. The all items retail price index rose by 4.4 per cent over the same period. Since 1998 food prices have risen by only 14 per cent while prices of all items have increased by 27 per cent.

Chart 7.8 Changes in retail price indices; United Kingdom

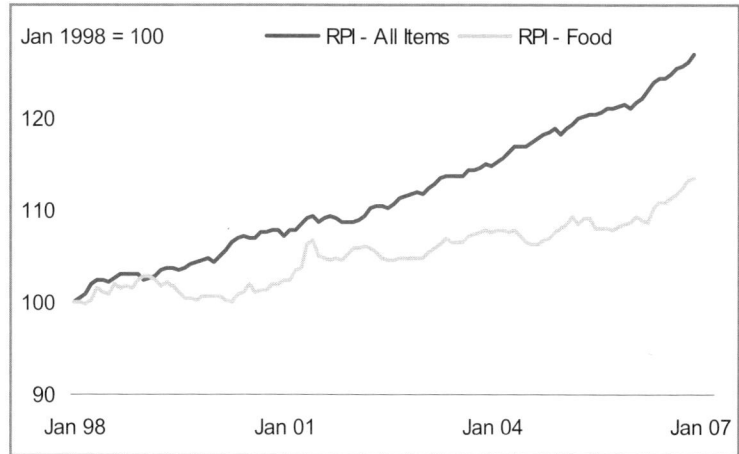

Jan 1998 = 100 — RPI - All Items — RPI - Food

Source: Retail Price Index (ONS)

2006

Chapter **8** Overseas Trade

Summary

In 2005:

* the value of food, feed and drink exports was £9.9 billion, a rise of 2.5 per cent over 2004;

* the value of food, feed and drink imports increased by 6.8 per cent to £23 billion;

* the trade gap in food, feed and drink widened by 10 per cent to £13 billion;

* principal destinations for exports were the Irish Republic (19 per cent), France (13 per cent), USA (8.8 per cent), Spain (8.4 per cent) and Germany (5.9 per cent);

* the most important trade partners for imports were France (13 per cent), the Netherlands (12 per cent), the Irish Republic (9.4 per cent), Germany (7.5 per cent) and Spain (5.6 per cent).

Introduction

1 The Overseas Trade Statistics presented in this chapter are based on data collected by HM Revenue and Customs and are compiled from returns made by importers and exporters. Before the completion of the Single Market in the European Union at the end of 1992 all overseas trade data for the United Kingdom were compiled from Customs declarations made by traders. Since the beginning of 1993 the collection of trade statistics has been divided into two categories: that transacted between the United Kingdom and countries outside the European Union (extra-EU trade); and that between the United Kingdom and its European Union partners (intra-EU trade). Extra-EU trade statistics are compiled, as before, from Customs declarations by importers, exporters and their agents; intra-EU trade statistics are compiled using a system linked to traders' VAT returns, known as Intrastat.

2 The trade statistics shown here may not match those shown in the commodities tables in Chapter 5 where for example, trade in meat includes the carcase weight equivalent of trade in live animals and trade in milk is of raw milk before processing and not of processed and packaged milk and cream.

Trade in food, feed and drink (chart 8.1, table 8.1)

3 The value of exports of food, feed and drink was 23 per cent lower in real terms in 2005 than at its peak in 1995. This is a consequence of the combination of the strength of sterling, disease related issues and lower world commodity prices. The value of imports was 7.3 per cent higher in real terms in 2005 than in 1996. As a consequence, the trade gap in food, feed and drink has widened by 44 per cent in real terms between 1996 and 2005 to £13 billion.

Chart 8.1 Trade in food, feed and drink in real terms at 2005 prices; United Kingdom

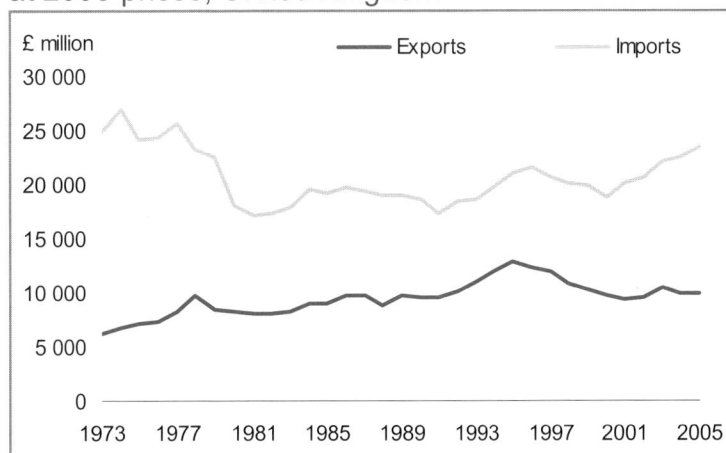

4   Table 8.1 shows the value of trade at current prices. The value of food, feed and drink exports was £9.9 billion in 2005, 2.5 per cent up on 2004 when it stood at £9.7 billion, while the value of food, feed and drink imports was £23 billion in 2005, 6.8 per cent higher than in 2004 when it stood at £22 billion.

Table 8.1 Trade in food, feed and drink by SITC division at current prices; United Kingdom

Enquiries: Dave Rimmer on +44 (0)1904 456406   email: david.j.rimmer@defra.gsi.gov.uk

£ million   Calendar years

SITC division Code	Title	Average of 1995-97	2001	2002	2003	2004	2005
Exports							
01	Meat	1 130.5	418.7	513.8	603.9	667.0	727.6
02	Dairy	763.2	612.2	619.3	760.5	782.2	720.4
03	Fish	705.7	745.6	762.3	891.4	885.8	939.5
04	Cereals	1 435.8	1 085.0	1 135.5	1 344.4	1 240.7	1 240.2
05	Fruit and Veg	460.3	394.8	432.2	472.6	508.0	515.0
06	Sugar	421.7	357.1	325.7	342.4	375.0	340.9
07	Coffee, tea, etc.	682.0	593.8	615.6	628.1	605.7	626.4
08	Animal feed	389.9	291.5	311.1	330.5	315.2	315.1
09	Misc.	484.3	605.8	621.1	683.3	714.4	732.6
11	Drink	3 158.0	3 240.6	3 329.0	3 502.5	3 373.9	3 507.5
22 + S4	Oils	271.5	160.8	249.7	321.8	234.1	276.5
	Total	9 902.9	8 505.7	8 915.2	9 881.4	9 701.9	9 941.8
Imports							
01	Meat	2 366.5	2 775.9	2 891.8	3 365.7	3 540.2	3 721.8
02	Dairy	1 131.5	1 279.1	1 324.6	1 538.4	1 652.7	1 746.8
03	Fish	1 177.3	1 449.9	1 438.8	1 439.0	1 474.2	1 696.4
04	Cereals	1 130.8	1 247.6	1 310.2	1 391.0	1 459.5	1 511.1
05	Fruit and Veg	4 068.2	4 221.1	4 528.0	4 930.9	5 099.9	5 643.7
06	Sugar	847.4	788.0	792.3	858.4	897.7	958.9
07	Coffee, tea, etc.	1 268.7	1 093.0	1 169.3	1 194.4	1 236.1	1 382.3
08	Animal feed	826.5	788.1	757.4	902.7	927.7	928.4
09	Misc.	859.5	833.5	888.0	1 062.1	1 156.9	1 184.9
11	Drink	2 216.9	2 926.8	3 118.1	3 323.5	3 574.5	3 722.4
22+S4	Oils	1 011.1	864.2	872.1	937.7	922.1	932.0
	Total	16 904.3	18 267.1	19 090.6	20 943.8	21 941.5	23 428.7

Defra's aggregate 'Food, Feed and Drink' is composed of the following divisions from the Standard International Trade Classification:

01   Meat: meat from cattle, sheep, pigs, goats, poultry, horses etc.; preparations including blood, juices, sausages, livers, offal.

02   Dairy: includes milk (skimmed or otherwise), butter, buttermilk, cream, yoghurt, ice cream, whey, cheese and curd, all types of eggs both in and out of shell.

03   Fish: All types of edible marine life excluding mammals, fresh, frozen, processed, prepared or preserved.

04   Cereals: includes rice, wheat, barley, oats, maize, grain sorghum and preparations including sweet biscuits, waffles, gingerbread, uncooked/unstuffed pasta.

05   Fruit and vegetables: includes fresh, frozen or prepared fruit (except crystallised) and vegetables, nuts (except groundnuts), vegetable and fruit juices of all kinds except wine (see division 11), jams, marmalades, fruit or nut puree/paste etc.

06   Sugar: includes both natural sugar and sugar confectionery (but not chocolate or cocoa), both natural and artificial honey, and liquorice.

07   Coffee, tea, etc.: includes all types of tea, coffee (e.g. green, decaffeinated), extracts and substitutes thereof; cocoa and chocolate (of all kinds): all kinds of spices.

08   Animal feed: includes hay, fodder, bran, sharps and other residues derived from cereals or leguminous plants, oil-cake and other solid residues, other residues, brewing dregs, all types of pet or animal food.

09   Miscellaneous: includes margarine, shortening, homogenised products or preparations not elsewhere specified, sauces, vinegar, soups, yeasts, cooked/stuffed pasta, food preparations for infant use.

11   Drink: includes alcoholic drinks of all kinds; also natural or artificial mineral and aerated waters sweetened or otherwise.

22+S4   Oils: includes groundnuts (peanuts), soya beans, sunflower seeds, rape seeds, palm nuts, linseed, poppy seeds etc., lard, pig fat, olive oil, rape oil, corn oil, linseed oil, beeswax etc.

Division 00, which covers all live animals, is excluded from the aggregate 'Food, Feed and Drink' because it includes non-food animals, particularly race horses.

S4 stands for Section 4 in the SITC and covers animal and vegetable oils, fats and waxes.

Trading partners (charts 8.2, 8.3)

5 Principal destinations of food, feed and drink exports to European Union countries in 2005 were the Irish Republic (£1.8 billion), France (£1.2 billion), Spain (£836 million) and Germany (£582 million). The principal countries in the European Union from which food, feed and drink were imported into the United Kingdom in 2005 were France (£3.0 billion), the Netherlands (£2.9 billion), the Irish Republic (£2.2 billion) and Germany (£1.8 billion).

6 Principal non-EU destinations of food, feed and drink exports in 2005 were the USA (£877 million), South Korea (£179 million) and Canada (£161 million) while the main non-EU countries from which food, feed and drink were imported into the United Kingdom were the USA (£730 million) and Brazil (£606 million).

Exports and imports (charts 8.4, 8.5)

7 Between 1996 and 2005, in real terms at 2005 prices:

- exports of highly processed foods and drink, such as confectionery, canned meats, jams, alcoholic drinks and ice cream, fell by 14 per cent;

- exports of lightly processed foods and drinks, i.e. goods that retain their raw recognisable form, such as meat, cheese and butter, powdered milk, flour and sugar, fell by 20 per cent;

- exports of unprocessed commodities, such as fresh fruit and vegetables, honey, eggs, milk and cream, and unmilled cereals, fell by 45 per cent.

Chart 8.2 Trade in food, feed and drink by country of destination 2005; United Kingdom

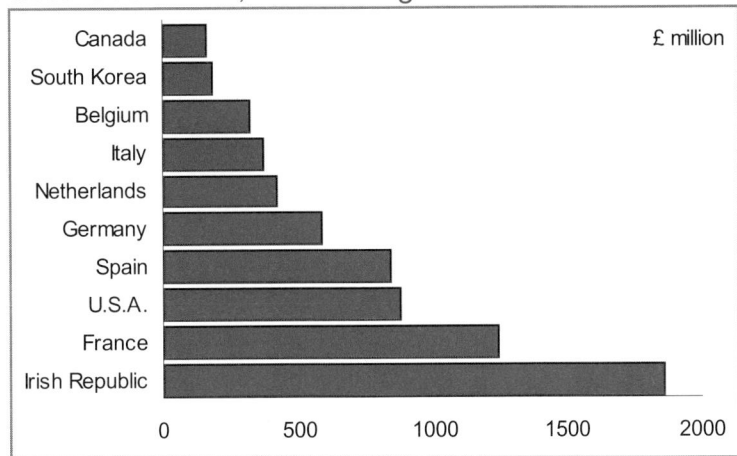

Chart 8.3 Trade in food, feed and drink by country of despatch 2005; United Kingdom

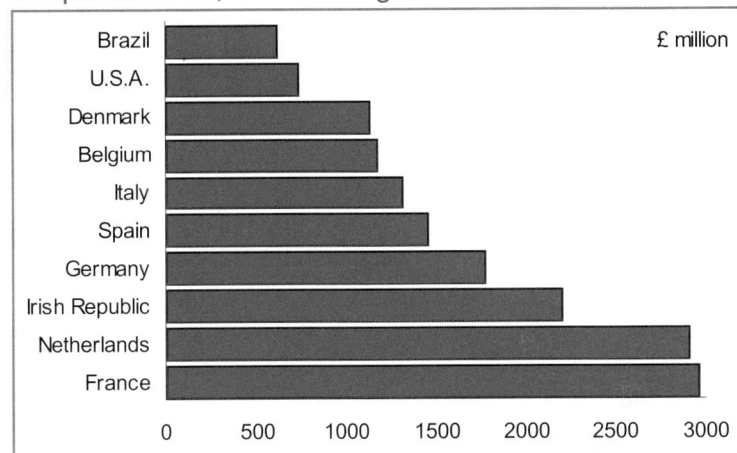

Chart 8.4 Exports of food, feed and drink by degree of processing in real terms; United Kingdom

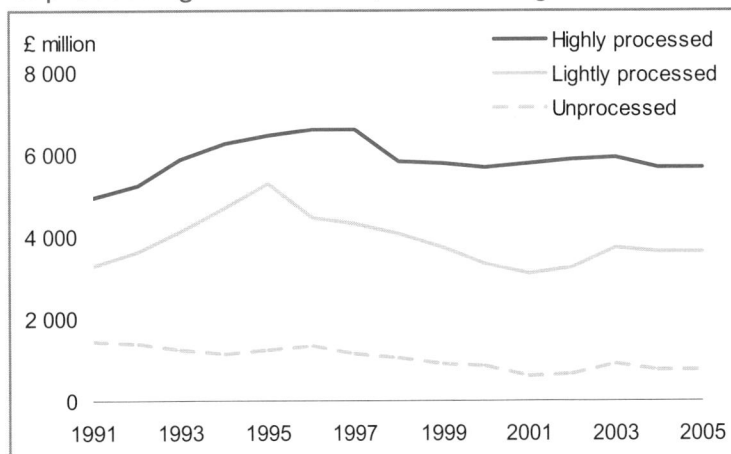

2006

8 Between 1996 and 2005, in real terms at 2005 prices:

- imports of highly processed foods and drink increased by 28 per cent;

- imports of lightly processed foods and drinks fell by 0.3 per cent;

- imports of unprocessed commodities increased by 0.1 per cent.

Chart 8.5 Imports of food, feed and drink by degree of processing in real terms; United Kingdom

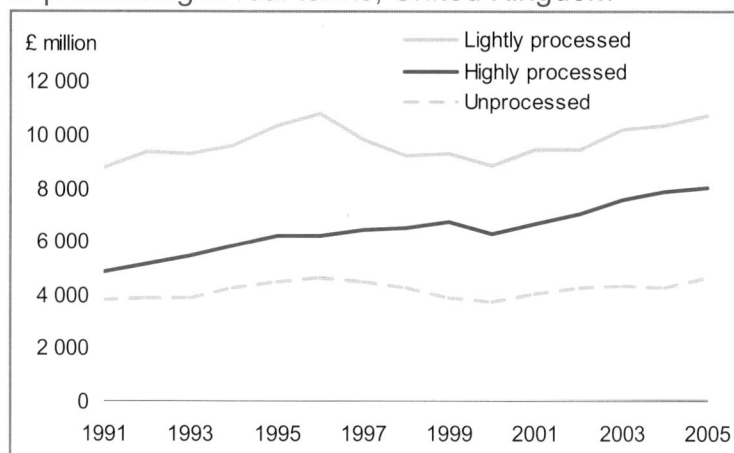

Trade in key commodities (table 8.2, 8.3)

9 Between 1996 and 2005, in real terms at 2005 prices:

- the value of exports of whisky fell by 17 per cent to £2.4 billion; the value of wine imports increased by 29 per cent to £2.4 billion;

- the value of exports of lamb and mutton fell by 44 per cent (exports were banned during the outbreak of foot and mouth disease in 2001 but partially recovered in 2002 and 2003);

- the value of beef exports fell by 86 per cent and the value of imports increased by 54 per cent (the pattern of beef exports reflects the export ban on beef between March 1996 and November 2005);

- the value of pork imports rose by 66 per cent while exports declined by 67 per cent over the same period reflecting the fall in pig production in the United Kingdom and the ban imposed during the outbreak of foot and mouth disease in 2001;

- the value of poultrymeat imports increased by 36 per cent while the value of exports fell by 7.5 per cent;

- all trade in breakfast cereal increased with the value of imports more than doubling and exports increasing by 8.4 per cent;

- the value of cheese exports increased by 14 per cent while imports increased by 9.4 per cent.

Table 8.2 Trade in key commodities in real terms at 2005 prices; United Kingdom

Enquiries: Dave Rimmer on +44 (0)1904 456406   email: david.j.rimmer@defra.gsi.gov.uk

£ million		Average of 1995-97	2001	2002	2003	2004	Calendar years 2005
Whisky	Imports	60.1	75.6	75.5	89.8	93.8	100.0
	Exports	2 949.4	2 572.3	2 522.9	2 554.3	2 366.4	2 417.1
Wine	Imports	1 830.3	2 049.7	2 208.3	2 321.0	2 412.2	2 355.7
	Exports	119.4	132.3	149.9	150.4	121.7	128.6
Cheese	Imports	737.4	724.5	705.0	787.6	833.5	853.8
	Exports	175.7	163.2	167.5	190.0	207.3	219.5
Poultrymeat	Imports	533.3	630.0	615.2	701.3	760.1	761.0
	Exports	233.0	183.9	155.9	181.1	199.5	208.5
Beef and veal	Imports	413.5	434.6	498.3	585.3	628.3	583.3
	Exports	322.4	20.8	19.7	21.0	20.7	25.5

continued

Table 8.2 continued

£ million		Average of 1995-97	2001	2002	2003	Calendar years 2004	2005
Wheat, unmilled	Imports	156.3	161.6	160.5	124.9	96.0	135.0
	Exports	487.6	148.7	129.4	309.1	213.7	198.8
Lamb and mutton	Imports	308.6	215.9	248.5	266.9	291.1	292.0
	Exports	365.9	86.9	155.4	202.2	194.3	213.8
Pork	Imports	299.8	371.7	360.7	491.2	511.0	590.1
	Exports	312.3	42.4	80.9	68.8	94.9	104.2
Breakfast cereals	Imports	47.7	71.8	82.5	80.2	94.2	98.6
	Exports	265.1	282.4	277.8	292.5	286.4	297.5
Milk and cream	Imports	74.5	44.9	34.2	31.6	34.8	36.2
	Exports	176.5	114.9	120.0	177.5	144.2	172.8
Bacon and ham	Imports	727.0	629.0	619.4	659.2	563.4	528.0
	Exports	22.0	22.8	33.3	40.9	35.4	27.7
Butter	Imports	289.0	271.4	277.2	297.6	286.8	309.5
	Exports	173.9	88.5	77.2	79.4	60.9	73.2
Eggs and egg products	Imports	45.1	56.5	71.4	89.0	88.0	77.1
	Exports	29.2	25.5	34.4	30.8	33.7	27.5

Table 8.3 Trade in key commodities by volume; United Kingdom

Enquiries: Dave Rimmer on +44 (0)1904 456406   email: david.j.rimmer@defra.gsi.gov.uk

Thousand tonnes (unless otherwise specified)		Average of 1995-97	2001	2002	2003	Calendar years 2004	2005
Whisky (million litres)	Imports	8.2	11.6	13.8	16.3	14.6	13.5
	Exports	271.0	287.7	267.9	277.9	273.4	284.1
Wine (million litres)	Imports	846.0	1 036.0	1 128.2	1 220.0	1 333.7	1 315.1
	Exports	32.9	20.0	28.5	24.5	21.8	21.4
Cheese	Imports	241.3	274.4	285.2	315.6	334.7	352.9
	Exports	55.3	67.9	82.3	89.8	93.3	96.3
Poultrymeat	Imports	232.6	291.4	317.1	346.6	396.4	406.4
	Exports	187.0	222.0	243.8	268.3	265.5	304.6
Beef and veal	Imports	134.2	193.4	226.1	269.4	280.6	239.9
	Exports	114.3	5.4	5.3	5.7	6.5	8.9
Wheat, unmilled	Imports	920.3	1 304.8	1 367.6	984.7	776.4	1 200.7
	Exports	3 543.8	1 626.1	1 624.0	3 661.5	2 528.2	2 494.8
Lamb and mutton	Imports	129.0	93.2	101.8	111.5	116.2	110.1
	Exports	127.7	30.4	61.1	75.8	76.7	85.2
Pork	Imports	149.6	239.2	275.9	380.5	383.5	432.0
	Exports	169.5	35.9	89.5	69.4	84.3	91.5
Breakfast cereals	Imports	24.7	52.1	55.7	61.0	66.9	78.8
	Exports	126.5	160.2	159.9	159.1	152.8	168.0
Milk and cream	Imports	156.5	110.1	63.9	52.5	70.8	79.0
	Exports	187.8	149.0	159.4	312.0	339.4	592.2
Bacon and ham	Imports	243.8	281.3	291.6	303.2	301.7	283.4
	Exports	6.6	7.3	10.7	13.9	13.2	10.6
Butter	Imports	112.3	115.2	116.0	118.4	113.7	128.6
	Exports	59.6	40.8	38.8	44.4	34.8	45.1
Eggs and egg products	Imports	27.5	54.2	69.0	70.4	67.1	78.7
	Exports	14.7	10.5	18.8	17.6	15.1	13.7

Notes to Table 8.2 and Table 8.3

Whisky	includes bourbon, scotch (malted and blended) and other whiskies.
Wine	includes grape must, vermouth and wine of fresh grapes (sparkling and still).
Cheese	includes grated or powdered, processed, blue-veined and fresh (e.g. curd).
Poultrymeat (inc. poultry offal)	includes carcase meat, cuts and offal (inc. liver).
Beef and veal	includes carcase meat and cuts, both bone-in and boneless.
Wheat, unmilled	includes durum, other wheat (inc. spelt) and meslin.
Lamb and mutton	includes carcase meat and cuts, both bone-in and boneless.
Pork	includes carcase meat and cuts, both bone-in and boneless.
Breakfast cereals	includes cereal grains worked or prepared for breakfast cereals
Milk and cream	includes milk (inc. skimmed milk) and cream, not concentrated or sweetened.

Trade with EU 24 countries (charts 8.6 to 8.17)

10 This section describes the trade in several key commodities between the United Kingdom and the other 24 Member States of the European Union (the EU 24 countries).

Bacon and ham

11 Imports of bacon and ham from the EU 24 countries have been far in excess of exports for many years. Total imports have fluctuated but have risen in recent years to reach 283 thousand tonnes in 2005. In 2005, the Netherlands and Denmark accounted for 84 per cent of all imported bacon and ham.

Chart 8.6 Trade with EU 24 countries: bacon and ham

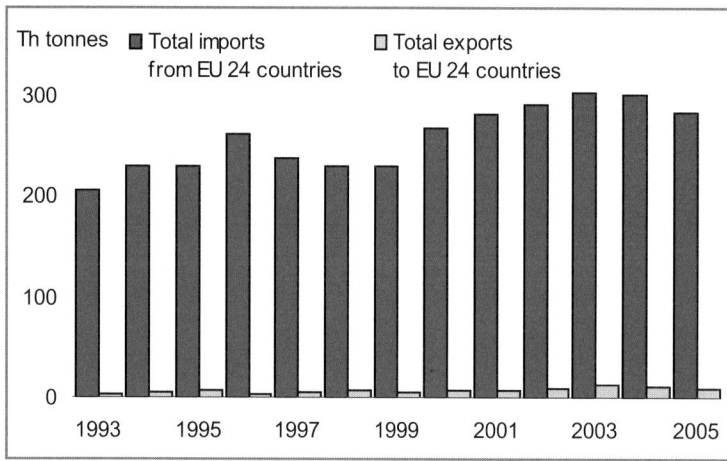

Chart 8.7 Trade with EU 24 countries: imports of bacon and ham 2005

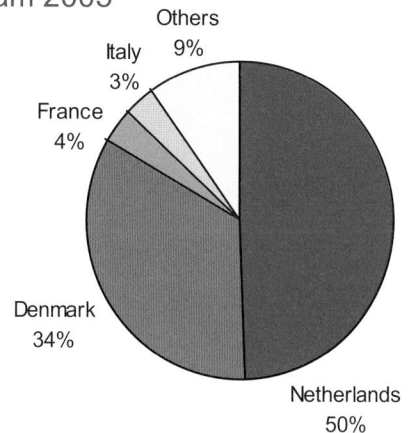

Pork

12 Exports of pork to the EU 24 countries grew strongly in 1997 and 1998. Since 1998 exports have declined rapidly. The dip in 2001 is the result of a ban on exports during the outbreak of foot and mouth disease that year. Imports have outperformed exports except in the two strong years for exports in 1997 and 1998. Imports rose to 427 thousand tonnes in 2005 while exports increased slightly to 80 thousand tonnes. Denmark and the Netherlands accounted for over half of the imports of pork in 2005 with a further 20 per cent contributed by Germany and France.

Chart 8.8 Trade with EU 24 countries: pork

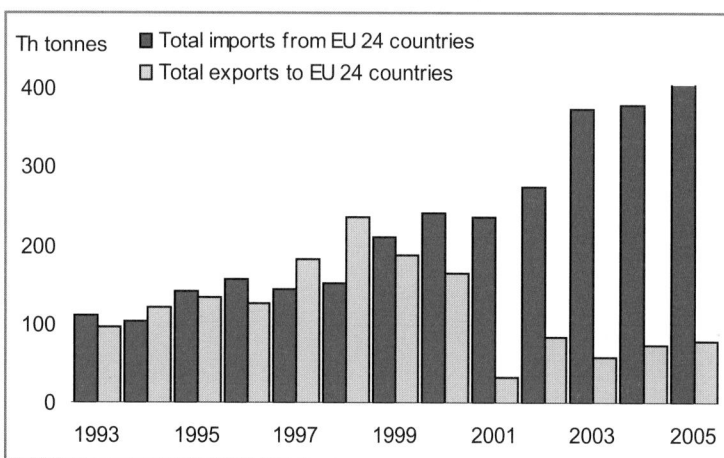

Chart 8.9 Trade with EU 24 countries: imports of pork 2005

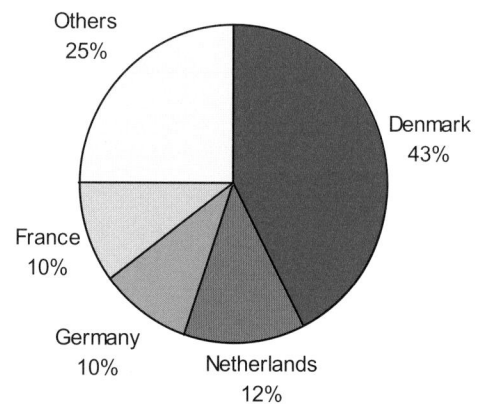

Lamb and mutton

13 The United Kingdom has exported much more lamb and mutton to the EU 24 countries than it has imported from these countries for many years. Exports peaked in 1995 but have since declined. The ban on exports during the outbreak of foot and mouth disease shows in the dip in 2001 followed by a recovery to 85 thousand tonnes for 2005. Seventy-two per cent of all lamb and mutton exported to the EU 24 countries in 2005 went to France with a further 21 per cent going to Belgium, Luxembourg, Germany and Italy.

Chart 8.10 Trade with EU 24 countries: lamb and mutton

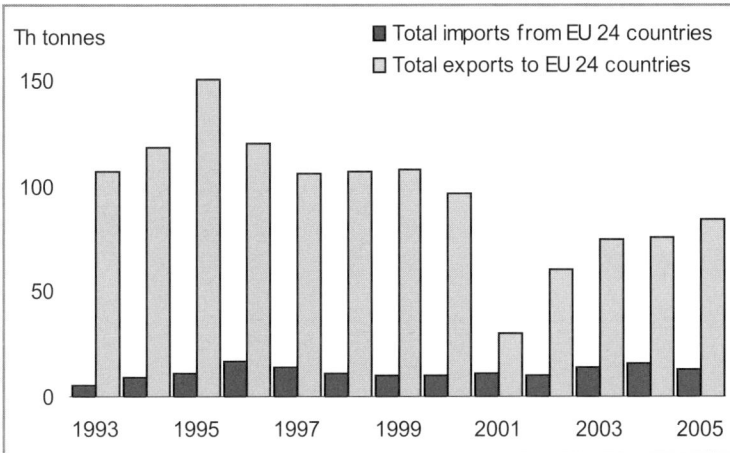

Th tonnes

- Total imports from EU 24 countries
- Total exports to EU 24 countries

150

100

50

0

1993   1995   1997   1999   2001   2003   2005

Chart 8.11 Trade with EU 24 countries: exports of lamb and mutton 2005

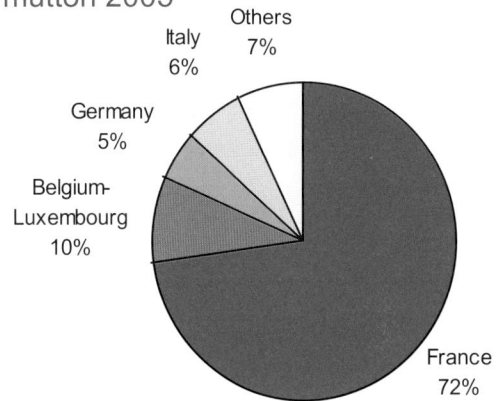

Italy 6%
Others 7%
Germany 5%
Belgium-Luxembourg 10%
France 72%

Beef and veal

14 Following the Government's announcement of a link between BSE and new variant CJD, exports of beef originating in the United Kingdom were banned from March 1996. The small amounts of exports seen here from 1997 are of beef and veal of non-UK origin which have been imported into the United Kingdom and then exported. Since the ban began, imports from the EU 24 countries have risen strongly reaching 176 thousand tonnes in 2005. The Irish Republic accounted for 78 per cent of the imports in 2005 with the Netherlands, Germany and Italy accounting for a further 14 per cent.

Chart 8.12 Trade with EU 24 countries: beef and veal

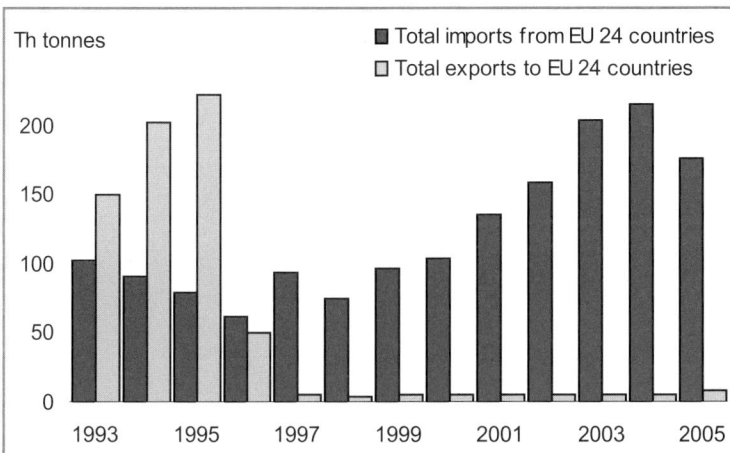

Th tonnes

- Total imports from EU 24 countries
- Total exports to EU 24 countries

200

150

100

50

0

1993   1995   1997   1999   2001   2003   2005

Chart 8.13 Trade with EU 24 countries: imports of beef and veal 2005

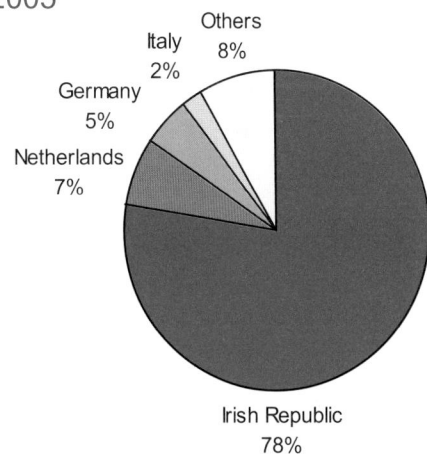

Italy 2%
Others 8%
Germany 5%
Netherlands 7%
Irish Republic 78%

Milk and cream

15 Since 1998 imports have been in decline. Exports have risen sharply since 2002 reaching 592 thousand tonnes in 2005. In 2005, three-quarters of milk and cream exports went to the Irish Republic with a further 10 per cent exported to Belgium, Luxembourg and Germany.

Chart 8.14 Trade with EU 24 countries: milk and cream

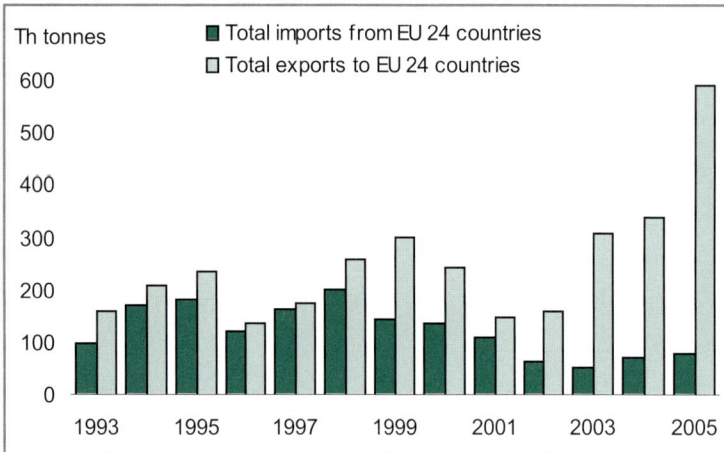

Th tonnes
- ■ Total imports from EU 24 countries
- ☐ Total exports to EU 24 countries

Chart 8.15 Trade with EU 24 countries: exports of milk & cream 2005

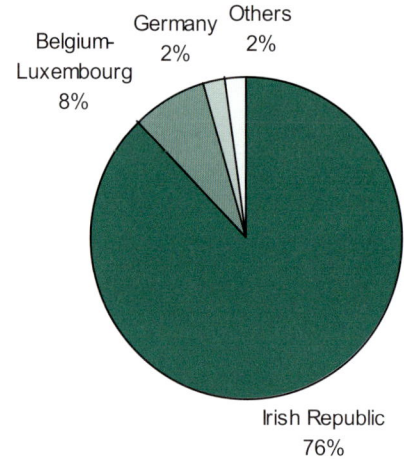

Belgium-Luxembourg 8%
Germany 2%
Others 2%
Irish Republic 76%

Unmilled wheat

16 Exports of unmilled wheat to the EU 24 countries have exceeded imports from these countries. The drop in exports in 2001 and 2002 was due to poor harvests resulting from bad weather. In 2005, exports stood at 2,478 thousand tonnes, of which almost 60 per cent went to Spain. A further 32 per cent went to Portugal, France and the Irish Republic.

Chart 8.16 Trade with EU 24 countries: unmilled wheat

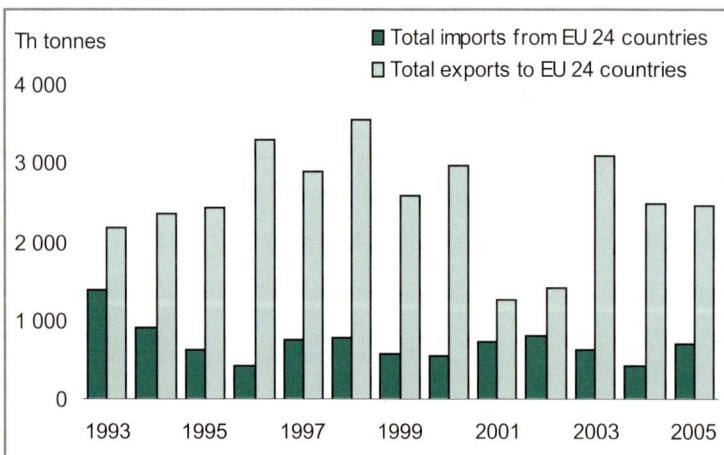

Th tonnes
- ■ Total imports from EU 24 countries
- ☐ Total exports to EU 24 countries

Chart 8.17 Trade with EU 24 countries: exports of unmilled wheat 2005

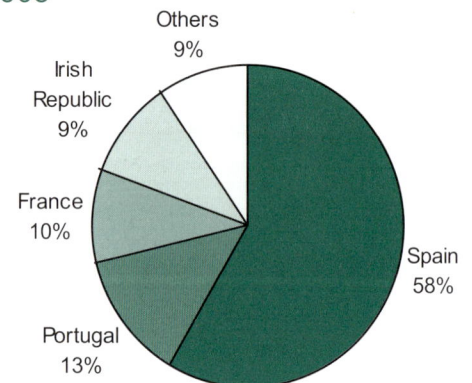

Others 9%
Irish Republic 9%
France 10%
Portugal 13%
Spain 58%

Chapter **9** Accounts

Summary

In 2006:

- Total Income from Farming is estimated to have risen by 10 per cent in current prices, or by 6.9 per cent in real terms, to £2.7 billion, as increases in the value of output largely due to higher prices more than offset higher input costs;

- the value of total output at market prices rose by 4.3 per cent to £15 billion;

- the value of intermediate consumption rose by 2.6 per cent with high oil prices leading to a 5.3 per cent rise in energy costs;

- gross value added at market prices rose by 7.3 per cent;

- net value added at factor cost rose by 4.6 per cent to £5.7 billion;

- labour costs fell by 0.8 per cent and rents fell by 4.9 per cent.

At market prices, the value of output of:

- cereals was £1.6 billion, 14 per cent higher than in 2005 as prices moved closer to the higher prices seen in late 2003 and early 2004;

- oilseed rape rose by 17 per cent to £307 million as a result of higher prices, which were a reflection of global demand for both food and non-food uses;

- sugar beet fell by 37 per cent to £168 million due to lower production and prices;

- fresh vegetables rose by 9.1 per cent to £986 million;

- plants and flowers fell by 4.4 per cent to £744 million;

- potatoes was £625 million, 24 per cent higher than in 2005, as higher prices more than offset a fall in production;

- livestock production also rose, by 7.5 per cent to £5.2 billion, led by an increase of 13 per cent in the value of output of cattle;

- milk production fell by £3.6 million due mainly to lower prices;

- egg production rose by 2.0 per cent to £357 million.

In 2005:

- net worth rose by 7.5 per cent or 5.2 per cent in real terms, to £130 billion;

- total assets increased by 5.1 per cent while liabilities rose by 4.7 per cent.

Introduction

1 This chapter shows a sequence of inter-related accounts for agriculture including current accounts, accumulation accounts and balance sheets. These accounts conform to internationally agreed accounting principles required by both the United Kingdom's National Accounts and by Eurostat, the statistical office of the European Union.

2 The production and income account provides details of the industry's outputs, inputs and generation of income; the balance sheets show the total assets and liabilities for agriculture at the end of each calendar year together with their net worth and the accumulation accounts analyse the various components of changes in the assets and liabilities of agriculture and record changes in net worth. The net worth shown in the balance sheets incorporates changes due to all of the accumulation accounts.

Total Income from Farming

3 Total Income from Farming (TIFF) in the United Kingdom is estimated to have risen in 2006 by 10 per cent in current prices, or by 6.9 per cent in real terms, to £2.7 billion. In real terms, TIFF remains below the high levels of the late eighties but is now 41 per cent above the low point of 2000.

4 Total Income from Farming is income generated by production within the agriculture industry, including subsidies. It represents business profits plus remuneration for work done by owners and other unpaid workers. It is sensitive to small percentage changes in the values of outputs and inputs. This sensitivity, the provisional nature of the figures for the latest year, and revisions made to previously published figures for earlier years as methodology or data sources improve, all need to be borne in mind when using the figures.

Production and income account at current prices (tables 9.1, 9.2, charts 9.1, 9.2)

5 In 2006 the total value of output at market prices increased by 4.3 per cent to £15 billion. The value of intermediate consumption increased by 2.6 per cent and gross value added at market prices increased by 7.3 per cent. The Single Payment, introduced in 2005, is not included as output as it is decoupled from production. However, Single Payment is included in Total Income from Farming, in accordance with National Accounting conventions.

6 The increased value of production for many outputs in 2006 was largely a result of higher prices than those seen in 2005, with the notable exception of sugar beet and milk, offsetting a 0.9 per cent fall in the volume of output. Input costs rose by 2.6 per cent, with high oil prices leading to a 5.3 per cent increase in energy costs.

7 Gross value added for the industry, which represents its contribution to national GDP, increased by 7.3 per cent at market prices. Interest payments increased by 4.3 per cent. Compensation of employees fell by 0.8 per cent as a result of the falling labour force.

8 Net value added at factor cost is the best measure of value added by the industry because it includes all subsidies, the bulk of which following the introduction of the Single Payment Scheme in 2005 are no longer included in output. It makes no allowance for interest, rent or labour costs. In 2006, net value added at factor cost was £5.7 billion, a 4.6 per cent rise compared to 2005.

9 Total Income from Farming is derived by deducting interest, rent and paid labour costs from net value added at factor cost. Labour costs fell slightly, by 0.8 per cent, rent cost fell by 4.9 per cent but interest payments rose by 4.3 per cent.

Definition of terms used in tables 9.1 and 9.2

The following list is provided to aid the user with the terms used in tables 9.1 and 9.2.

Term	Table 9.1 reference number	Definition
Agricultural industry		All activities taking place within businesses that carry out any agricultural .activities. These businesses include all farms and specialist agricultural contractors.
Capital formation in livestock	8	Production of animals that will be used as the means of production, e.g. breeding animals.
Other agricultural activities	10	Agricultural activities that do not result in sales of final product, e.g. quota leasing, contract work.
Inseparable non-agricultural activities	11	Non-agricultural activities which are included within the business level accounts and are inseparable, e.g. some cases of bed and breakfast and recreation facilities.
Output at market prices	12	Output excluding subsidies. The output of the agricultural industry includes some non-agricultural activities and transactions within the industry.
Basic prices		Market price plus directly paid subsidies that are linked to production of specific product.
Subsidies (less taxes) on product	13	Subsidies and taxes linked to the production of an agricultural product. All subsidies are recorded on an 'as due' basis.
Intermediate consumption	24	Consumption of goods and services, e.g. feed, seeds, fertiliser, pesticides.
Gross value added	25	Gross output less intermediate consumption.
Consumption of fixed capital	27	The reduction in value (at current prices) of capital assets used in the production process, e.g. buildings, plant, machinery, vehicles and livestock.
Net value added	28	Gross value added at basic prices less consumption of fixed capital.
Compensation of employees	30	The full costs of employees to the business including national insurance contributions.
Other subsidies on production	32	Subsidies and taxes not linked to production of a specific product, e.g. Single Payment Scheme, agri-environment payments, animal disease compensation.
Net value added at factor cost	33	Net value added at basic prices plus other subsidies (less taxes) on production
Total Income from Farming (TIFF)	36	Income to those with an entrepreneurial interest in the agricultural industry, e.g. farmers, partners, spouses and most other family workers.

2006

Chart 9.1 Main components of the production and income account in 2006 (£ billion); United Kingdom

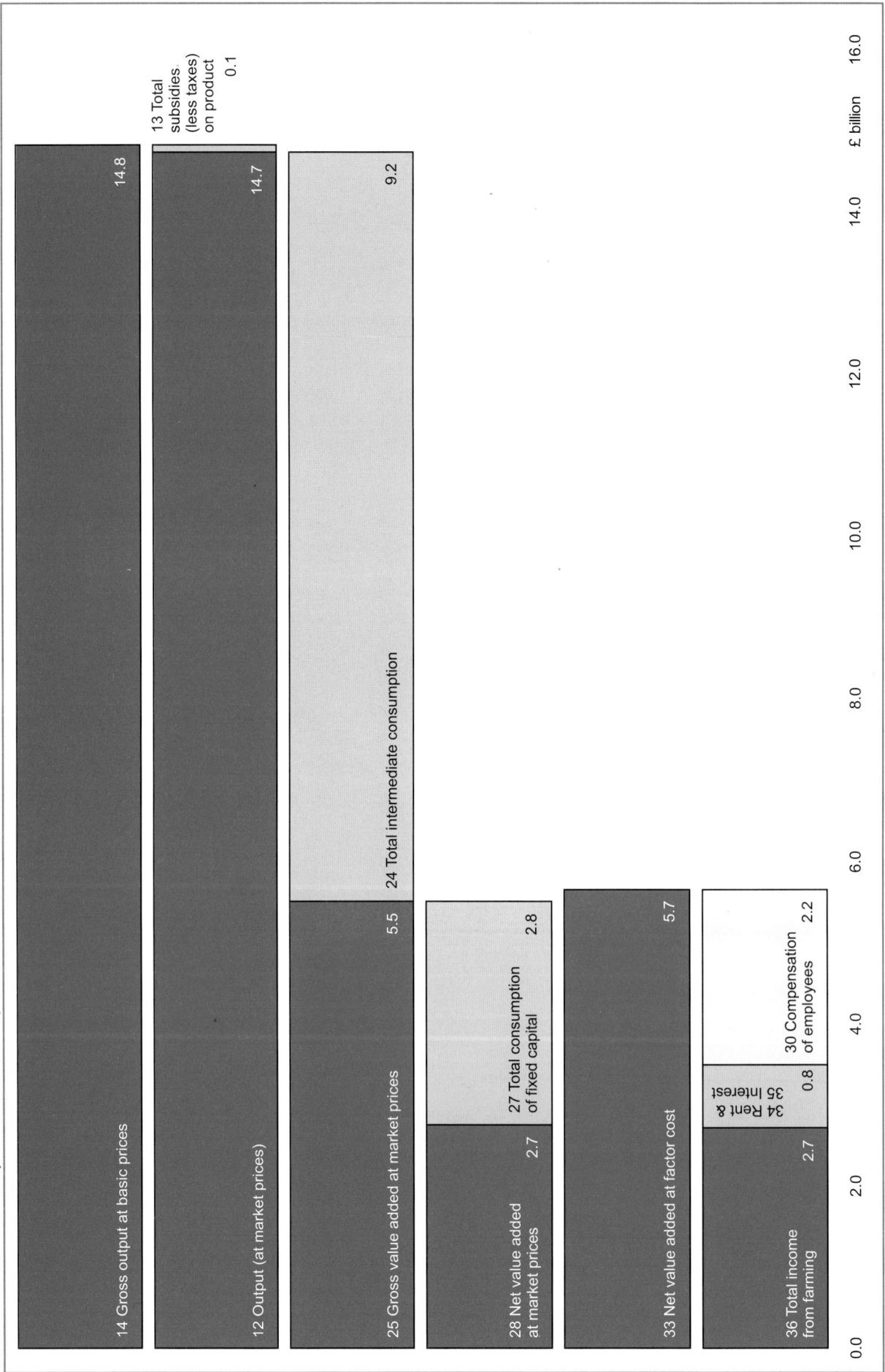

14 Gross output at basic prices — 14.8

13 Total subsidies (less taxes) on product — 0.1

12 Output (at market prices) — 14.7

24 Total intermediate consumption — 9.2

25 Gross value added at market prices — 5.5

27 Total consumption of fixed capital — 2.8

28 Net value added at market prices — 2.7

33 Net value added at factor cost — 5.7

34 Rent & 35 Interest — 0.8

30 Compensation of employees — 2.2

36 Total income from farming — 2.7

£ billion

0.0 2.0 4.0 6.0 8.0 10.0 12.0 14.0 16.0

Chart 9.2 Changes in value of output and inputs between 2005 and 2006 (£ million)

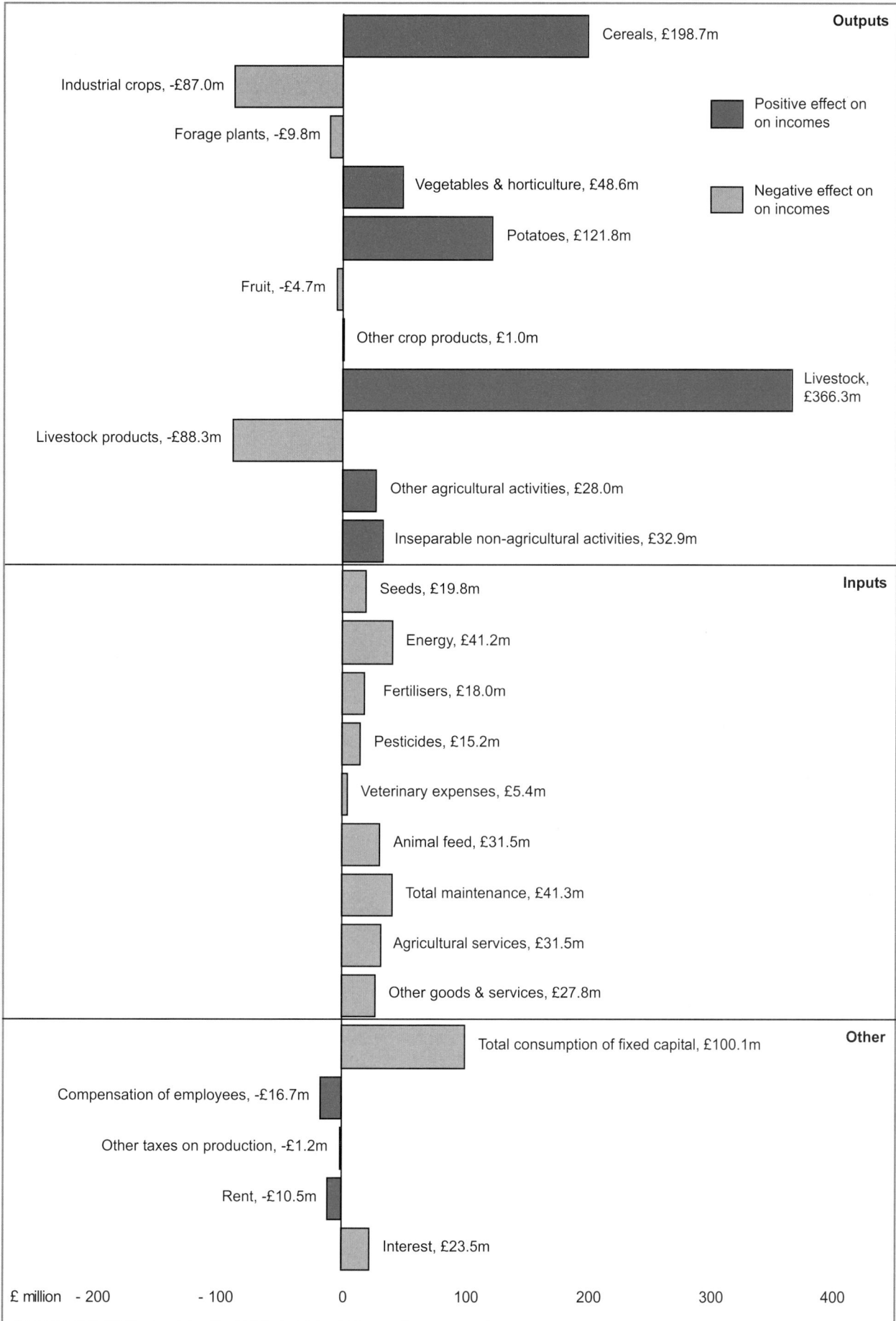

Table 9.1 Production and income account at current prices; United Kingdom

Enquiries: Christine Holleran on +44 (0)1904 455080   email: christine.holleran@defra.gsi.gov.uk

£ million | | | | | | Calendar years
	Average of 1995-97	2002	2003	2004	2005	2006 (provisional)
Output at market prices (a)						
1 Output of cereals	2 429	1 455	1 608	1 692	1 415	1 614
wheat	1 588	1 033	1 094	1 217	1 001	1 158
rye	3	1	1	2	1	2
barley	780	382	467	425	375	412
oats and summer cereal mixtures	57	37	45	47	37	42
other cereals	1	1	1	1	1	1
2 Output of industrial crops	881	860	813	799	807	720
oil seeds	259	220	314	266	279	315
oilseed rape	245	217	304	257	262	307
other oil seeds	14	3	10	9	17	8
sugar beet	347	283	280	278	269	168
other industrial crops	275	357	219	254	259	237
fibre plants	3	1	2	1	1	1
hops	18	7	6	6	5	4
other industrial crops (b)	254	348	211	247	253	231
3 Output of forage plants	95	90	104	93	95	85
4 Output of vegetables and horticultural products	1 685	1 591	1 673	1 611	1 682	1 730
fresh vegetables	1 025	841	901	824	904	986
plants and flowers	660	750	772	787	778	744
5 Output of potatoes (including seeds)	707	480	517	654	503	625
6 Output of fruit	249	251	310	316	382	377
7 Output of other crop products including seeds	39	26	32	31	32	33
Total crop output (sum 1 - 7)	6 085	4 753	5 055	5 195	4 915	5 183
8 Output of livestock	5 835	4 567	4 835	4 832	4 879	5 245
primarily for meat	5 167	3 865	4 101	4 181	4 223	4 447
cattle	1 487	1 146	1 227	1 278	1 389	1 568
pigs	1 245	687	672	679	678	687
sheep	827	613	698	726	683	702
poultry	1 466	1 261	1 343	1 332	1 302	1 315
other animals	142	158	161	166	171	175
gross fixed capital formation	667	702	734	651	656	798
cattle	359	389	444	333	410	526
pigs	17	8	7	8	7	8
sheep	165	178	155	178	113	138
poultry	127	128	128	132	127	126
9 Output of livestock products	3 804	2 834	3 031	3 040	2 992	2 903
milk	3 418	2 466	2 629	2 611	2 593	2 501
eggs	321	314	337	380	350	357
raw wool	40	19	21	20	20	16
other animal products	24	34	45	29	30	30
Total livestock output (8 + 9)	9 639	7 401	7 866	7 872	7 870	8 148
10 Other agricultural activities	742	644	651	697	642	670
agricultural services	579	601	592	637	631	662
leasing out quota	163	43	58	60	11	8
11 Inseparable non-agricultural activities	353	560	594	636	703	736
12 Output (at market prices) (sum 1 to 11)	16 820	13 357	14 166	14 400	14 130	14 737
of which:						
transactions within the agricultural industry						
feed wheat	67	39	79	103	87	90
feed barley	199	143	159	149	138	167
feed oats	15	10	11	12	10	12
seed potatoes	28	15	6	13	12	23
straw	227	306	177	209	211	188
contract work	579	601	592	637	631	662
leasing of quota	163	43	58	60	11	8
total capital formation in livestock	667	702	734	651	656	798
13 Total subsidies (less taxes) on product (c)	2 492	2 131	2 174	2 387	206	85
14 Gross output at basic prices (12 + 13)	19 312	15 489	16 340	16 787	14 336	14 822

continued

Table 9.1 continued

	Average of 1995-97	2002	2003	2004	2005	2006 (provisional)
Intermediate consumption						
15 Seeds	367	275	287	303	310	329
16 Energy	623	647	600	670	771	812
electricity	239	235	205	210	229	246
fuels	384	412	395	460	541	566
17 Fertilisers	992	752	696	776	769	787
18 Pesticides	637	531	501	577	546	561
19 Veterinary expenses	298	250	253	279	273	278
20 Animal feed (d)	3 010	2 223	2 372	2 517	2 391	2 423
compounds	1 846	1 377	1 348	1 450	1 321	1 436
straights	883	654	774	804	836	717
feed purchased from other farms	280	192	250	264	234	269
21 Total maintenance (e)	1 097	960	971	1 017	999	1 040
materials	729	636	642	663	654	680
buildings	368	324	329	353	345	360
22 Agricultural services	579	601	592	637	631	662
23 Other goods and services (e)(f)	2 256	2 097	2 187	2 399	2 322	2 350
24 Total intermediate consumption (sum 15 to 23)	9 859	8 338	8 459	9 175	9 010	9 242
25 Gross value added at market prices (12 - 24)	6 961	5 020	5 707	5 226	5 119	5 495
26 Gross value added at basic prices (14 - 24)	9 453	7 151	7 881	7 613	5 325	5 580
27 Total consumption of fixed capital	2 630	2 583	2 645	2 528	2 655	2 755
equipment	1 283	1 262	1 206	1 194	1 207	1 201
buildings (e)(g)	662	688	691	671	671	679
livestock	685	632	748	662	777	875
cattle	374	353	441	362	490	581
pigs	16	8	8	9	7	7
sheep	173	142	173	168	151	162
poultry	122	129	126	124	128	125
28 Net value added at market prices (25 - 27)	4 330	2 437	3 062	2 698	2 464	2 740
29 Net value added at basic prices (26 - 27)	6 823	4 568	5 237	5 085	2 670	2 825
30 Compensation of employees (h)	1 882	1 966	1 917	2 009	2 177	2 161
31 Other taxes on production	- 80	- 81	- 83	- 96	- 102	- 103
32 Other subsidies on production (c)	233	565	622	594	2 836	2 932
33 Net value added at factor cost (29 + 31 + 32)	6 976	5 053	5 775	5 583	5 405	5 654
34 Rent	220	255	269	240	215	205
rent paid (i)	271	341	361	336	309	302
rent received (j)	- 77	- 86	- 92	- 96	- 94	- 97
35 Interest (k)	588	483	450	511	548	571
36 Total income from farming (33 - 30 - 34 - 35)	4 285	2 348	3 140	2 824	2 465	2 718

(a) Output is net of VAT collected on the sale of non-edible products. Figures for output at market prices exclude subsidies on products.

(b) Includes straw and minor crops.

(c) "Subsidies (less taxes) on product": payments linked to the production of agricultural products. "Other subsidies on production": payments not linked to production from which agricultural producers can benefit as a consequence of engaging in agricultural activities e.g. Single Payment Scheme, agri-environment schemes.

(d) For years prior to 1992 the split between compounds and straights was derived from the split present in later years.

(e) Landlords' expenses are included within total maintenance, other goods and services and total consumption of fixed capital of buildings.

(f) Includes livestock and crop costs, water costs, insurance premiums, bank charges, professional fees, rates, and other farming costs.

(g) A more empirically based methodology for calculating landlords' consumption of fixed capital was introduced in 2000. The new series has been linked with the old one using a smoothing procedure for the transition year of 1996.

(h) Excludes the value of work done by farm labour on own account capital formation in buildings and works.

(i) Rent paid on all tenanted land (including 'conacre' land in Northern Ireland) less landlords' expenses, landlords' consumption of fixed capital and the benefit value of dwellings on that land.

(j) Rent received by farming landowners from renting of land to other farmers less landlords' expenses. This series starts in 1996 following a revision to the methodology of calculating net rent.

(k) Interest charges on loans for current farming purposes and buildings and works less interest on money held on short term deposit.

Table 9.2 Changes in outputs and inputs; United Kingdom

Enquiries: Christine Holleran on +44 (0)1904 455080   email: christine.holleran@defra.gsi.gov.uk

£ million   Calendar years

	Current price value		Changes %		
	2005	2006	value	volume	price
Output at market prices (a)					
1 Output of cereals	1 415	1 614	14	- 2	16
wheat	1 001	1 158	16	- 1	17
rye	1	2	17	-	17
barley	375	412	10	- 4	15
oats and summer cereal mixtures	37	42	12	- 4	17
other cereals	1	1	-	- 3	3
2 Output of industrial crops	807	720	- 11	- 8	- 3
oil seeds	279	315	13	- 4	18
oilseed rape	262	307	17	- 2	19
other oil seeds	17	8	- 54	- 45	- 16
sugar beet	269	168	- 37	- 18	- 24
other industrial crops	259	237	- 9	- 4	- 5
fibre plants	1	1	25	25	-
hops	5	4	- 18	- 17	- 1
other industrial crops (b)	253	231	- 9	- 4	- 5
3 Output of forage plants	95	85	- 10	- 12	1
4 Output of vegetables and horticultural products	1 682	1 730	3	- 5	9
fresh vegetables	904	986	9	- 2	11
plants and flowers	778	744	- 4	- 10	6
5 Output of potatoes (including seeds)	503	625	24	3	21
6 Output of fruit	382	377	- 1	7	- 8
7 Output of other crop products including seeds	32	33	3	- 2	5
Total crop output (sum 1 - 7)	4 915	5 183	5	- 3	9
8 Output of livestock	4 879	5 245	8	1	6
primarily for meat	4 223	4 447	5	1	5
cattle	1 389	1 568	13	5	8
pigs	678	687	1	- 1	2
sheep	683	702	3	- 1	4
poultry	1 302	1 315	1	- 2	3
other animals	171	175	3	- 1	3
gross fixed capital formation	656	798	22	4	17
cattle	410	526	28	2	25
pigs	7	8	24	26	- 2
sheep	113	138	23	13	9
poultry	127	126	- 1	- 1	-
9 Output of livestock products	2 992	2 903	- 3	- 1	- 2
milk	2 593	2 501	- 4	- 1	- 3
eggs	350	357	2	- 3	6
raw wool	20	16	- 16	- 7	- 10
other animal products	30	30	-	-	-
Total livestock output (8 + 9)	7 870	8 148	4	-	3
10 Other agricultural activities	642	670	4	- 1	5
agricultural services	631	662	5	-	5
leasing out quota	11	8	- 31	- 31	-
11 Inseparable non-agricultural activities	703	736	5	3	2
12 Output (at market prices) (sum 1 to 11)	14 130	14 737	4	- 1	5
of which:					
transactions within the agricultural industry					
feed wheat	87	90	4	- 12	17
feed barley	138	167	21	5	16
feed oats	10	12	29	7	21
seed potatoes	12	23	92	59	21
straw	211	188	- 11	- 5	- 6
contract work	631	662	5	-	5
leasing of quota	11	8	- 31	- 31	-
total capital formation in livestock	656	798	22	4	17
13 Total subsidies (less taxes) on product (c)	206	85	- 59	. .	. .
14 Gross output at basic prices (12 + 13)	14 336	14 822	3	- 1	4

continued

Table 9.2 continued

	Current price value		Changes %		
	2005	2006	value	volume	price
Intermediate consumption					
15 Seeds	310	329	6	2	4
16 Energy	771	812	5	..	..
electricity	229	246	7	- 2	10
fuels	541	566	4	- 5	10
17 Fertilisers	769	787	2	- 3	6
18 Pesticides	546	561	3	-	3
19 Veterinary expenses	273	278	2	- 8	11
20 Animal feed (d)	2 391	2 423	1	- 4	6
compounds	1 321	1 436	9	6	3
straights	836	717	- 14	- 20	8
feed purchased from other farms	234	269	15	- 1	16
21 Total maintenance (e)	999	1 040	4	- 1	5
materials	654	680	4	- 1	5
buildings	345	360	4	-	5
22 Agricultural services	631	662	5	-	5
23 Other goods and services (e)(f)	2 322	2 350	1	- 4	6
24 Total intermediate consumption (sum 15 to 23)	9 010	9 242	3	- 3	6
25 Gross value added at market prices (12 - 24)	5 119	5 495	7	3	4
26 Gross value added at basic prices (14 - 24)	5 325	5 580	5	3	2
27 Total consumption of fixed capital	2 655	2 755	4	- 3	7
equipment	1 207	1 201	-	- 2	1
buildings (e)(g)	671	679	1	- 3	4
livestock	777	875	13	- 4	17
cattle	490	581	19	- 5	25
pigs	7	7	- 6	- 7	1
sheep	151	162	7	- 1	8
poultry	128	125	- 3	- 3	-
28 Net value added at market prices (25 - 27)	2 464	2 740	11	10	1
29 Net value added at basic prices (26 - 27)	2 670	2 825	6	9	- 3
30 Compensation of employees (h)	2 177	2 161	- 1	- 5	4
31 Other taxes on production	- 102	- 103	1	..	..
32 Other subsidies on production (c)	2 836	2 932	3	..	..
33 Net value added at factor cost (29 + 31 + 32)	5 405	5 654	5	9	- 4
34 Rent	215	205	- 5	..	..
rent paid (i)	309	302	- 2	..	..
rent received (j)	- 94	- 97	3	..	..
35 Interest (k)	548	571	4	..	..
36 Total income from farming (33 - 30 - 34 - 35)	2 465	2 718	10	102	- 45

(a) Output is net of VAT collected on the sale of non-edible products. Figures for output at market prices exclude subsidies on products.

(b) Includes straw and minor crops.

(c) "Subsidies (less taxes) on product": payments linked to the production of agricultural products. "Other subsidies on production": payments not linked to production from which agricultural producers can benefit as a consequence of engaging in agricultural activities e.g. Single Payment Scheme, agri-environment schemes.

(d) For years prior to 1992 the split between compounds and straights was derived from the split present in later years.

(e) Landlords' expenses are included within total maintenance, other goods and services and total consumption of fixed capital of buildings.

(f) Includes livestock and crop costs, water costs, insurance premiums, bank charges, professional fees, rates, and other farming costs.

(g) A more empirically based methodology for calculating landlords' consumption of fixed capital was introduced in 2000. The new series has been linked with the old one using a smoothing procedure for the transition year of 1996.

(h) Excludes the value of work done by farm labour on own account capital formation in buildings and works.

(i) Rent paid on all tenanted land (including 'conacre' land in Northern Ireland) less landlords' expenses, landlords' consumption of fixed capital and the benefit value of dwellings on that land.

(j) Rent received by farming landowners from renting of land to other farmers less landlords' expenses. This series starts in 1996 following a revision to the methodology of calculating net rent.

(k) Interest charges on loans for current farming purposes and buildings and works less interest on money held on short term deposit.

Balance sheets (table 9.3)

10 The value of net worth rose by 5.2 per cent in real terms to £130 billion. The total value of assets rose by 5.1 per cent in real terms to £140 billion. The total value of liabilities increased by 7.0 per cent (4.7 per cent in real terms) to £11 billion.

11 At current prices, net of depreciation and excluding the value of quota, the value of fixed assets rose by 7.6 per cent to £131 billion. Within this, the value of land and buildings, which forms the greater part of the total, rose by 8.3 per cent to £119 billion, led by the continued rise in land prices. The value of current assets rose by 6.1 per cent to £10 billion. Long and medium-term liabilities rose by 2.9 per cent to £5.1 billion while short-term liabilities rose by 11 per cent to £5.7 billion. Short term loans rose by 11 per cent to £5.7 billion, with bank overdrafts rising by 21 per cent to £3.5 billion.

Table 9.3 Aggregate balance sheets for agriculture; United Kingdom

Enquiries: Sarah Tumber on +44 (0)1904 455084   email: sarah.tumber@defra.gsi.gov.uk

£ million					As at December each year	
	Average of 1995-97	2001	2002	2003	2004	2005 (provisional)
At current prices						
Assets						
Fixed: (a)						
Land and buildings	76 446	94 718	97 365	97 029	101 958	119 427
Plant, machinery and vehicles	8 236	7 421	7 346	7 113	6 954	7 125
Breeding livestock	5 209	3 645	3 942	3 783	3 799	3 978
Total fixed	89 891	105 783	108 652	107 925	112 711	130 530
Current:						
Trading livestock	3 106	2 100	1 908	2 605	2 853	2 320
Crops and stores	2 975	2 236	2 194	2 031	2 412	2 042
Debtors, cash deposits	3 991	4 096	3 991	4 259	4 891	5 598
Total current	10 072	8 432	8 093	8 895	10 157	9 959
Total assets	99 963	114 215	116 745	116 820	122 868	140 490
Liabilities						
Long and medium-term:						
AMC and SASC (b)	1 224	1 377	1 339	1 334	1 313	1 363
Building societies and institutions	292	396	379	389	460	457
Bank loans	1 781	2 367	2 202	2 284	2 435	2 403
Family loans	336	430	449	450	529	538
Other	170	232	248	271	263	338
Total long and medium-term	3 803	4 802	4 617	4 728	5 000	5 099
Short-term:						
Leasing	213	95	94	113	130	121
Hire purchase	687	479	517	593	724	602
Trade credit	1 278	1 250	1 193	1 238	1 423	1 388
Bank overdrafts	2 533	3 015	2 814	2 991	2 949	3 485
Other	152	114	118	128	120	128
Total short-term	4 863	4 953	4 735	5 063	5 347	5 726
Total liabilities	8 665	9 755	9 352	9 790	10 347	10 825
Net worth	91 298	104 460	107 394	107 030	112 522	129 664
In real terms (as deflated by the retail price index):						
Indices 2000 = 100						
Total assets	97	100	102	99	101	109
Total liabilities	98	100	95	97	100	98
Net worth	97	100	102	99	101	110

(a) The valuations of land, buildings and breeding livestock are at average market prices; those of plant, machinery and vehicles are replacement cost, net of consumption of fixed capital.

(b) Agricultural Mortgage Company (AMC) and Scottish Agricultural Securities Corporation (SASC).

Capital account (table 9.4)

12 The capital account in table 9.4 shows estimates of changes in the assets held by the agricultural sector in the United Kingdom. The provisional estimate of gross fixed capital formation in buildings, works, plant, machinery and vehicles in 2006 is £1.8 billion, a fall of 1.4 per cent compared to 2005. Consumption of fixed non-livestock assets also rose slightly, by 0.1 per cent to £1.9 billion.

13 Capital formation and capital consumption in livestock measure the value of output due to the production and depreciation of breeding animals, mainly dairy cows, beef cows, ewes, sows and egg laying poultry. In 2006, the value of capital formation in livestock rose by 22 per cent to £798 million. Consumption of fixed capital in livestock, which is approximated by assuming that all depreciation takes place at the time animals leave the breeding herds, rose by 13 per cent to £875 million, led by an increase of 19 per cent in capital consumption in cattle.

14 Changes in inventories contribute to income. Stocks of crops fell by £99 million in 2006 with large falls for wheat, barley and potatoes following decreased production and increased prices. The value of work-in-progress livestock fell by £42 million as increased prices were generally offset by decreased numbers.

Table 9.4 Accumulation accounts; United Kingdom

Enquiries: Sarah Tumber on +44 (0)1904 455084   email: sarah.tumber@defra.gsi.gov.uk

£ million

	Average of 1995-97	2002	2003	2004	2005	2006 (provisional)
Capital account						
Gross fixed capital formation	2 586	2 168	2 369	2 457	2 431	2 548
Acquisitions less disposals of non-livestock assets:	1 919	1 466	1 635	1 806	1 775	1 750
buildings and works	549	423	495	571	667	647
plant and machinery	1 125	848	916	996	899	892
vehicles	245	195	224	238	209	211
Capital formation in livestock (a):	667	702	734	651	656	798
cattle	359	389	444	333	410	526
sheep	165	178	155	178	113	138
pigs	17	8	7	8	7	8
poultry	127	128	128	132	127	126
Consumption of fixed capital	2 630	2 583	2 645	2 528	2 655	2 755
Non-livestock assets:	1 946	1 950	1 897	1 865	1 878	1 880
buildings and works	662	688	691	671	671	679
plant and machinery	1 076	1 057	1 002	985	998	993
vehicles	207	205	204	209	209	208
Livestock (b):	685	632	748	662	777	875
cattle	374	353	441	362	490	581
sheep	173	142	173	168	151	162
pigs	16	8	8	9	7	7
poultry	122	129	126	124	128	125
Changes in inventories	88	151	- 136	104	- 45	- 141
stocks of crops	132	137	- 177	112	- 21	- 99
work-in-progress livestock	- 44	15	40	- 8	- 24	- 42
Total Income from Farming	4 285	2 348	3 140	2 824	2 465	2 718
Other capital grants and payments not included in the production and income account	71	41	21	26	36	61

(a) Capital formation in livestock is estimated by valuing the number of entries to the breeding herds at the entry price less the disposal price.
(b) Consumption of fixed capital in livestock is estimated by valuing the disposals from the breeding herds at the entry price less the disposal price.

Revaluation account (table 9.5)

15 Revaluation or holding gains, measures the change in value between the time of production and the end of the accounting period due to changes in price, and rose by £695 million in 2006. The value of work-in progress of non-breeding livestock production and of replacement animals for breeding herds rose with the exception of sheep. The value of work-in-progress of crop production increased in 2006 by £387 million. Revaluation is not included in the production and income account and therefore does not contribute to income.

Table 9.5 Revaluation account; United Kingdom
Enquiries: Tim Marsh on +44 (0)1904 455089   email: tim.marsh@defra.gsi.gov.uk

£ million					Calendar years
	2002	2003	2004	2005	2006 (provisional)
Livestock production work-in-progress (non-breeders)					
cattle	248	113	- 177	- 214	137
sheep	77	16	- 25	- 33	- 14
pigs	40	41	- 85	48	45
poultry (broilers, ducks, geese and turkeys)	-	22	- 16	10	1
Total	365	193	- 304	- 189	169
Replacement animals for breeding herds					
cattle	109	- 93	13	- 78	144
sheep	33	8	- 13	- 14	- 6
pigs	1	1	- 1	1	1
Total	142	- 84	- 1	- 91	139
Crop production work-in-progress					
wheat	- 137	356	- 275	2	180
barley	- 18	81	- 67	- 1	55
potatoes	- 80	235	- 157	36	112
other crops (oats, oilseeds, apples and pears)	12	9	- 36	11	39
Total	- 223	680	- 535	47	387
Total holding gains	284	789	- 840	- 232	695

Interest (table 9.6)

16 Revised figures for 2005 show that interest charges payable on farmers' borrowings for agricultural purposes, including land purchases net of interest on short-term deposits, rose by 7.5 per cent in 2005 to £548 million. The level of borrowing, rose as did the average interest rate. In 2006, interest charges are estimated to have risen by 4.3 per cent to £571 million due to an increase in the level of farmers' borrowings.

Table 9.6 Interest; United Kingdom
Enquiries: Tim Marsh on +44 (0)1904 455089   email: tim.marsh@defra.gsi.gov.uk

£ million (unless otherwise specified)					Calendar years
	Average of 1995-97	2002	2003	2004	2005	2006 (provisional)
Interest rates						
average bank base lending rate in the UK	6.4%	4.0%	3.7%	4.4%	4.6%	4.5%
average rate of interest on bank advances to agriculture	9.0%	6.1%	5.7%	6.5%	6.7%	6.6%
Interest charges (all lending to the farm business) on:						
bank advances	390	325	316	342	377	..
AMC and SASC loans (a)	109	94	84	96	96	..
instalment credit	67	43	45	53	51	..
leased assets	18	6	6	6	5	..
other credit (b)	41	40	35	42	47	..
less interest earned on money held on short-term deposit	37	25	22	30	29	..
Total	588	483	463	509	548	571

(a) Agricultural Mortgage Company (AMC) and Scottish Agricultural Securities Corporation (SASC).
(b) Interest paid on other institutional credit and that from private sources.

Changes in volume of capital assets (table 9.7)

17 The volume of gross fixed capital formation fell by 1.1 per cent with an increase of 3.8 per cent in livestock assets being offset by a fall in the volume of non-livestock assets. The volume of consumption of fixed capital has fallen sharply since 1996 and a 2.7 per cent fall in 2006 continued the trend. Consumption of fixed capital in livestock fell by 3.8 per cent in 2006 while consumption of fixed capital in non-livestock assets fell by 2.7 per cent.

Table 9.7 Changes in volume of capital assets; United Kingdom

Enquiries: Sarah Tumber on +44 (0)1904 455084   email: sarah.tumber@defra.gsi.gov.uk

Indices 2000 = 100

	Average of 1995-97	2002	2003	2004	2005	2006 (provisional)
Total volume of gross fixed capital formation						
Gross fixed capital formation:	151.5	116.2	123.1	132.8	127.4	126.0
non livestock:	167.8	116.3	131.6	146.0	140.5	136.2
buildings and works	168.8	113.8	130.1	151.6	174.9	165.9
plant and machinery	173.0	117.1	131.2	143.9	126.1	123.3
vehicles	143.6	118.0	135.7	141.4	122.5	122.3
livestock	117.9	115.9	106.6	107.1	102.0	105.8
Total volume of capital consumption						
Consumption of fixed capital	104.2	93.9	93.2	92.3	93.4	90.9
non livestock:	105.6	98.5	96.6	95.4	93.1	91.1
buildings and works	104.7	103.0	100.2	97.8	94.2	91.6
plant and machinery	107.6	95.2	93.5	92.7	91.2	89.4
vehicles	98.4	101.0	101.1	101.2	100.0	98.3
livestock	97.6	81.2	83.4	83.3	92.3	88.8

Chapter **10** Productivity

Summary

In 2006:

* total factor productivity rose by 2.1 per cent;

* the volume of final output at market prices fell by 0.9 per cent;

* the volume of all inputs fell by 3.2 per cent;

* the volume of total labour in annual work units (or full-time person equivalent) fell by 3.1 per cent as the shift to part-time working continued and the head count of total labour fell;

* labour productivity as measured by net value added at market prices per annual work unit increased by 13 per cent.

Over the longer term:

* since 1973, productivity has grown by 54 per cent, the volume of final output at market prices has increased by 22 per cent and the volume of all inputs has fallen by 21 per cent.

Introduction

1 A key measure of agriculture's economic performance and a key component of its competitiveness is its productivity, that is, how efficiently the agricultural industry uses the resources that are available to turn inputs into outputs. It is a key measure of the economic sustainability of United Kingdom farming and food, an important driver of farm incomes and an essential foundation for the environmental and social contributions which farming and food make.

2 Productivity measures are based on the ratio of the volume of outputs and the volume of inputs. However, measuring productivity is not straightforward and comparisons need to be interpreted carefully both because of practical problems in obtaining robust data and because productivity performance, particularly in agriculture, is often shaped by factors outside farmers' control, such as climate, topography and location, which are not easily susceptible to change.

3 The headline measure, total factor productivity, shows the volume of output leaving the industry per unit of all inputs including fixed capital and labour. It encompasses all businesses engaged in farming activities, including specialist contractors. Labour productivity measures the volume of net value added per unit of all labour (paid and entrepreneurial) and is a key component of total factor productivity.

4 Volume indices for outputs refer to the value of production at market prices, i.e. excluding subsidies.

Productivity (chart 10.1, table 10.1)

5 Total factor productivity increased by 2.1 per cent in 2006 as the volume of final output (gross output at market prices less transactions in the industry) fell by 0.9 per cent and the volume of all inputs (including fixed capital, paid and entrepreneurial labour) fell by 3.2 per cent.

6 Over the longer term, since 1973, the productivity of the agriculture industry in the United Kingdom has increased by 54 per cent. The volume of final output has increased by 22 per cent while the volume of all inputs has fallen by 21 per cent. Labour productivity in 2006, as measured by net value added per annual work unit, was five times its 1973 value.

Chart 10.1 Productivity; United Kingdom

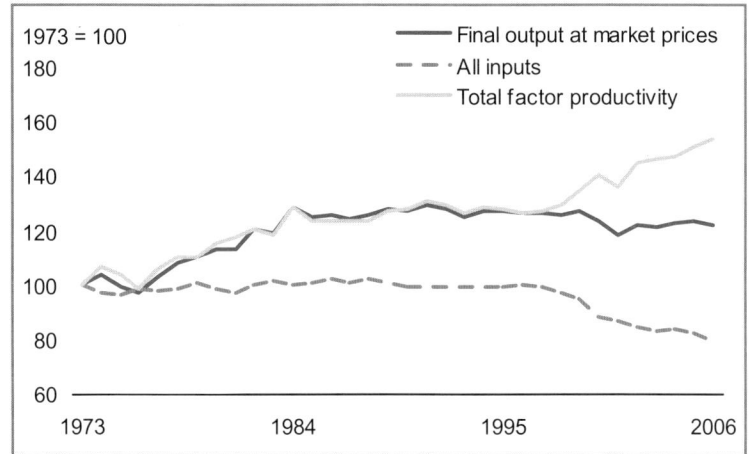

Table 10.1 Productivity; United Kingdom

Enquiries: Christine Holleran on +44 (0)1904 455080   email: christine.holleran@defra.gsi.gov.uk

Volume indices 2000 = 100   Calendar years

	Average of 1995-97	2002	2003	2004	2005	2006 (provisional)
Final output at market prices (gross output less transactions within the industry)	102.6	98.9	97.9	99.4	99.9	98.7
All inputs (including fixed capital, paid and entrepreneurial labour)	112.9	95.9	93.7	95.0	92.8	89.8
Net value added at market prices per AWU of all labour (a)	65.0	123.3	124.5	123.4	138.5	157.0
Total factor productivity (b)	90.8	103.1	104.5	104.7	107.6	109.9

(a) An annual work unit (AWU) represents the equivalent of an average full-time person engaged in agriculture.
(b) Final output per unit of all inputs (including fixed capital and labour).

Productivity at the farm level (England and Wales) (table 10.2)

7 Analysis of Farm Business Survey data for England and Wales from 1982 to 2002 shows that most farm types exhibit a relatively high degree of efficiency with the majority of farms close to the efficient frontier (Defra research project http://statistics.defra.gov.uk/esg/reports/agri.asp). Frontier farms of all types are becoming more efficient through time due to technical change, which ranges from 5.8 per cent per year for cereal farms to 1.6 per cent a year for poultry farms (table 10.2). However, while the frontier of productive efficiency is being pushed out by technical change, evidence suggests that the average farm is falling behind that advancing frontier. Change in mean annual efficiency from 1982 to 2002 (shown as average per annum percentages) shows that farms of all types (except cereal and poultry farms) have on average become relatively less efficient compared to the frontier. The issue of scale of operation dominates the difference between the farms that are most efficient, and that define the frontier, and

Table 10.2 Productivity at the farm level; England and Wales

Enquiries: Christine Holleran on +44 (0)1904 455080   email: christine.holleran@defra.gsi.gov.uk

	Farm Type							
	Cereals	Dairy	Sheep	Beef	Poultry	Pigs	General Cropping	Mixed
Number of farms in sample	702	1431	592	402	85	199	1094	1093
Technical change (average per annum)	5.8%	2.0%	2.0%	3.3%	1.6%	3.5%	4.2%	5.2%
Approximate efficiency Change (average per annum)	0.00%	-0.43%	-0.76%	-0.24%	0.00%	-0.48%	-0.95%	-0.95%

Source: Defra research project

those that are least efficient. However this does not exclusively mean that large farms (in terms of area or herd size) are more efficient than small farms, but that on average larger farms are more efficient.

International comparison of productivity (chart 10.2)

8   An international comparison of total factor productivity is made in chart 10.2 using total factor productivity relative to the USA (Defra research project http://statistics.defra.gov.uk/esg/reports/agri.asp). Over the period 1973 to 2002 the United Kingdom shows only modest productivity growth compared to other countries shown in the chart; increasing at a rate of 34 per cent to achieve a 2002 level higher only than Ireland and Sweden (not shown).

9   The United Kingdom began the period with a high growth rate but switched to a low rate in 1984. The highest growth rate is that of Spain, which began the period in second from last place, but grew by 170 per cent to achieve a 2002 level of total factor productivity behind only the Netherlands and the USA.

Chart 10.2 Total factor productivity - International comparison 1973 to 2002

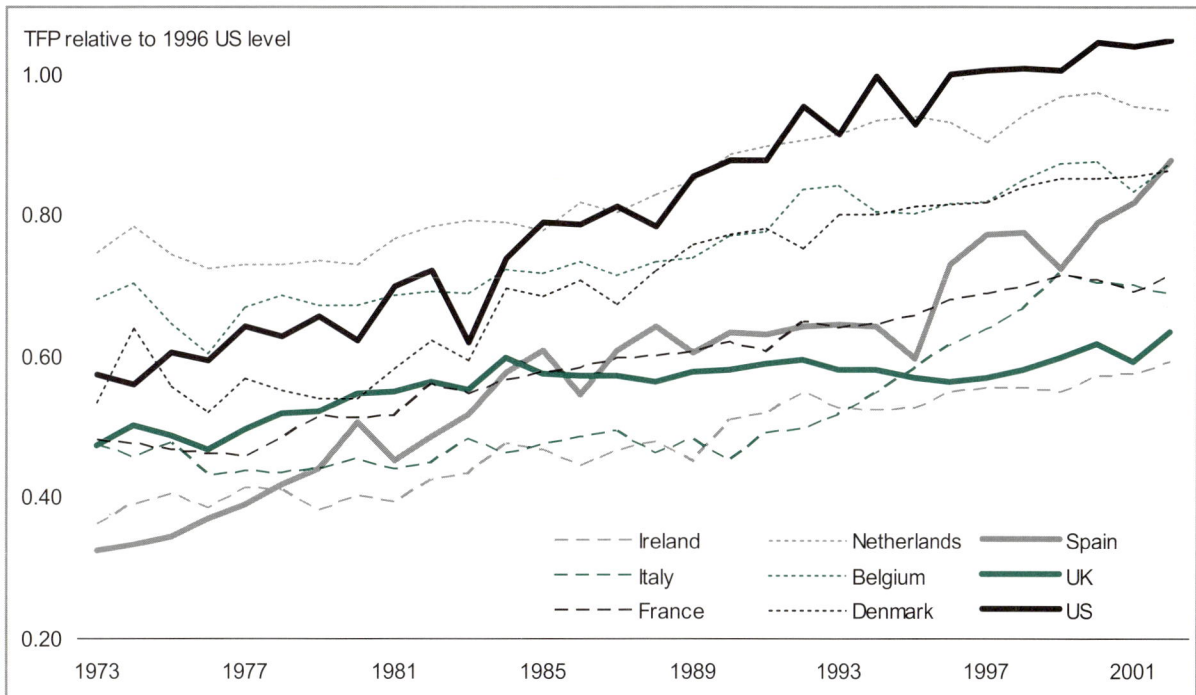

Source: Defra research project

Volume indices (table 10.3)

10   In 2006, the volume of output of:

* cereals fell by 1.9 per cent with the largest fall in output of barley;

* industrial crops fell by 8.1 per cent with a large fall in output of sugar beet;

* forage plants fell by 12 per cent;

* vegetables and horticultural products fell by 5.4 per cent mainly due to a fall of 10 per cent in output of plants and flowers;

* potatoes rose by 2.9 per cent;

* fruit rose by 7.2 per cent;

* livestock production rose by 1.1 per cent;

- livestock products fell by 1.2 per cent as output of milk and eggs both fell;

- other agricultural activities fell by 0.5 per cent as the leasing out of quota fell by 31 per cent;

- inseparable non-agricultural activities rose by 2.6 per cent.

11 The volume of consumption of:

- seeds rose by 2.4 per cent;

- electricity fell by 2.3 per cent and fuels by 5.3 per cent;

- fertilisers fell by 3.2 per cent;

- pesticides fell slightly by 0.2 per cent;

- veterinary expenses fell by 7.9 per cent;

- animal feeds fell by 4.2 per cent particularly due to a fall of 21 per cent in straights feed;

- maintenance fell by 0.7 per cent as consumption of both materials and buildings fell;

- agricultural services was unchanged;

- other goods and services fell by 4.5 per cent.

Table 10.3 Output and input volume indices; United Kingdom

Enquiries: Christine Holleran on +44 (0)1904 455080   email: christine.holleran@defra.gsi.gov.uk

Indices 2000 = 100

	Average of 1995-97	2002	2003	2004	2005	2006 (provisional)
Outputs at market prices						
1 Output of cereals	97.4	95.9	89.9	93.0	88.3	86.6
wheat	90.7	95.9	86.0	93.3	89.4	88.5
rye	130.3	90.9	86.4	86.4	86.4	86.4
barley	115.4	94.3	97.8	89.0	85.2	81.6
oats and summer cereal mixtures	93.5	103.5	113.3	116.0	84.7	81.4
other cereals	73.1	109.1	107.3	104.6	105.1	102.1
2 Output of industrial crops	107.5	105.7	109.3	105.7	103.7	95.3
oil seeds	125.7	124.1	153.3	139.9	168.0	161.4
oilseed rape	122.4	127.2	153.8	140.6	165.8	163.0
other oil seeds	213.5	42.7	138.1	121.3	208.8	114.6
sugar beet	109.9	105.3	101.0	99.6	95.7	78.8
other industrial crops	102.1	97.2	91.9	93.1	75.5	72.4
fibre plants	155.4	40.3	67.3	47.7	31.4	39.3
hops	185.5	94.5	72.4	72.4	61.9	51.1
others (a)	98.3	97.6	92.5	94.0	76.1	73.2
3 Output of forage plants	89.8	117.2	115.6	111.4	113.4	100.2
4 Output of vegetables and horticultural products	103.4	96.1	93.5	95.2	95.0	89.8
fresh vegetables	109.0	88.3	87.8	88.1	91.1	89.7
plants and flowers	96.6	106.6	101.3	104.8	100.4	90.3
5 Output of potatoes (including seeds)	109.4	106.8	92.1	101.3	92.2	95.0
6 Output of fruit	107.0	99.8	109.7	127.7	149.6	160.3
7 Output of other crop products including seeds	96.1	69.0	83.0	84.6	81.9	80.3
Total crop output	101.9	98.9	95.7	98.7	96.8	93.8
8 Output of livestock	108.3	97.4	95.9	98.1	99.1	100.2
primarily for meat	107.3	95.3	95.1	97.5	99.4	100.0
cattle	109.5	102.6	105.9	104.3	112.6	118.1
pigs	119.5	87.4	77.5	78.3	78.5	77.9
sheep	99.0	81.8	83.4	88.5	89.5	88.7
poultry	103.7	99.4	101.0	106.8	104.2	101.8
other animals	99.6	99.8	99.3	99.1	99.6	98.9

continued

Table 10.3 continued

Indices 2000 = 100   Calendar years

	Average of 1995-97	2002	2003	2004	2005	2006 (provisional)
gross fixed capital formation	117.9	115.9	106.6	107.1	102.0	105.8
cattle	117.9	110.6	109.4	101.6	104.2	106.7
pigs	163.2	127.6	101.0	94.7	80.3	101.5
sheep	164.4	173.6	126.4	149.4	117.2	132.3
poultry	103.1	95.3	95.0	98.0	94.0	93.3
9 Output of livestock products	101.3	102.9	104.1	101.7	101.2	100.0
milk	101.5	102.3	103.5	100.3	99.6	98.7
eggs	98.3	107.0	105.3	114.0	115.1	111.1
raw wool	106.2	86.3	84.4	85.7	87.9	82.1
other animal products	114.3	139.6	173.9	105.3	105.2	105.3
Total livestock output	105.4	99.6	99.1	99.5	100.0	100.2
10 Other agricultural activities	111.2	100.7	101.5	106.5	96.2	95.7
agricultural services	90.9	102.5	100.9	106.3	103.3	103.3
leasing out quota	356.0	80.9	107.4	107.2	19.6	13.6
11 Inseparable non-agricultural activities	80.1	108.2	110.9	113.5	120.4	123.6
12 Output (at market prices)	103.3	99.7	98.4	100.1	99.4	98.6
of which:						
transactions within the agricultural industry						
feed wheat	110.3	103.2	163.3	221.7	218.0	192.7
feed barley	98.3	114.9	108.1	98.0	101.9	107.1
feed oats	83.0	97.1	96.7	93.7	75.6	80.5
seed potatoes	140.6	110.7	56.2	77.6	100.5	159.9
straw	99.0	95.8	89.9	90.9	71.3	67.5
contract work	90.9	102.5	100.9	106.3	103.3	103.3
leasing of quota	356.0	80.9	107.4	107.2	19.6	13.6
total capital formation in livestock	117.8	116.0	106.7	107.2	102.0	105.9
13 Total subsidies (less taxes) on product	. .	. .	. .	. .	. .	. .
14 Gross output at basic prices	103.1	99.5	98.5	100.0	99.8	98.9
Intermediate consumption						
15 Seeds	110.9	99.1	98.8	99.9	100.9	103.4
16 Energy						
electricity	105.6	110.3	89.6	86.6	85.4	83.4
fuels	114.5	95.8	83.5	89.0	81.2	76.9
17 Fertilisers	121.2	91.2	78.2	79.4	71.2	68.9
18 Pesticides	96.8	95.8	90.5	99.4	92.1	91.9
19 Veterinary expenses	118.0	100.0	97.6	104.6	104.2	95.9
20 Animal feed	106.3	101.3	105.5	107.4	110.8	106.1
compounds	111.1	102.3	102.2	103.3	99.8	105.4
straights	99.3	96.7	107.9	110.2	127.8	101.8
feed purchased from other farms	99.8	111.2	120.0	125.8	126.6	125.3
21 Total maintenance (b)	124.6	96.2	92.7	93.1	86.3	85.7
materials	119.5	91.0	86.4	85.5	78.8	78.1
buildings	135.9	108.3	107.0	110.8	103.8	103.6
22 Agricultural services	90.9	102.5	100.9	106.3	103.3	103.3
23 Other goods and services (b) (c)	119.8	92.4	99.0	103.7	95.5	91.3
24 Total intermediate consumption	112.1	97.0	96.4	99.6	95.5	92.5
25 Gross value added at market prices	88.9	104.1	101.8	100.8	106.8	110.3
26 Gross value added at basic prices	93.1	102.3	101.0	100.4	106.4	109.7
27 Total consumption of Fixed Capital	104.2	93.9	93.2	92.3	93.4	90.9
equipment	106.0	96.1	94.7	94.1	92.6	90.8
buildings (b)	104.7	103.0	100.2	97.8	94.2	91.6
livestock	97.6	81.2	83.4	83.3	92.3	88.8
cattle	92.9	76.0	81.0	80.9	92.2	87.8
pigs	117.6	99.3	79.4	79.6	69.3	64.5
sheep	95.0	78.9	78.1	79.0	86.6	85.5
poultry	101.5	98.8	96.2	94.7	98.1	95.6
28 Net value added at market prices	75.0	116.6	112.2	111.2	123.6	135.8
29 Net value added at basic prices	87.7	107.7	105.9	105.5	116.1	126.7

(a) Includes straw and minor crops.

(b) Landlords' expenses are included within total maintenance, other goods and services and total consumption of fixed capital of buildings.

(c) Includes livestock and crop costs, water costs, insurance premiums, bank charges, professional fees, rates, and other farming costs.

Labour (table 10.4)

12 The total cost of paid labour fell by 0.8 per cent to £2.2 billion in 2006 as the average wage increased while paid labour input fell by 4.7 per cent. The volume of the total labour force fell by 3.1 per cent and has fallen by 65 per cent since 1973 reflecting the outflow of labour from the industry. The volume of paid labour has fallen by twice as much as the volume of entrepreneurial labour in that time.

Table 10.4 Costs and volumes of labour engaged in agricultural work (a); United Kingdom

Enquiries: Sarah Tumber on +44 (0)1904 455084   email: sarah.tumber@defra.gsi.gov.uk

						Calendar years
	Average of 1995-97	2006	2006	2006	2006	2006 (provisional)
Paid labour costs (£ million) (b)	1 882	1 966	1 917	2 009	2 177	2 161
Annual work unit (thousand) (c)						
Entrepreneurial labour	241	211	205	203	201	196
Paid labour	144	105	97	98	97	93
Labour force	385	316	301	301	298	289

(a) This table shows the cost and volume of paid labour relating to agricultural work only and excludes time spent on the construction of farm buildings

(b) Includes payments in kind to workers and employer and employee National Insurance contributions, redundancy payments, Workers Pension Scheme (up to 1990) and the cost of trainees.

(c) An annual work unit represents the equivalent of an average full-time person engaged in agriculture.

Chapter **11** Payments and Public Expenditure

Summary

In 2006:

- total payments made to farmers less levies are expected to be about the same as in 2005 at £3.0 billion;

- payments linked to production are expected to fall by £121 million to £85 million;

- payments not linked to production, including the Single Payment Scheme, are expected to rise by 3.4 per cent to £2.9 billion;

- the Single Payment Scheme is estimated to total £2.4 billion after deductions for modulation;

- payments through agri-environment schemes are expected to have risen by 24 per cent to £346 million;

- payments through less favoured areas support schemes are expected to fall by 1.2 per cent to £144 million;

- payments of animal disease compensation are expected to fall by 32 per cent to £37 million.

Introduction

1 This chapter gives details of direct subsidy payments and other payments received by farmers that are included in the production and account shown in chapter 9. It also includes other information on public expenditure under the CAP and on national grants and subsidies.

Payments and levies linked to agricultural production (chart 11.1, table 11.1)

2 In 2006, payments that are still linked to production fell from £206 million to £85 million, as a result of the Over Thirty Month Scheme being replaced by the Older Cattle Disposal Scheme in January 2006. The Older Cattle Disposal Scheme is an exceptional market support measure providing for disposal of and compensation for cattle born before 1 August 1996; it started on 23 January 2006 and will end on 31 December 2008.

3 Other schemes linked to production are the Scottish Beef Calf Scheme, Area Payment for Nuts, Aid for Energy Crops and Protein Crop Premium, totalling £31 million in 2006.

Chart 11.1 Payments (less levies) made to farmers; United Kingdom

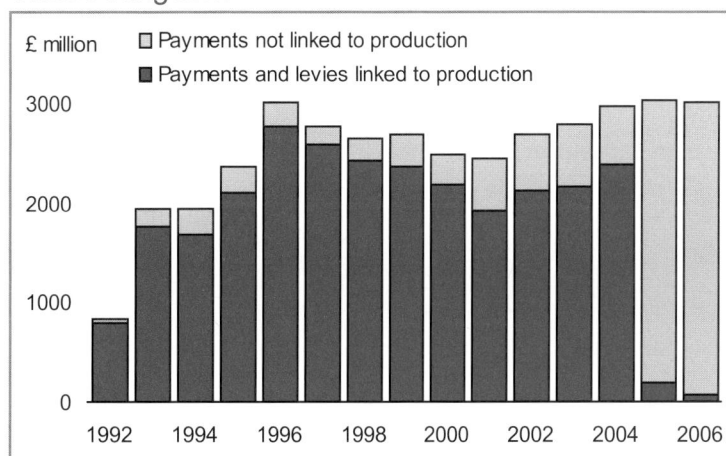

Table 11.1 Direct payments to farmers and levies recorded in the production and income account; United Kingdom

Shows payments after deduction for modulation where appropriate.

Enquiries: Keith Seabridge on +44 (0)1904 455081   email: keith.seabridge@defra.gsi.gov.uk

£ million					Calendar years	
	Average of 1995-97	2002	2003	2004	2005	2006 (provisional)
Payments and levies linked to the production of agricultural products						
Crop subsidies						
Arable area payments on:	1 106	875	925	900	..	..
Other crop subsidies (a)	18	2	3	12	11	14
Livestock subsidies:						
Beef Special Premium	251	236	238	267	..	..
Beef Marketing Payment Scheme	58	..	..	..	..	..
Suckler Cow Premium	330	203	208	229	..	..
Slaughter Premium	..	133	136	157	..	..
Extensification Payment Scheme	..	137	145	159	..	..
Calf Processing Aid Scheme	46	..	..	..	..	..
Over Thirty Month Scheme	443	237	199	204	178	17
Older Cattle Disposal Scheme	..	..	..	..	..	37
Hill Livestock Compensatory Allowance - cattle	53	..	..	..	..	..
Beef National Envelope	19	34	34	37	..	..
Scottish Beef Calf Scheme	..	..	..	..	18	18
Sheep Annual Premium	370	264	276	305	..	..
Sheep National Envelope	..	10	10	18	..	..
Hill Livestock Compensatory Allowance - sheep	55	..	..	..	..	..
Dairy subsidies (b)	..	..	..	108	..	..
less milk superlevy	- 37	..	..	- 8	- 1	..
Total coupled payments less levies	2 492	2 131	2 174	2 387	206	85
Payments not linked to production						
Single Payment Scheme	..	..	..	..	2 358	2 405
Arable Area Payments on set-aside	149	143	177	129	..	..
Animal disease compensation (c)	9	54	61	49	54	37
Less favoured areas support schemes (d)	..	166	160	153	146	144
Agri-environment schemes:						
Countryside Stewardship Scheme, Arable Stewardship Scheme, Entry Level Pilot, Environmental Stewardship Scheme	13	55	72	105	119	198
Countryside Premium, Rural Stewardship & Land Management Contract Schemes	2	9	13	17	17	13
Tir Cymen, Tir Gofal, Tir Cynnal	4	15	16	18	20	24
Countryside Management Scheme	..	3	3	6	6	9
Organic Aid & Organic Farming Schemes	-	27	21	12	10	10
Environmentally Sensitive Areas Scheme	36	72	84	88	91	79
Nitrate Sensitive Areas Scheme	5	2	-	..	..	..
Other (e)	7	15	16	16	16	..
Weather Aid	..	5	..	..	..	..
Total decoupled payments	233	565	622	594	2 836	2 932
Total all payments less levies	2 725	2 697	2 796	2 982	3 042	3 017
Capital grants and other payments not included in the production and income account	75	41	21	26	36	61

(a) CAP hops and herbage seeds support; hemp and flax aid; protein crop premium; area aid for nuts; energy crops aid.

(b) Dairy premium and additional dairy premium.

(c) Tuberculosis, brucellosis, salmonella, Chernobyl, Newcastle and Aujeszky's disease, swine fever and avian influenza compensation and BEIC egg scheme, where applicable.

(d) Tir Mynydd in Wales, Less Favoured Area Compensatory Allowance Scheme in Northern Ireland, Less Favoured Areas Support Scheme in Scotland and Hill Farm Allowance in England. In Scotland, the 2006 figure for Less Favoured Area Support Scheme (LFASS) excludes £40 million which was announced by SEERAD in January. These payments will be added to the 2006 TIFF estimates in due course, in line with the TIFF standard methodology of accruing payments to the scheme year.

(e) Includes remnants of closed schemes not recorded elsewhere.

Payments not linked to production (charts 11.1, 11.2, table 11.1)

4 Decoupled payments, including the Single Payment Scheme and other payments made to farmers by virtue of being engaged in agricultural activities, are expected to increase from £2.8 billion to £2.9 billion.

5 Payments made through the Single Payment Scheme are estimated to total £2.4 billion after deductions for modulation in 2006. An increase in the amount deducted from the Single Payment by modulation in 2006 was offset by an uplift in the value of dairy entitlements and the addition of compensation arising from reform of the sugar regime of the Common Agricultural Policy. The production and income account shown in chapter 9 is prepared on an accruals basis and payments through the Single Payment Scheme are therefore recorded in the year in which the claim is made rather than when payments are made.

6 Payments to farmers taking part in agri-environment schemes are expected to rise by 25 per cent to £346 million, mainly due to payments starting to be made to farmers in England who have entered the Environmental Stewardship Scheme.

7 Payments to farmers under the less favoured areas support schemes (Hill Farm Allowance in England, Tir Mynydd in Wales, Less Favoured Area Support Scheme in Scotland and Less Favoured Area Compensatory Allowance in Northern Ireland) fell slightly, by 1.2 per cent to £144 million.

Chart 11.2 Payments made through agri-environment schemes; United Kingdom

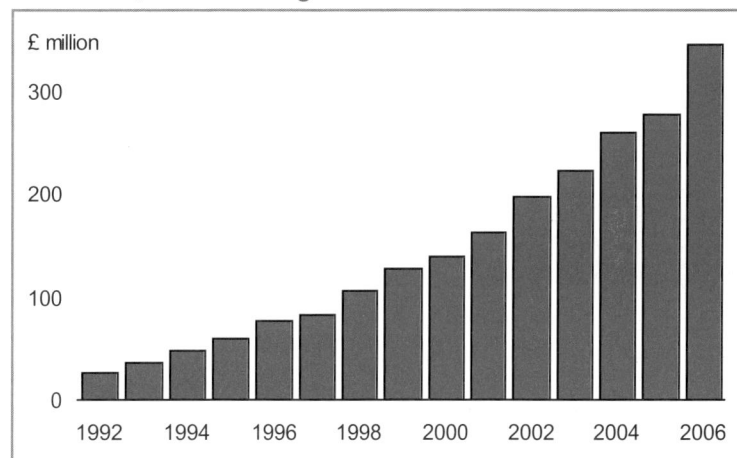

8 Payments of animal disease compensation, principally for cattle slaughtered as a result of bovine tuberculosis control measures, are expected to have fallen by 32 per cent to £37 million in 2006, due to a combination of the introduction of table valuations for determining compensation payments in England and a fall in the number of cattle compulsorily slaughtered in 2006 compared to 2005.

Public expenditure on agriculture (table 11.2)

9 Table 11.2 shows public expenditure under the Common Agricultural Policy, national grants and subsidies. The table does not include other expenditure of benefit to farmers and the farming community such as expenditure on animal health, research, advice and education.

10 The figures for the financial year 2005/06 represent actual expenditure recorded in the Rural Payments Agency (RPA) resource account for the year ended 31 March 2006 combined with actual expenditure figures for the national agriculture departments. The figures for 2006/07 are the latest estimates of expenditure.

11 Total expenditure in 2005/06 was £3.7 billion. Direct payments, mostly through the Single Payment Scheme, amounted to £3.0 billion while expenditure on market support measures, including the Over Thirty Month Scheme, was £570 million. Total expenditure in 2006/07 is forecast to be £3.5 billion.

Table 11.2 Public expenditure under CAP and national grants and subsidies (a); United Kingdom

Enquiries: Rural Payments Agency on 0118 958 3626   email: Mark.Coulson@rpa.gsi.gov.uk

£ million	Financial years	
	2005/06	2006/07 (forecast)
A. Total direct product subsidies		
Arable Area Payments Scheme	1	-
of which EU funded (%)	100%	100%
Livestock subsidies		
cattle and calves	367	22
sheep	2	-
of which EU funded (%)	100%	100%
Milk	-	-
of which EU funded (%)	100%	100%
B. Total other subsidies		
Single Payment Scheme	2 373	2 695
of which EU funded (%)	100%	100%
Total rural, conservation, agri-environment (b)		
agri-environment and conservation schemes	228	314
rural schemes	61	49
Total special area support (c)		
less favoured areas	43	21
Total animal disease	-	-
C: Total capital grants, transfers and other payments		
Total other (structural and guidance)	32	37
D: Total CAP market support		
Cereals	1	4
of which EU funded (%)	100%	100%
Sugar	191	169
of which EU funded (%)	100%	100%
Milk products	57	48
of which EU funded (%)	95%	95%
Processed goods	17	15
of which EU funded (%)	100%	100%
Beef and veal (BSE)		
BSE (disposal)	88	45
TSE surveillance (d)	24	32
of which EU funded (%)	0%	0%
Beef and veal (BSE compensation)	161	37
of which EU funded (%)	70%	70%
Beef and veal (non-BSE)	-	-
of which EU funded (%)	100%	100%
Sheepmeat	-	-
of which EU funded (%)	100%	100%
Pigmeat	-	-
of which EU funded (%)	100%	100%
Others (e)	31	37
of which EU funded (%)	100%	100%
Total public expenditure (A + B + C + D)	3 678	3 526

Source: Rural Payment Agency

(a) The figures are net of receipts which are treated as negative expenditure.
(b) These schemes are partly EU funded. Funding varies from 35 to 50 per cent depending on the national contribution to the scheme.
(c) These schemes are partly EU funded. Funding varies from 15 to 20 per cent depending on the national contribution to the scheme.
(d) TSE - Transmissible Spongiform Encephalopathies.
(e) Includes fish, fresh fruit and vegetables, hops, protein and textile plants, seeds, wine, eggs and poultry.

Chapter **12** Rural Development Programme

Summary

- There are four rural development plans for the United Kingdom, which cover England, Wales, Scotland and Northern Ireland.

- Most spending provides support for less favoured areas, the environment and forestry.

- There has been a significant increase in the area of land under agreements and in the number of agreement holders under agri-environment schemes in 2006.

Introduction

1 The Agenda 2000 reforms of the Common Agricultural Policy (CAP) introduced a comprehensive rural development regulation (RDR), described as a new 'second pillar' to the CAP, in addition to existing schemes. This aimed to complement reforms in the agricultural market sectors in promoting a competitive, multi-functional sector and sought to encourage alternative sources of income in rural areas while supporting agri-environment measures (Council Regulation 1257/1999).

2 EU support for rural development is co-financed by the European Agricultural Guidance and Guarantee Fund (EAGGF) and Member States. Member States had the option to carry out modulation whereby funds were switched from the 'first pillar' of the CAP (market and income support) to the 'second pillar' and this was used in the United Kingdom to part-fund schemes.

3 Further reform of the CAP was agreed in June 2003, which aimed to further strengthen rural development by transferring further funds from the 'first pillar' to the 'second pillar'. At the same time, the scope of the rural development instruments was expanded (Council Regulation 1783/2003) and compulsory modulation was introduced; optional modulation is used in the United Kingdom in addition to compulsory modulation.

Rural Development Programme 2000-2006

4 Under the rural development regulation, each Member State was required to draw up territorially-based rural development plans at the most appropriate geographical level for 2000-2006. There are four rural development plans in the United Kingdom, which cover England, Scotland, Wales and Northern Ireland.

5 The priorities of each country in the United Kingdom were:

England:	Creating a productive and sustainable rural economy.
	Conserving and enhancing the rural environment.
Wales:	To create stronger agriculture and forestry sectors.
	To improve the economic competitiveness of rural communities and areas.
	To maintain and protect the environment and rural heritage.
Scotland:	To assist the viability and sustainability of Scottish farming.
	To encourage farming practices which contribute to the economic, social and environmental sustainability of rural areas.

Northern Ireland: The maintenance of a viable farming community within the Less Favoured Areas.
The conservation and enhancement of the agri-environment.
The afforestation of agricultural land.

6 Member States could choose from a range of measures. The measures chosen in the United Kingdom were:

Measure	England	Scotland	Wales	Northern Ireland
Investment in Agricultural Holdings	Yes		Yes	
Setting up of Young Farmers Training	Yes		Yes	
Early Retirement				
Less Favoured Areas and Areas with Environmental Restrictions	Yes	Yes	Yes	Yes
Meeting Standards				
Agri-environment and Animal Welfare	Yes	Yes	Yes	Yes
Food Quality		Yes		
Improving Processing and Marketing of Agricultural Products	Yes		Yes	
Forestry	Yes	Yes	Yes	Yes
Promoting the Adaptation and Development of Rural Areas	Yes		Yes	

Rural Development Programme 2007-2013

7 The four rural development plans for 2000 to 2006 ended on 31 December 2006. The plans for the second period from 2007 to 2013 are currently being prepared and the final detail informed by extensive consultation. Each Member State must also have a National Strategy Plan. The United Kingdom will submit a single National Strategy Plan, which will cover the four strategies for rural development in England, Wales, Scotland and Northern Ireland.

8 Finalisation of the rural development plans has been delayed as the EU regulation that would give legal basis to European Council agreement on modulation has been blocked by the European Parliament. Defra and the Devolved Administrations have announced contingency arrangements to enable certain rural development schemes to continue until programmes are agreed.

9 Further information on the rural development plans may be found at:

England: http://www.defra.gov.uk/erdp/default.htm
Wales: http://new.wales.gov.uk/topics/environmentcountryside/countryside_policy/
                  rural_development/?lang=en
Scotland: http://www.scotland.gov.uk/Topics/Rural/SRDPpage
Northern Ireland: http://www.dardni.gov.uk/index/rural-development/rural-development-
                  programme/about_the_rdp.htm

Payments made through key measures (table 12.1)

10 Table 12.1 shows payments made through two key measures: Less Favoured Areas and Areas with Environmental Restrictions; and Agri-environment and Animal Welfare, adopted by each of the countries of the United Kingdom through which most funding and support have been provided, as recorded in the production and income account shown in chapter 9. A significant amount of funding (not shown) also provides support for the Forestry measure, which has also been adopted by England, Wales, Scotland and Northern Ireland.

Table 12.1 Principal payments made through rural development plans

Enquiries: Keith Seabridge on +44 (0)1904 455081   email: keith.seabridge@defra.gsi.gov.uk

£ Million		2001	2002	2003	2004	Calendar years 2005
Less Favoured Areas and Areas with Environmental Restrictions						
England:	Hill Farm Allowance	42.5	39.0	39.5	34.9	27.3
Scotland:	Less Favoured Areas Support Scheme	62.0	63.5	62.7	60.7	61.0
Wales:	Tir Mynydd	42.2	40.2	34.0	35.7	35.8
Northern Ireland:	Less Favoured Areas Compensatory Allowance	24.6	23.5	23.7	22.1	21.8
Agri-Environment and Animal Welfare						
England:	Organic Farming Scheme	10.7	18.9	10.4	6.5	4.6
	Countryside Stewardship Scheme	42.0	54.0	70.2	103.3	117.4
	Environmentally Sensitive Areas Scheme	44.7	50.9	59.6	64.5	69.8
Wales:	Organic Farming Scheme	1.6	2.5	2.7	1.9	2.3
	Tir Gofal	5.9	11.1	13.4	16.9	19.1
	Environmentally Sensitive Areas Scheme	7.5	6.0	8.5	8.5	8.5
Scotland:	Organic Aid Scheme	4.6	4.7	7.2	3.5	2.5
	Rural Stewardship Scheme	..	3.2	7.2	5.8	5.0
	Environmentally Sensitive Areas Scheme	11.2	10.0	11.1	9.7	8.2
Northern Ireland:	Organic Farming Scheme	..	0.4	0.2	0.1	0.3
	Countryside Management Scheme	0.9	2.9	3.1	5.6	5.8
	New Environmentally Sensitive Areas Scheme (a)	6.6	5.0	5.2	5.7	4.9

(a) The Environmentally Sensitive Areas Scheme (ESA) in Northern Ireland ended in 2002 when it was replaced by the New Environmentally Sensitive Areas Scheme (NESA); existing agreements under the ESA Scheme continue to be honoured.

Take-up of agri-environment schemes (chart 12.1 tables 12.2,12.3)

11 Tables 12.2 and 12.3 shows the take-up of agri-environment schemes by area of land under management agreements and by the number of agreement holders, including those that were introduced prior to the Rural Development Programme 2000-2006 but where agreements have continued to be honoured.

12 There has been a significant increase in both area of land under agreement and number of agreement holders in 2006, mainly due to new agreements being made following the introduction of the Environmental Stewardship Scheme in England in 2005.

Chart 12.1 Land area under agri-environment management agreements; United Kingdom

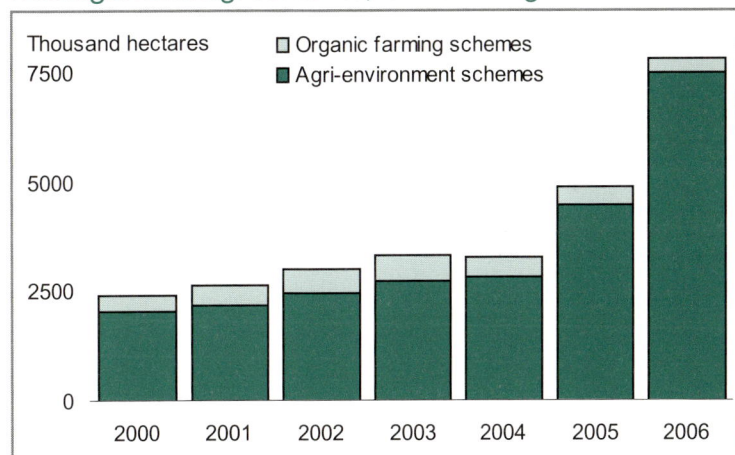

Thousand hectares
Organic farming schemes
Agri-environment schemes

Table 12.2 Agri-environment schemes - area under agreements

Enquiries: Keith Seabridge on +44 (0)1904 455081

email: keith.seabridge@defra.gsi.gov.uk

Thousand Hectares

31 December

	2001	2002	2003	2004	2005	2006
England						
Organic Farming Scheme	138	157	200	143	141	68
Countryside Stewardship Scheme	335	420	521	570	531	514
Environmentally Sensitive Areas Scheme	579	590	635	653	616	582
Environmental Stewardship Scheme						
Entry Level Scheme (a)	..	..	31	31	1 354	3 741
Organic Entry Level Scheme	..	..	..	..	21	180
Higher Level Scheme	..	..	..	..	..	83
Wales						
Organic Farming/Maintenance Schemes	37	48	55	55	68	81
Tir Cymen/Tir Gofal	99	116	120	115	332	354
Environmentally Sensitive Areas Scheme	180	173	161	171	127	77
Tir Cynnal	..	..	..	..	223	223
Scotland						
Organic Aid Scheme	264	342	339	269	167	127
Countryside Premium Scheme/Rural Stewardship Scheme	83	165	190	250	363	461
Environmentally Sensitive Areas Scheme	771	816	855	815	688	530
Land Management Contracts	..	..	..	..	..	..
Northern Ireland						
Organic Farming Scheme	4	5	5	5	6	10
Countryside Management Scheme	19	57	90	116	118	538
New Environmentally Sensitive Areas Scheme (b)	148	144	146	126	131	251

(a) Includes Entry Level Pilot Scheme

(b) The Environmentally Sensitive Areas Scheme (ESA) in Northern Ireland ended in 2002 when it was replaced by the New Environmentally Sensitive Areas Scheme (NESA); existing agreements under the ESA Scheme continue to be honoured.

Table 12.3 Agri-environment schemes - number of agreement holders

Enquiries: Keith Seabridge on +44 (0)1904 455081

email: keith.seabridge@defra.gsi.gov.uk

Rounded to nearest hundred

31 December

	2001	2002	2003	2004	2005	2006
England						
Organic Farming Scheme	1 800	2 000	2 600	1 800	1 700	800
Countryside Stewardship Scheme	13 900	15 400	16 900	17 800	16 700	15 600
Environmentally Sensitive Areas Scheme	11 300	12 000	12 500	13 000	11 500	9 600
Environmental Stewardship Scheme:						
Entry Level Scheme (a)	..	..	300	300	12 100	27 200
Organic Entry Level Scheme	..	..	..	..	300	1 400
Higher Level Scheme	..	..	..	..	..	1 200
Wales						
Organic Farming Scheme	400	500	500	600	700	800
Tir Cymen/Tir Gofal	1 700	1 800	2 400	3 000	3 200	3 300
Environmentally Sensitive Areas Scheme	2 400	2 400	2 600	2 300	1 700	1 000
Tir Cynnal	..	..	..	..	3 400	3 400
Scotland						
Organic Aid Scheme	500	600	700	600	500	400
Countryside Premium Scheme/Rural Stewardship Scheme	1 700	1 800	1 900	2 900	4 600	6 200
Environmentally Sensitive Areas Scheme	2 700	2 900	2 900	2 800	2 400	2 000
Land Management Contracts	..	..	..	..	..	..
Northern Ireland						
Organic Farming Scheme	100	100	100	100	100	100
Countryside Management Scheme	400	1 300	2 400	2 900	5 200	8 900
New Environmentally Sensitive Areas Scheme (b)	4 200	4 400	4 400	4 400	3 500	4 400

(a) Includes Entry Level Pilot Scheme

(b) The Environmentally Sensitive Areas Scheme (ESA) in Northern Ireland ended in 2002 when it was replaced by the New Environmentally Sensitive Areas Scheme (NESA); existing agreements under the ESA Scheme continue to be honoured.

Chapter **13** Organic Farming

Summary

In January 2006:

- the total area of land that was organically managed (either fully organic or in-conversion) fell by 8.1 per cent;

- permanent and temporary pasture accounted for 85 per cent of organically managed land in the United Kingdom;

- forty per cent of organically managed land in the United Kingdom was in Scotland, covering 247 thousand hectares;

- sixtyfive per cent of producers and growers and 83 per cent of processors and importers were located in England;

- twentynine per cent of organic livestock producers in the United Kingdom were located in the southwest region of England;

- there were 214 thousand cattle, 691 thousand sheep, 30 thousand pigs, 3,439 thousand poultry and 2.0 thousand other livestock, being reared organically in the United Kingdom.

Introduction

1 Organic farming is a method of farming that requires farmers to operate to a system based on ecological principles and which imposes strict limitations on the inputs that can be used in order to minimise damage to the environment and wildlife. Emphasis is placed on natural methods of production and pest control.

2 In partnership with the various organic sector bodies in the United Kingdom, Defra collected and published data on the organic sector during 2006. Work continues with the organic sector bodies to further develop the data collected and published. If you have any comments on the statistics shown here or on future requirements, contact the Organic Statistics team at: organic-stats@defra.gsi.gov.uk.

3 Some revisions have been made to 2004 and 2005 figures due to changes in methodology.

Organic and in-conversion land (table 13.1, chart 13.1)

4 The total area of land that was organically managed, either fully organic or in-conversion, fell by 8.1 per cent between January 2005 and January 2006 to 619 thousand hectares, having peaked in March 2003 at 741 thousand hectares following several years of very notable increases.

5 The late 1990s and early 2000s saw increases in the area of organically managed land for a variety of reasons. Significant factors operating during this period were: farmers seeking alternatives to conventional farming in response to falling farm incomes, the scope of organic farming being extended by the European Union to include livestock production in July 1999 and payment rates under organic farming support schemes being substantially increased.

6 The area of in-conversion land rose by 63 per cent between January 2005 and January 2006 to 86 thousand hectares while the area of fully organic land fell by 88 thousand hectares. This reduction was due to withdrawals of organic land in Scotland. The area of organic land rose in the other countries of the United Kingdom. Of the total organically managed land in the United Kingdom, 86 per cent was fully organic in January 2006.

Chart 13.1 Organically managed land; United Kingdom

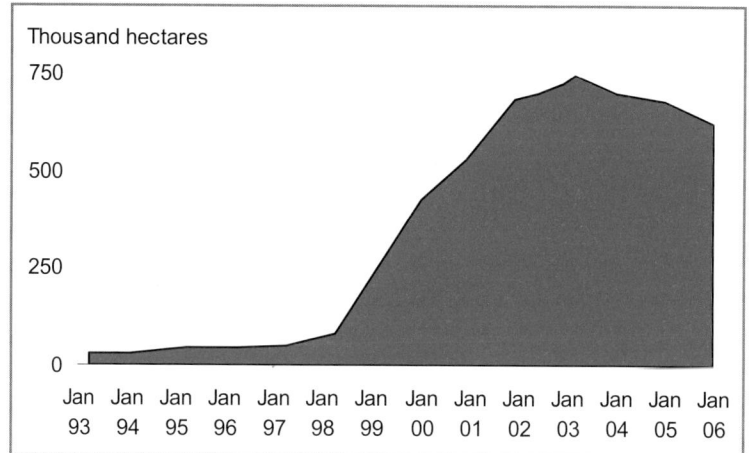

7 Permanent and temporary pasture accounted for 85 per cent of fully organic or in-conversion land in the United Kingdom. The remainder was made up of cereals and other crops, vegetables including potatoes, set-aside, woodland and other uses.

Regional analysis (tables 13.1 to 13.3)

8 Fortyseven per cent of the United Kingdom's organically managed land is in England covering 291 thousand hectares, 40 per cent is in Scotland, 11 per cent in Wales and 1.5 per cent in Northern Ireland. Fiftyfive per cent of organically managed land in England is situated in the southwest and southeast of the country. As a percentage of the total area in the United Kingdom, Scotland is down 11 percentage points on 2005 due to a few extensive hill farms pulling out of the sector.

9 Despite 40 per cent of the organically managed land being in Scotland, only 14 per cent of organic producers and growers are found there. Sixtyfive per cent are located in England, 16 per cent in Wales and 5.1 per cent in Northern Ireland. Over half of producers and growers in England are located in the southwest and southeast of the country. Eightythree per cent of processors and importers of organic food in the United Kingdom are located in England with 9.3 per cent in Scotland, 5.3 per cent in Wales and 2.3 per cent in Northern Ireland.

Table 13.1 Organic and in-conversion land

Enquiries: Organic Statistics Team on +44 (0)1904 455557   email: organic-stats@defra.gsi.gov.uk

Thousand hectares

	March 2003	January 2004	January 2005	January 2006
Land, in-conversion				
North East	15.3	6.8	4.6	6.6
North West	7.7	2.6	2.5	3.2
Yorkshire & Humberside	2.3	1.7	1.3	2.3
East Midlands	2.9	1.6	1.2	2.4
West Midlands	6.0	3.7	2.4	3.2
Eastern	4.1	3.0	2.4	2.6
South West	18.0	10.8	9.1	22.0
South East (inc. London)	11.5	6.5	5.4	10.7
England	67.8	36.8	28.8	53.2
Wales	13.7	8.0	8.6	12.8
Scotland	121.3	20.4	13.7	16.7
Northern Ireland	1.5	0.8	1.6	3.2
United Kingdom	204.3	66.0	52.7	86.0

continued

Table 13.1 continued

Thousand hectares

	March 2003	January 2004	January 2005	January 2006
Land, fully organic				
North East	12.4	20.5	25.3	29.3
North West	15.1	19.9	18.8	18.9
Yorkshire & Humberside	7.0	8.1	8.6	9.0
East Midlands	12.0	16.1	13.4	13.2
West Midlands	23.4	25.5	26.8	27.0
Eastern	7.8	9.7	10.3	11.8
South West	78.1	86.2	90.5	94.0
South East (inc. London)	28.3	34.3	34.9	35.2
England	184.0	220.2	229.6	238.4
Wales	41.4	50.2	55.6	58.0
Scotland	307.3	351.9	331.6	231.2
Northern Ireland	4.1	6.6	5.0	6.3
United Kingdom	536.9	629.0	621.8	533.9

Table 13.2 Organic and in-conversion land use; United Kingdom
Enquiries: Organic Statistics Team on +44 (0)1904 455557   email: organic-stats@defra.gsi.gov.uk

Thousand hectares

	March 2003	January 2004	January 2005	January 2006
Land, in-conversion				
Cereals	11.2	7.0	4.1	10.3
Other crops	6.5	1.9	2.7	3.5
Fruit & nuts (nuts not included in Mar 03)	0.4	0.2	0.2	0.2
Vegetables (including potatoes)	3.0	1.9	1.3	1.3
Herbs & ornamentals (included nuts in Mar 03)	-	0.1	-	0.2
Temporary pasture	18.1	12.7	10.4	15.9
Set aside	3.5	2.3	1.3	1.4
Permanent pasture (a)	159.1	38.1	27.2	47.5
Woodland	1.1	0.7	0.6	3.5
Field margins	-	..	..	..
Non cropping	0.2	0.3	2.9	1.1
Environmental schemes	0.3	..	..	..
Other	-	0.3	1.7	1.1
Unknown	0.8	0.5	0.1	0.1
Total	204.3	66.0	52.7	86.0
Land, fully organic				
Cereals	25.7	35.4	35.1	37.4
Other crops	14.1	7.5	10.2	7.3
Fruit & nuts (nuts not included in Mar 03)	1.5	1.4	1.5	1.5
Vegetables (including potatoes)	9.7	11.7	12.7	12.4
Herbs & ornamentals (included nuts in Mar 03)	0.2	0.2	0.2	0.6
Temporary pasture	58.9	77.3	80.3	82.0
Set aside	3.4	4.6	4.6	2.3
Permanent pasture (a)	413.9	481.3	467.8	380.9
Woodland	5.6	4.8	5.2	3.3
Field margins	0.1	..	..	..
Non cropping	1.4	0.9	1.3	2.4
Environmental schemes	0.1	..	..	..
Other	-	3.0	2.4	3.2
Unknown	2.4	0.8	0.4	0.4
Total	536.9	629.0	621.8	533.9

(a) Includes rough grazing.

Table 13.3 Organic producers, growers, processors and importers - regional breakdown

Enquiries: Organic Statistics Team on +44 (0)1904 455557   email: organic-stats@defra.gsi.gov.uk

Number of businesses

	March 2003	January 2004	January 2005	January 2006
Producers and growers				
North East	73	74	83	101
North West	171	169	176	168
Yorkshire & Humberside	136	134	149	138
East Midlands	220	218	237	221
West Midlands	330	325	337	335
Eastern	248	258	259	253
South West	1 026	1 020	1 123	1 152
South East (inc. London)	418	409	463	417
England	2 622	2 607	2 027	2 785
Wales	618	623	667	688
Scotland	725	689	653	595
Northern Ireland	139	153	174	217
United Kingdom	4 104	4 072	4 321	4 285
Processors and/or importers (a)				
North East	34	31	19	28
North West	122	130	107	143
Yorkshire & Humberside	118	126	121	141
East Midlands	175	191	154	195
West Midlands	138	139	114	143
Eastern	224	249	209	255
South West	333	353	242	380
South East (inc. London)	393	450	387	484
England	1 537	1 669	1 353	1 769
Wales	103	112	85	112
Scotland	152	174	152	197
Northern Ireland	33	35	36	50
United Kingdom	1 825	1 990	1 626	2 128

(a) Processers and importers include abattoirs, bakers, storers and wholesalers. The recorded location depends on the address registered with the Sector Bodies and so larger businesses may be recorded at their headquarters.

Livestock statistics (tables 13.4, 13.5)

10 Twentynine per cent of organic livestock producers are located in the southwest region of England. Around 63 per cent of organic livestock producers in the United Kingdom are found in England. There were 214 thousand cattle, 691 thousand sheep, 30 thousand pigs, 3,439 thousand poultry and 2.0 thousand other livestock, being reared organically in the United Kingdom. The figures are based on annual inspections of organic holdings conducted by certification bodies.

Table 13.4 Producers of organic and in-conversion livestock

Enquiries: Organic Statistics Team on +44 (0)1904 455557   email: organic-stats@defra.gsi.gov.uk

Number of producers

	January 2004	January 2005	January 2006
North East	49	44	54
North West	122	87	102
Yorkshire & Humberside	82	54	82
East Midlands	135	110	125
West Midlands	196	162	196
Eastern	99	69	86
South West	761	553	724
South East (inc. London)	220	162	201
England	1 664	1 241	1 570
Wales	469	402	502
Scotland	385	293	296
Northern Ireland	119	110	140
United Kingdom	2 637	2 046	2 508

Table 13.5 Estimates of organic and in-conversion livestock numbers (a); United Kingdom
Enquiries: Organic Statistics Team on +44 (0)1904 455557   email: organic-stats@defra.gsi.gov.uk

Thousand head

	January 2004	January 2005	January 2006
Cattle	126.8	174.8	214.3
Sheep	440.7	571.6	691.0
Pigs	48.8	43.7	30.0
Poultry	2 166.2	2 431.6	3 439.5
Goats	0.7	0.5	0.5
Other livestock	1.0	1.2	1.5

(a) Certification bodies record production data at various times of the year so figures should be treated with care as they will not represent an exact snapshot of organic livestock farming.

Annex

11 An annex to this chapter with a summary of the background to organic farming and a map of the distribution of organic holdings in the United Kingdom can be found on the Defra website at: http://statistics.defra.gov.uk/esg/publications/auk/default.asp.

2006

Chapter **14** Animal Health and Welfare

Summary

- Indicators, which measure progress within livestock sectors in England towards the aims of the Animal Health and Welfare Strategy for Great Britain, were published on 24 November 2006.

- During 2006, the Department of Agriculture and Rural Development in Northern Ireland published its Animal Health and Welfare Strategy, which reflects Northern Ireland's geographical position within the island of Ireland.

- The rate of confirmed incidence of Bovine Tuberculosis (bTB) in 2005 was the highest of recent years (excluding 2001), however provisional 2006 data shows a drop in the confirmed incidence rate.

- At the end of 2005, 94 per cent of the cattle herds in Great Britain were considered officially bTB free, compared to 96 per cent at the end of 2004.

Introduction

1 The aim of this section is to provide a focus on key high profile issues and to signpost readers to more detailed information and statistics on a wide range of animal health and welfare issues across the United Kingdom.

2 The Animal Health and Welfare Strategy, published in June 2004, sets an overarching direction for the future of Animal Health and Welfare in Great Britain (http://www.defra.gov.uk/animalh/ahws/default.htm) The strategy for Great Britain is being implemented at a national, devolved level, reflecting the individual circumstances in each country. However, all administrations are working towards the vision of improved animal health and welfare and the aim of developing a new partnership in which a lasting and continuous improvement to animal health and welfare can be made.

3 Within England, the strategy is overseen by an independent advisory group, the England Implementation Group (EIG). Defra has worked with the EIG to develop indicators which report progress towards the stated aims of the strategy within England.

4 The first suite of indicators, looking at progress within livestock sectors, was published on the 24 November 2006. Many of these indicators are still in development, however work is in place for further development and regular updates of the indicators. The indicators can be found at http://www.defra.gov.uk/animalh/ahws/eig/indicators/index.htm with updates that are published at regular intervals.

5 Indicators are being developed, in conjunction with the EIG, to develop measures which monitor progress towards the strategy outcomes for companion animals, including pets, animals for sport and aquaculture. These will be developed during 2007 along with further development of the livestock indicators.

6 The Scottish Animal Health and Welfare Advisory Group has identified a number of industry priorities, against which progress is being monitored. More information on the group and its priorities can be found at:

http://www.scotland.gov.uk/Topics/Agriculture/animal-welfare/AHWStrategy/Introduction. Work is ongoing to develop measures in Wales.

7   During 2006, the Department of Agriculture and Rural Development in Northern Ireland published its Animal Health and Welfare Strategy (http://www.dardni.gov.uk/animal-health-and-welfare-strategy.pdf). This reflects Northern Ireland's relative geographical position within the island of Ireland but is consistent with the principles of the strategy for Great Britain.

Animal Health

8   Animal Health and Welfare within Great Britain is comprehensively reported through the Chief Veterinary Officer's (CVO) report published annually at http://www.defra.gov.uk/animalh/cvo/report/index.htm. The Department of Agriculture and Rural Development in Northern Ireland publishes animal health bulletins on a regular basis via the internet at http://www.dardni.gov.uk/index/dard-statistics.

9   Bovine Tuberculosis (bTB) continues to be a disease affecting a small percentage of the national cattle herd but provides an ongoing challenge to both industry and government. Due to laboratory procedures there is a time-lag in confirmed incidents so the final results for 2006 are not yet available. Table 14.1 shows results for 2005, broken down by region and country plus total results for 2004.

10   During 2005, 4.4 per cent fewer tests were carried out on unrestricted herds in Great Britain than in 2004 (46,617 compared with 48,790). However, the number of new herd incidents in Great Britain increased from 3,349 in 2004 to 3,670 in 2005 (up 9.6 per cent). Infection was confirmed in 2,079 of these new incidents (up 18 per cent on previous year).

11   The number of confirmed incidents recorded is standardised using the number of tests carried out to give a confirmed bTB incidence rate (calculated as "number of incidents" divided by "number of unrestricted tests"). In 2005, this gives a confirmed new incidence rate of 4.5 per cent, which can be interpreted as "for every 100 tests in unrestricted cattle herds, an average of 4.5 new confirmed incidents were detected". This is an increase from 2004 when 3.6 per cent of tests resulted in a new confirmed incident.

12   With the exception of 2001 and 2002, which were affected by the outbreak of foot and mouth disease, the confirmed incidence of bTB in Great Britain has been steadily increasing over the past twenty years. The incidence rate in 2005 was the highest incidence rate over the last twenty years (excluding 2001, when testing was focussed on the most "at risk" herds). However, provisional 2006 data shows a reversal in this trend, with a drop in the confirmed incidence rate.

13   A total of 5,680 cattle herds were under restrictions due to a bTB incident at some time during 2005 in Great Britain, compared with 5,239 herds in 2004. This figure includes new herd incidents plus any incidents disclosed in previous years and still unresolved in 2005. At the end of 2005, a total of 5,782 cattle herds were under bTB restrictions. This figure includes herds that were subject to restrictions for reasons other than a bTB incident (e.g. an overdue tuberculin test). At the end of 2005, 94 per cent of the cattle herds in Great Britain were considered officially bTB free, compared to 96 per cent at the end of 2004.

14   Constant disease surveillance work is carried out by all United Kingdom rural affairs departments, monitoring not only known threats but also new and emerging diseases.

15   The global spread of Avian Influenza has continued during 2006, meaning that the United Kingdom is at continued risk of infection via a number of different pathways including legal or illegal trade and migratory birds. In April 2006, Highly Pathogenic H5N1 Avian Influenza was found in a dead wild

2006

Table 14.1 Bovine tuberculosis: summary statistics for the testing of animals and herds 2005
Enquiries: Jennifer Lees on +44 (0)1904 456582

email: jennifer.lees@defra.gsi.gov.uk

SVS Region/Country	West Region, England	North Region, England	East Region, England	England total	Wales total	Scotland total	Great Britain total 2005	Great Britain total 2004	Northern Ireland total 2005	Northern Ireland total 2004
Cattle herds										
1. Total number of cattle herds registered on Vetnet	23 486	25 132	12 856	61 474	14 898	14 599	90 971	93 489	28 263	28 568
2. ...of which were under TB2 restrictions because of a TB incident at some time during the reporting period	3 756	540	134	4 430	1 184	66	5 680	5 239	..	..
TB tests carried out (in year to date)										
3. Total number of unrestricted herd tests	20 658	9 839	3 035	33 535	9 153	3 929	46 617	48 790	30 263	32 443
4. Total number of cattle tested	2 730 274	803 816	154 313	3 688 403	928 466	231 188	4 848 057	4 638 761	1 776 099	1 865 762
TB incidents (started in year to date)										
5. Total new herd TB incidents	2 399	405	95	2 899	734	37	3 670	3 349	1 792	2 324
6. ...of which are considered confirmed new TB incidents (i.e. CNIs)	1 436	207	31	1 674	396	9	2 079	1 765	1 012	1 384
7. ...of which are considered unconfirmed TB incidents	953	197	64	1 214	333	28	1 575	1 581	780	940
8. ...of which are still unclassified TB incidents (pending culture results)	10	1	-	11	5	-	16	3	-	-
Animals slaughtered (In year to date, excluding any reactors awaiting slaughter on the date of the data download)										
9. As Reactors (inc. IRx3)	18 226	1 661	226	20 113	5 520	112	25 745	19 975	10 479	15 086
10. As Inconclusive Reactors (IRs)	320	68	25	413	138	17	568	494	..	..
11. As Direct Contacts (DCs)	1 662	842	64	2 568	1 119	52	3 739	2 595	1 208	673
12. Slaughterhouse cases reported to the SVS (of which confirmed)	401 (283)	98 (51)	30 (24)	529 (358)	36 (22)	26 (10)	591 (390)	387 (201)	609 (n/a)	849 (616)
Herds under TB2 restrictions at the end of the month (due to a TB incident, overdue TB test, etc)										
13. Herds under movement restriction on 31 December 2005 (and 31/12/2004 under GB Total 2004)	2 903	756	305	3 964	1 654	164	5 782	3 745	..	..

(a) Figures for Great Britain and Northern Ireland should not be added to arrive at totals for the United Kingdom because of differences in methodology.

Whooper Swan in Cellardyke, Fife. In line with European Commission legislation on findings of wild birds, restrictions on the movement of poultry and poultry products in the area were put in place and an extensive surveillance programme was established to identify any further disease present. No further cases of Highly Pathogenic Avian Influenza were found and restrictions were lifted on 1 May 2006. The working assumption remains that the Whooper Swan originated outside the United Kingdom. Also during April 2006, a low pathogenic strain of Avian Influenza, H7N3, was found at three commercial poultry premises in Norfolk. Surveillance and tracing was carried out, showing no further spread. Restrictions were ceased on 26 May 2006.

Animal Welfare

16 Defra and the devolved administrations in Scotland, Wales and Northern Ireland have an important and active role in developing national and EU legislation and in educating livestock keepers in standards of welfare. Farm premises; farming practices including animal transportation; markets and slaughterhouses are all assessed against legal requirements, and enforcement used where necessary. Inspections carried out against the EU requirements and welfare codes contribute to animal welfare surveillance, along with targeted State Veterinary Service (SVS) visits and scanning visits by the SVS, Meat Hygiene Service (MHS) and Veterinary Laboratory Agency (VLA). In Northern Ireland many of these checks fall to the Veterinary Service (VS).

17 Visits are made as part of programmed compliance checks or where the livestock keeper has requested an inspection ("compliance" or "elective" respectively). Where an allegation of poor welfare has been made, a visit is undertaken as a matter of urgency and these are referred to as "complaint" visits. Targeted visits are undertaken where there is possible cause for concern for the welfare for livestock. Targeted and complaint inspection results are reported jointly in the statistics that are produced.

18 The CVO Report provides fuller details of these inspections along with in depth analysis and commentary, and should be regarded as the main reference point.

19 The following graphs show a summary of results from welfare inspections on farm.

On farm welfare

20 The SVS carried out 6,348 welfare inspections at 3,794 visits during 2006 (1.7 inspections per visit) on farms to check that legislation and the welfare codes are being followed. At these visits, assessments

Chart 14.1 Results of SVS assessments of the welfare of animals on farm in Great Britain between 1 January and 31 December 2006 during complaint and target visits

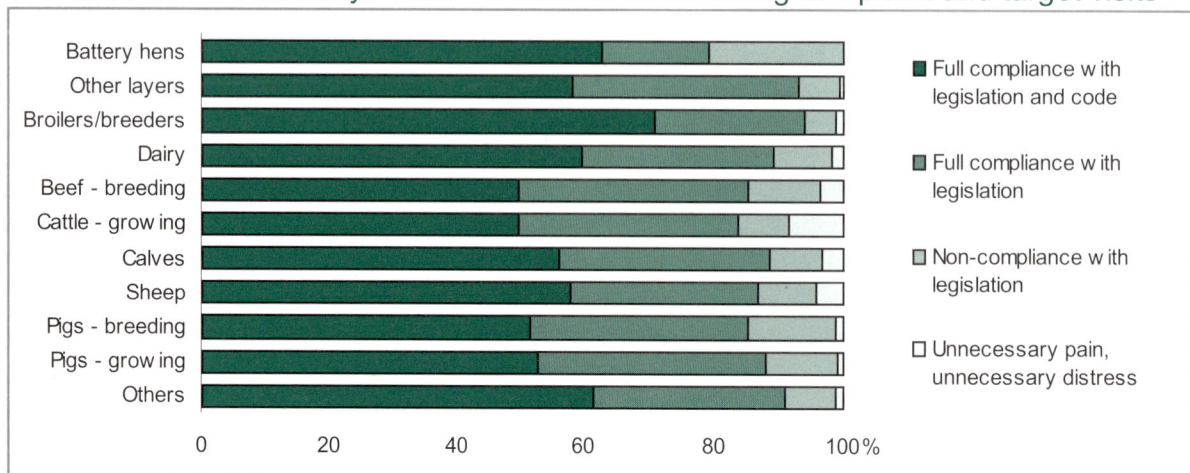

Chart 14.2 Results of SVS assessments of the welfare of animals on farm in Great Britain between 1 January and 31 December 2006 during programme and elective visits

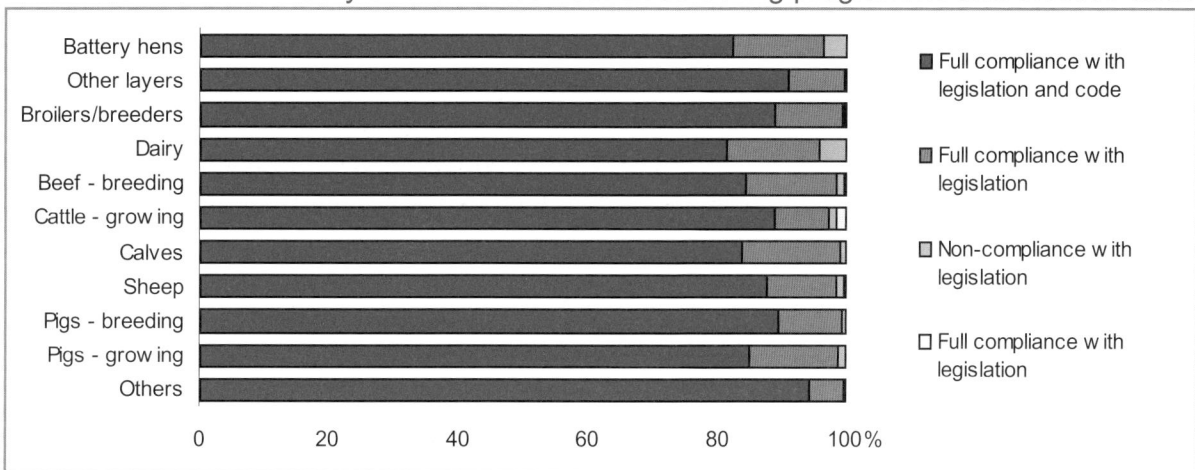

(Chart legend: Full compliance with legislation and code; Full compliance with legislation; Non-compliance with legislation; Full compliance with legislation. Categories listed: Battery hens, Other layers, Broilers/breeders, Dairy, Beef - breeding, Cattle - growing, Calves, Sheep, Pigs - breeding, Pigs - growing, Others. Axis 0 to 100%)

are made covering a wide range of issues from disease treatment, feed and water, freedom of movement, housing, staffing and records.

21 Results from on farm welfare assessments show that there was a high level of compliance on farms, with 91 per cent of assessments at visits achieving either "full compliance with legislation and code" or "full compliance with legislation". Overall 3 per cent of assessments revealed a level of non compliance which was deemed to cause 'unnecessary pain, unnecessary suffering'.

22 Where visits are based on complaints or are targeted, 13 per cent of the visits showed "non-compliance with legislation" or "unnecessary pain, unnecessary distress", compared to 1 per cent of visits carried out as elective or programmed visits. This follows the same trend as 2005 when 14 per cent of complaint and targeted visits showed some level of non-compliance compared with 1 per cent of elective and programmed visits.

23 During 2006 the Veterinary Service in Northern Ireland carried out 659 welfare inspections on farms. Of this total 52 per cent were complaint or targeted with the remaining 48 per cent programmed or elective.

24 Of the programmed and elective visits 87 per cent achieved an overall visit assessment of "compliance with legislation", of which 73 per cent complied with both legislation and code. Non compliance was

Chart 14.3 Results of VS assessments of the welfare of animals on farm in Northern Ireland between 1 January and 31 December 2006 during complaint and target visits

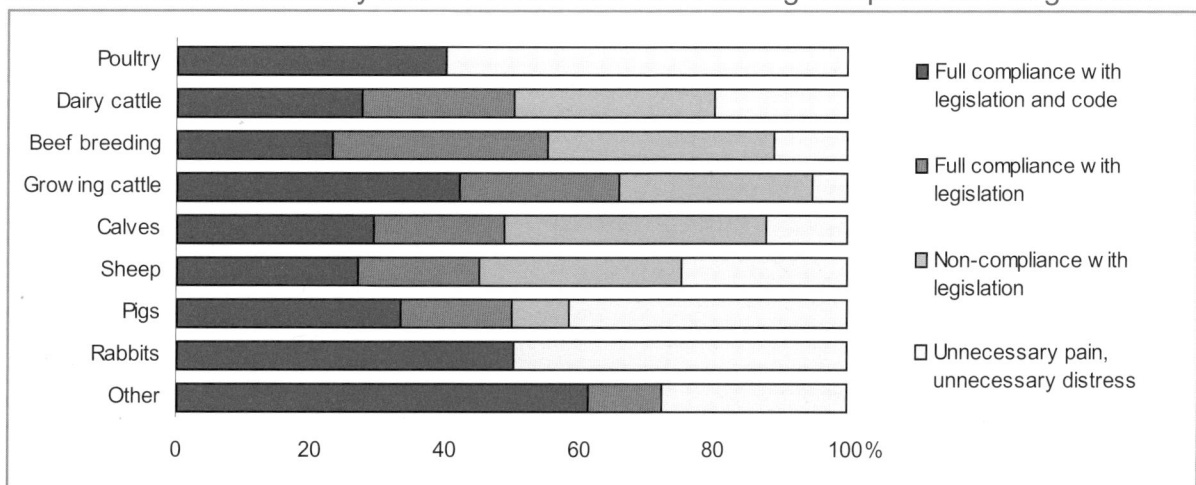

(Chart legend: Full compliance with legislation and code; Full compliance with legislation; Non-compliance with legislation; Unnecessary pain, unnecessary distress. Categories listed: Poultry, Dairy cattle, Beef breeding, Growing cattle, Calves, Sheep, Pigs, Rabbits, Other. Axis 0 to 100%)

Chart 14.4 Results of VS assessments of the welfare of animals on farm in Northern Ireland between 1 January and 31 December 2006 during programme and elective visits

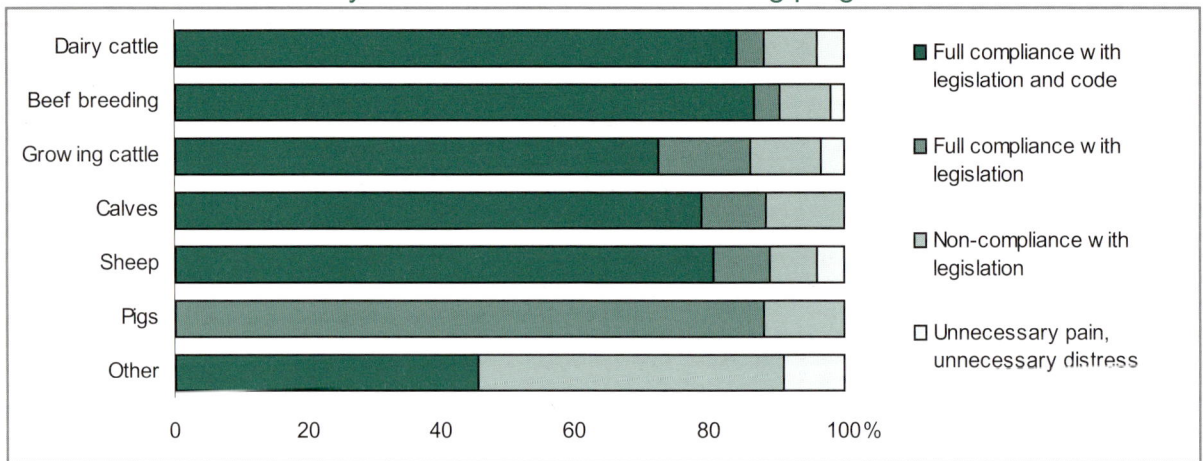

found on 13 per cent of visits with 2 per cent assessed as "unnecessary pain and unnecessary distress" to the animals.

25 Of the complaint and targeted visits 52 per cent of visits achieved compliance with legislation and 30 per cent of visits showed evidence of compliance with both legislation and code. However, in this group of visits 18 per cent were assessed to be at a level where unnecessary pain and distress is caused.

Chapter **15** Environment

2006

Summary

- Agricultural activities cover about three quarters of the land area in the United Kingdom .

- In 2005, around one third of habitat SSSIs on agriculturally managed land were in a favourable condition and one third were recovering.

- Around 6 million hectares of farmland in the United Kingdom are managed under agri-environment schemes.

- The index of farmland bird populations declined by about half between 1978 and 1993, and has remained relatively stable since.

- Agricultural emissions of methane have fallen by 11 per cent over the 10 years up to 2004.

- Agricultural emissions of nitrous oxide have fallen by 12 per cent over the 10 years up to 2004.

- Ammonia emissions from agriculture have reduced by 9 per cent over the 10 years to 2004.

- Nitrate levels in rivers in England fell steadily between 2000 and 2003 but have remained steady since. In Scotland, Wales and Northern Ireland they remain low.

- Phosphate levels in rivers in all countries except Wales have fallen slightly between 2000 and 2005, while Wales shows a slight increase.

- Total energy use by agriculture has fallen by a quarter over 10 years.

- Over the last 10 years, the use of nitrate and phosphate fertilisers has shown an overall decline.

Introduction

Chart 15.1 Environmental profile of the agricultural sector

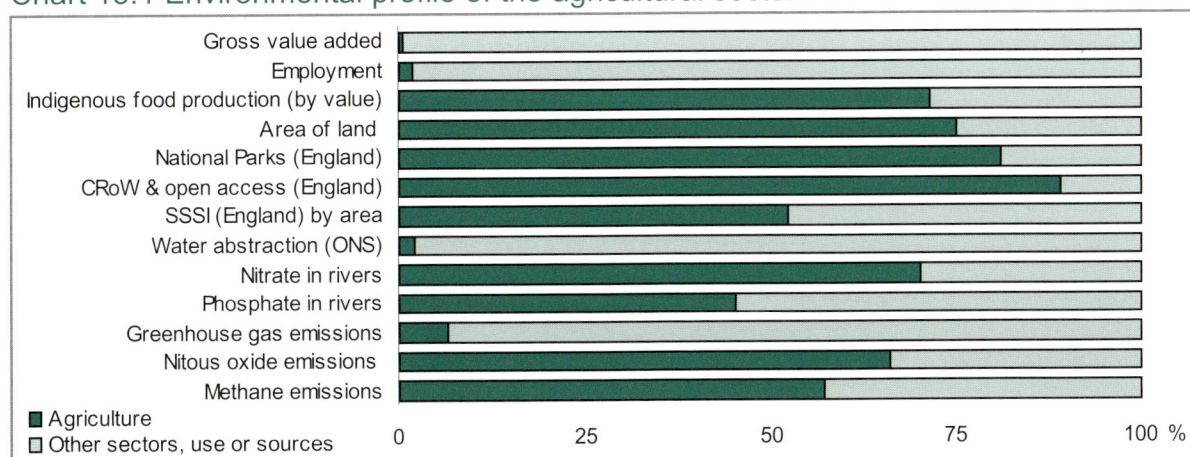

Source: Collated by Defra

1 In the United Kingdom, agricultural activities cover around three-quarters of the land area and produce two-thirds of United Kingdom food. The agricultural sector is made up of around 307,000 holdings varying widely in size and type. A range of different farming practices are employed involving: the way in which livestock are kept; the use of inputs such as soil and water as well as nutrient, land and waste management. The interaction between these practices and the local environmental characteristics affect the extent to which farming activities impact on the environment. The effects on the environment are significant and complex; farming activities can give rise to both positive and negative impacts on the environment operating at local, regional, national and global levels.

2 Chart 15.1 puts agriculture into context by bringing together data to summarise agriculture in comparison with other sectors in the United Kingdom. It shows the agricultural sector as a proportion of the United Kingdom (or England where stated). It includes the agricultural contribution to: the national economy; land protection and conservation; resources; pollution and emissions. It is intended to indicate the relative contribution of farming in different areas and as different baselines are used for comparison the figures should not be directly compared. The latest available data are used, the sources and units of which can be found in the specific tables and charts elsewhere in this publication.

Environmental impacts

3 This section brings together physical data to show the state and trend of the impacts of agriculture on the environment. This includes farm woodland, but not forests or other woodland. The data have been selected to put these impacts into context and show the agricultural contribution to environmental issues. They cover the major environmental issues where reliable sources exist.

Landscape

4 The countryside has been shaped and managed by agriculture for several thousand years. Traditional farming methods together with climatic conditions and the underlying geology have produced distinctive and unique regional landscapes. Local landscapes are shaped by natural landforms, local building materials, species and habitat types and land management practices. These have combined to create distinctive and unique character areas in the United Kingdom. Our ideas of landscape are rooted in history and local, regional and national cultures. National Parks and Areas of Outstanding Natural Beauty (AONB), National Scenic Areas in Scotland, are designated for various reasons including their landscape value.

5 Table 15.1 shows the area of designated land in National Parks and Areas of Outstanding Natural Beauty (AONB), Natural Scenic Areas (NSA) in Scotland. Map 15.1 shows their distribution in Great Britain.

Table 15.1 Designated National Parks and Areas of Outstanding Natural Beauty 2006 (a) (b) (c)

Enquiries: Barbara Norton on +44 (0)1904 455577   email: barbara.norton@defra.gsi.gov.uk

	England			Wales			Scotland			Northern Ireland		
	000 ha	Number	% of total land	000 ha	Number	% of total land	000 ha	Number	% of total land	000 ha	Number	% of total land
National parks	1 051	9	8	410	3	20	568	2	9	..	..	..
AONB / NSA	2 064	36	16	83	5	4	1 378	46	17	286	9	20

Source: Defra, English Nature, Department of Environment (Northern Ireland), Countryside Council for Wales, Welsh Assembly Government, Scottish Executive, Scottish Natural Heritage, National Trust and Scottish National Trust

(a) Generally AONBs and National Parks are mutually exclusive, however, some AONBs exist within the Broads and National Scenic Areas remain within the Scottish National Parks.

(b) The total number of AONBs in England and Wales is 40, as the Wye Valley AONB spans both countries, the respective areas are included in each country in this table.

(c) The percentage is included for comparison purposes. Areas of land are not always consistent in their inclusion of lakes, estuaries and other bodies of water.

Map 15.1 Designated areas in Great Britain

2006

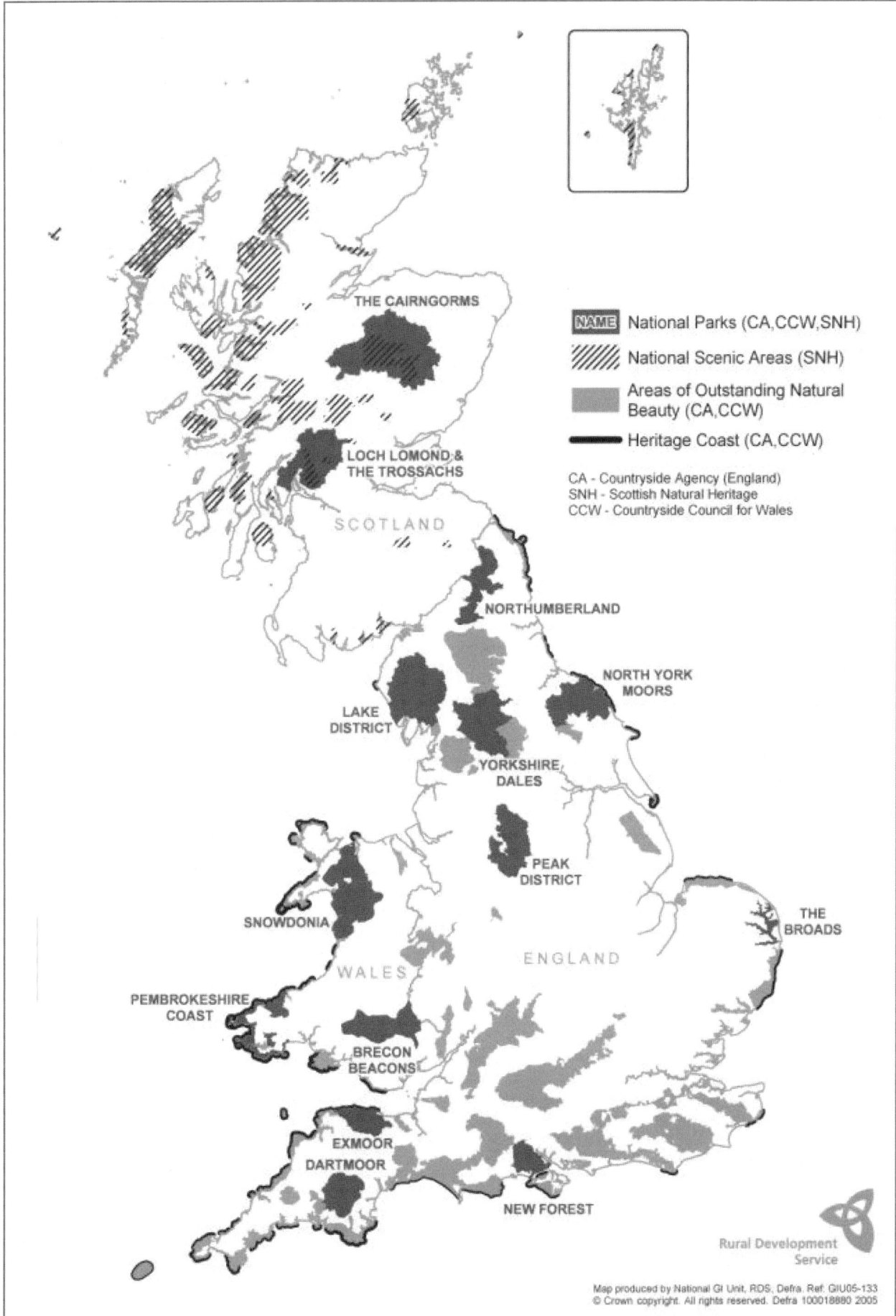

Legend:

- NAME — National Parks (CA,CCW,SNH)
- National Scenic Areas (SNH)
- Areas of Outstanding Natural Beauty (CA,CCW)
- Heritage Coast (CA,CCW)

CA - Countryside Agency (England)
SNH - Scottish Natural Heritage
CCW - Countryside Council for Wales

Map labels:
THE CAIRNGORMS
LOCH LOMOND & THE TROSSACHS
SCOTLAND
NORTHUMBERLAND
NORTH YORK MOORS
LAKE DISTRICT
YORKSHIRE DALES
PEAK DISTRICT
SNOWDONIA
THE BROADS
WALES
ENGLAND
PEMBROKESHIRE COAST
BRECON BEACONS
EXMOOR
DARTMOOR
NEW FOREST

Rural Development Service

Map produced by National GI Unit, RDS, Defra. Ref: GIU05-133
© Crown copyright. All rights reserved. Defra 100018880 2005

6   Agriculture can help conserve historic landscape by protecting features such as historic field patterns which are all part of our heritage. Local materials and vernacular building techniques make unique contributions to the visual impact of the countryside. Traditional buildings and field boundaries are important characteristic features of the landscape. Table 15.2 shows the stock and changes in stock of some landscape boundary features from the Countryside Surveys of 1990 and 1998. Further information can be found at: http://www naturalengland.org.uk/; http://www.snh.org.uk/; http://www.doeni.gov.uk/, http://www.ccw.gov.uk/; http://www.cs2000.org.uk/index.htm.

Table 15.2 Stock of linear landscape features in Great Britain, 1998 and changes 1990 to 1998

For definitions of linear landscape features used in Countryside Survey 2000 see Accounting for Nature: assessing habitats in the UK countryside.
Enquiries: Barbara Norton on +44 (0)1904 455577   email: barbara.norton@defra.gsi.gov.uk

	England and Wales			Scotland		
	1998 Length	Change in length 1990-1998		1998 Length	Change in length 1990-1998	
	thousand km		%	thousand km		%
Hedge	449.3	- 0.4	-	19.0	0.8	4.6
Remnant Hedge	52.3	- 13.5	- 20.9	5.3	- 0.9	- 20.0
Wall	105.8	- 2.7	- 2.5	87.1	- 1.5	- 1.7
Line of trees/shrubs/relict hedge and fence	70.0	15.5	30.8	11.1	1.4	14.0
Line of trees/shrubs/relict hedge	83.4	19.6	31.4	13.3	2.4	22.2
Bank/grass strip	70.0	- 1.9	- 2.5	12.4	0.8	6.3
Fence	423.2	25.6	6.6	233.7	8.6	3.9
Total	1 253.9	42.3	3.5	382.0	11.7	3.2

Source: CS2000, Defra e-Digest of Environmental Statistics

Habitats and species

7   By interacting with environmental factors such as soil type, climatic conditions and existing populations of flora and fauna, agriculture creates, maintains and supports semi-natural habitats, but can also damage them. Agricultural land use and other factors, such as recreational use, impact on habitats and species in a complex and diverse manner.

8   Changes were made in 2005 (CAP reform) to the way subsidies are paid to farmers. Farmers now have to farm in an environmentally responsible way to meet the cross compliance criteria to receive their single farm payment. This means keeping land in good agricultural and environmental condition. Further support for environmental issues comes from various agri-environment schemes. Tables of payments, areas of land and number of agri-environment agreements are in chapter 12.

9   Table 15.3 shows the stock of broad habitats in the United Kingdom and the relative dominance in terms of area of habitat on land under intensive agriculture. The flora and fauna will not only vary between the different habitats, but also within the individual habitats depending on local features.

10 National Nature Reserves (NNR) are of national importance. Sites of Special Scientific Interest (SSSIs) and Areas of Special Scientific Interest (ASSIs) in Northern Ireland protect and conserve the most important wildlife and geological sites in the United Kingdom. The Natura 2000 sites, Special Protection Areas (birds), Special Areas of Conservation (habitats) and Ramsar (wetlands) sites are internationally important sites for species and habitats usually designated within the SSSIs and ASSIs. Table 15.4 shows the areas of these designated habitats in the countries of the United Kingdom.

Table 15.3 Stock of broad habitat areas in the United Kingdom 1998

For definitions of broad habitats used in Countryside Survey 2000 see the definitions page in the Land section of the e-Digest
Enquiries: Barbara Norton on +44 (0)1904 455577

email: barbara.norton@defra.gsi.gov.uk

Broad Habitat	England and Wales 000 ha	%	Scotland 000 ha	%	Northern Ireland 000 ha	%	United Kingdom 000 ha	%
Woodland habitats								
Broadleaved, Mixed and Yew Woodland	1 171	7.7	300	3.7	51	3.7	1 522	6.2
Coniferous Woodland	380	2.5	993	12.4	61	4.4	1 435	5.9
Intensive agriculture								
Improved Grassland	4 431	29.1	1 051	13.1	568	41.0	6 050	24.7
Arable and Horticultural	4 609	30.3	639	8.0	59	4.3	5 307	21.7
Semi-natural habitats								
Neutral Grassland	444	2.9	168	2.1	254	18.3	867	3.5
Bog	180	1.2	2 038	25.4	148	10.7	2 367	9.7
Dwarf Shrub Heath	485	3.2	1 002	12.5	13	0.9	1 500	6.1
Acid Grassland	547	3.6	748	9.3	28	2.0	1 324	5.4
Fen, Marsh and Swamp	210	1.4	337	4.2	53	3.8	600	2.5
Bracken	273	1.8	166	2.1	4	0.3	443	1.8
Calcareous Grassland	38	0.2	27	0.3	1	0.1	66	0.3
Sediment and rock	204	1.3	168	2.1	9	0.6	189	0.8
Water								
Standing Open Water and Canals	106	0.7	85	1.1	..	..	..	..
Rivers and Streams	43	0.3	21	0.3	..	..	..	..
Developed habitats								
Built up and Gardens	1 180	7.7	151	1.9	..	..	..	..
Boundary and Linear Features	411	2.7	87	1.1	..	..	..	..
Unsurveyed urban land	426	2.8	37	0.1	..	..	..	..
Unclassified	93	0.6	2	-	143	10.3	..	..
Total	15 230	100.0	8 020	100.0	1 385	100.0	24 495	100.0

Source: Countryside Survey 2000, Northern Ireland Countryside Survey 2000, e-Digest of Environmental Statistics

Table 15.4 Designated areas for habitats and species 2006 (a)

Enquiries: Barbara Norton on +44 (0)1904 455577

email: barbara.norton@defra.gsi.gov.uk

	England 000 ha	Number	% of total land	Wales 000 ha	Number	% of total land	Scotland 000 ha	Number	% of total land	Northern Ireland 000 ha	Number	% of total land
LNR	34	1 016	-	5	57	-	9	36	-	3	39	-
NNR	86	213	1	24	66	1	117	66	1	2	9	-
SSSI / ASSI	1 073	4 113	8	264	1 021	13	1 008	1 451	13	94	226	7
SAC	887	235	7	107	73	5	963	238	12	66	52	5
SPA	636	79	5	137	19	7	625	138	8	109	15	8
Ramsar	331	70	3	26	10	1	313	51	4	78	21	6

Natura 2000 (b)

Source: Defra, English Nature, Department of Environment (Northern Ireland), Countryside Council for Wales, Welsh Assembly Government, Scottish Executive and Scottish Natural Heritage

a) The percentage is included for comparison purposes. Areas of land are not always consistent in their inclusion of lakes, estuaries and other bodies of water.
b) Natura 2000 sites can be in more than one designation and are on SSSIs and/or NNR.

11 Chart 15.2 shows the condition of those Sites of Special Scientific Interest (Areas of Special Scientific Interest in Northern Ireland), A/SSSIs, for the United Kingdom (2005) that are habitats under mainly agricultural management. These are shown by the number of features (not area as previously used). The A/SSSIs do not include features that have not been assessed, including all Welsh SSSIs, and are assessed on a six year rolling programme. Arable & improved grassland features are only in England.

Chart 15.2 Condition of agriculturally managed A/SSSIs 2005; United Kingdom

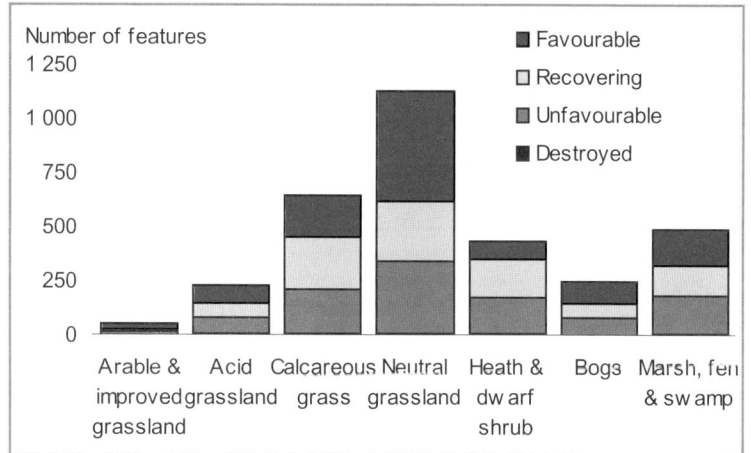

Source: Natural England, Scottish Natural Heritage, Countryside Council for Wales and Department of Environment (Northern Ireland)

12 Chart 15.3 shows, by number of features, the Special Areas of Conservation features, SACs, (2005) for habitats on mainly agriculturally managed land. Only those sites that can be identified as being predominately agriculturally managed have been included in the bogs and marsh, fen & swamp categories.

Chart 15.3 Condition of agriculturally managed SACs 2005; United Kingdom

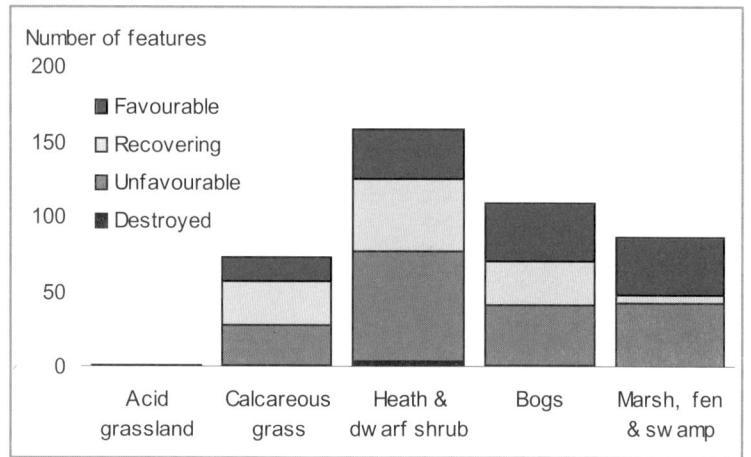

Source: Natural England, Scottish Natural Heritage, Countryside Council for Wales and Department of Environment (Northern Ireland)

13 Chart 15.4 shows the main reasons for adverse conditions, unfavourable and recovering, on all A/SSSIs and SACs. Agricultural activities account for about a third of damage to all A/SSSIs and SACs. Indirect damage can be caused on areas outside agriculture, such as sensitive habitats or bodies of water by air or water pollution. All data in this section (A/SSSIs & SACs) are extracted from those used in the JNCC Common Standards Monitoring report,

Chart 15.4 Reasons for adverse conditions on A/SSSIs and SACs 2005; United Kingdom

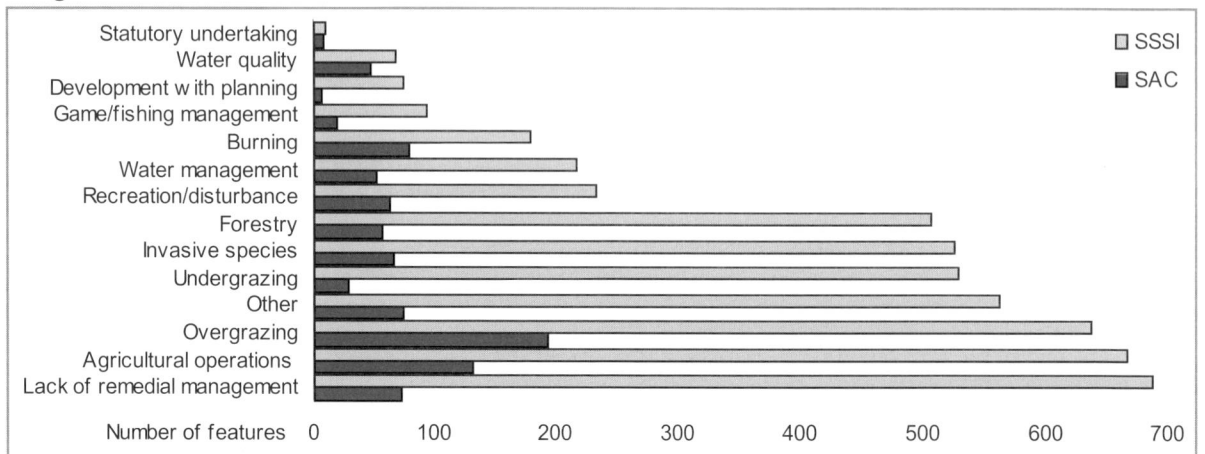

Source: Natural England, Scottish Natural Heritage, Countryside Council for Wales and Department of Environment (Northern Ireland)

2006. Further details of the report including the non agricultural features, background and definitions can be found at: http://www.jncc.gov.uk/page-2217.

14 Farming activities carried out in an environmentally responsible manner will help support, maintain and enhance the diversity of the landscapes, habitats and food sources for farmland wildlife. Much of our flora and fauna have adapted to agricultural systems, the common names of wild species indicate their historic relationship with farming, such as corncrake, barn owl, hedge sparrow, field poppy, corn cockle and corn flower.

15 Chart 15.5 shows the trends in farmland bird populations since 1970. Bird populations are considered good indicators of the state of wildlife since they have a wide habitat distribution and are near the top of the food chain. Therefore, changes in the bird population reflect changes in habitat diversity and within the food chain. The chart shows that, although populations of farmland generalist species have remained fairly stable since 1970, populations of farmland specialists (those that breed or feed mainly or solely on farmland) had declined by over 60 per cent by the late 1990s and have since remained at this level since. Further information can be found at: http://defraweb/wildlife-countryside/index.htm, http://www.bto.org/; http://www.rspb.org.uk/, http://www.jncc.gov.uk/

Chart 15.5 Farmland bird index 1970 to 2005; United Kingdom

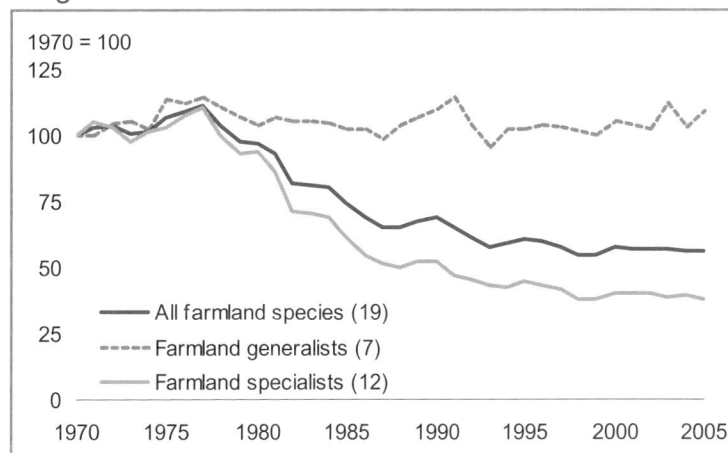

1970 = 100

- All farmland species (19)
- Farmland generalists (7)
- Farmland specialists (12)

Source: Defra/RSPB/BTO

16 Land under agricultural management can still provide many of the necessary functions that the natural land or wilderness delivers. The natural environment consists of ecosystems: functioning units of interacting plants, animals and micro-organisms with other non living elements. These provide beneficial goods and services for both ecological and economic functions including:

- filtering and purifying air water and soils, recharging aquifers;

- nutrient cycling, nitrogen fixation, carbon sequestration and soil formation;

- pest and disease control, climate regulation, mitigation of storms and floods, erosion control, regulation of rainfall and water supply;

- habitat provision and storehouse of genetic material;

- production of biomass, raw materials and food, pollination and seed dispersal;

- aesthetic, recreational and cultural opportunities.

17 Agriculture plays a role in providing many of the functions. Further information on ecosystems can be found at: http://www.defra.gov.uk/wildlife-countryside/natres/ecosystem.htm

Recreation

18 The countryside has been shaped and managed by agriculture for several thousand years. It is valued for recreation, providing landscapes, tranquillity and open space. The landscape is made more accessible for recreational activities, such as walking, cycling and horse riding, by the network of paths, bridleways and green lanes which cross farmland. Chart 15.6 shows the numbers taking part in some of these activities. Other recreational and educational activities include field studies and bird watching. Over 100 million visits are made to National Parks annually.

19 The area of open access has increased in England and Wales by an additional million hectares under the Countryside and Rights of Way Act 2000. In Scotland the Land Reform (Scotland) Act 2003 gives a right of responsible access to all land and inland water for recreational and educational purposes. Part 1 of the Act came into force in 2005. Further information can be found at: http://www.defra.gov.uk/wildlife-countryside/cl/accessopen /index.htm or http://www.outdooraccess-scotland.com/default.asp

Chart 15.6 Recreational activities in the countryside 2004; United Kingdom

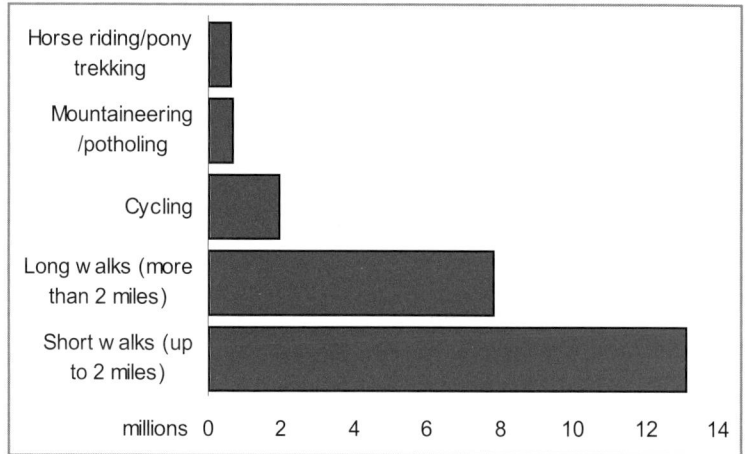

Source: UK Tourism Survey

Water

20 River and groundwater are important resources for agriculture. Water used for agriculture represents about 2 per cent of water abstracted. Agricultural use of water can have both positive and negative contributions to flooding, soil erosion and the recharge of aquifers.

21 Farming is a major source of water pollution, both diffuse, such as from fertiliser and pesticides spread on the land, and to a lesser extent from point sources such as runoff from livestock buildings. The key areas of concern are:

- nitrate pollution in surface and groundwater;
- phosphorus levels in surface water;
- contamination by pesticides;
- and other environmental problems including the harmful effects of soil erosion sediments and mineral salts resulting in impaired drinking water.

22 Chart 15.7 shows the lengths of rivers with nitrates levels over 30mg NO_3 per litre. In Northern Ireland, Wales and Scotland these remain low. In England levels have fallen overall since 2000 (though 2004 shows an increase) reflecting the decrease in fertiliser use (chart 15.12 and paragraph 40). Agriculture accounts for around 60 per cent (ADAS report 2004) of the nitrate in rivers.

Chart 15.7 Per cent of river length with nitrate levels greater than 30mg NO_3 per litre

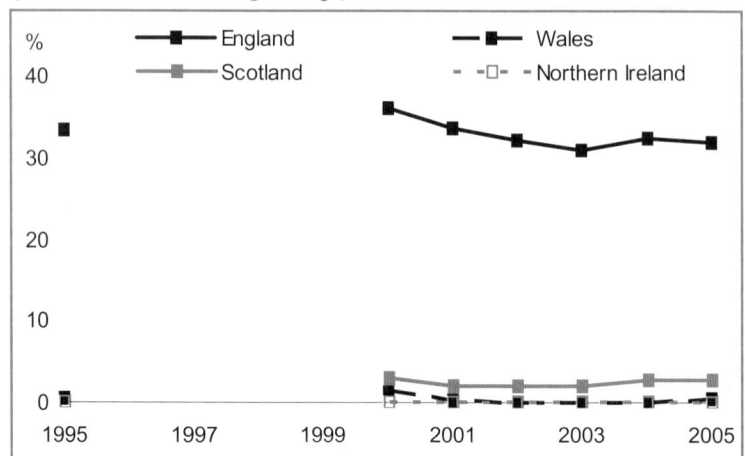

Source: Environment Agency, Scottish Environment Protection Agency, Environment & Heritage Service, Defra e-Digest of Environmental Statistics

23 Chart 15.8 shows phosphate levels in rivers by country. High levels in freshwater can cause eutrophication, which affects the ecological balance of the water environment leading to excessive plant growth. Agriculture accounts for around 29 per cent (White and Hammond 2006) of phosphates in river water. Further information can be found at: http://www.environment-agency.gov.uk/?lang=_e, http://www.sepa.org.uk/, http://www.doeni.gov.uk/.

Chart 15.8 Per cent of river length with phosphate levels greater than 0.1mg P per litre

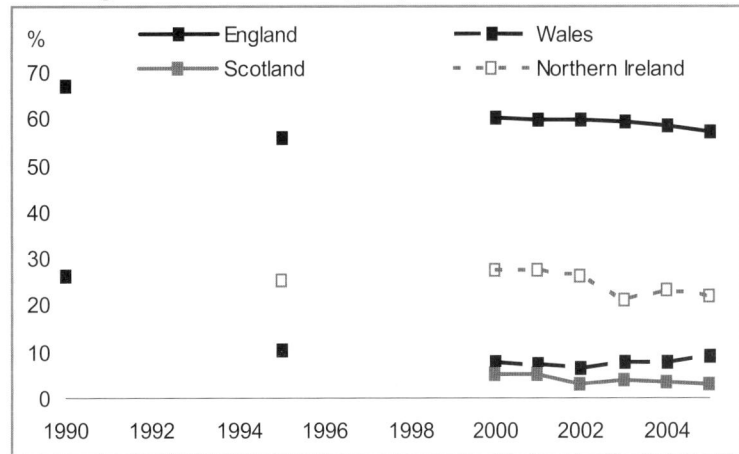

Source: Environment Agency, Scottish Environment Protection Agency, Environment & Heritage Service, Defra e-Digest of Environmental Statistics

Air

24 Emissions of carbon dioxide (CO_2), methane (CH_4) and nitrous oxide (N_2O) are of concern as they are greenhouse gasses and contribute to climate change. Methane and nitrous oxide have global warming potentials greater than carbon dioxide of 21 and 310 times respectively. Greenhouse gas emissions from agriculture account for around 7 per cent of total United Kingdom emissions. Ammonia mainly effects local air quality.

25 Chart 15.9 shows the United Kingdom methane (CH_4) emissions from all sources and that from agriculture. Agriculture accounts for 57 per cent of these emissions. Methane is generated as a result of enteric fermentation in ruminating animals. Over the last 30 years the emissions from agriculture have remained fairly constant at around a million tonnes per year. There has been an 11 per cent fall over the last 10 years, reflecting a general reduction in livestock numbers over this period.

26 Chart 15.10 shows the United Kingom emissions of nitrous oxide (N_2O) from all sources and that from

Chart 15.9 Methane emissions by source 1990 to 2004; United Kingdom

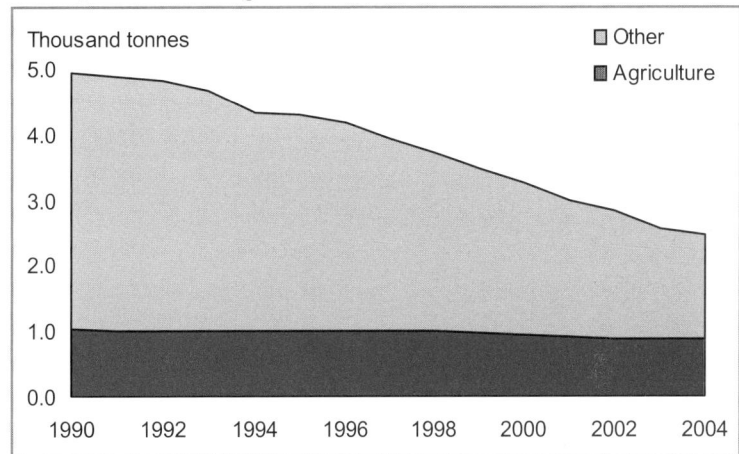

Source: Netcen, Defra e-Digest of Environmental Statistics

Chart 15.10 Nitrous oxide emissions by source 1990 to 2004; United Kingdom

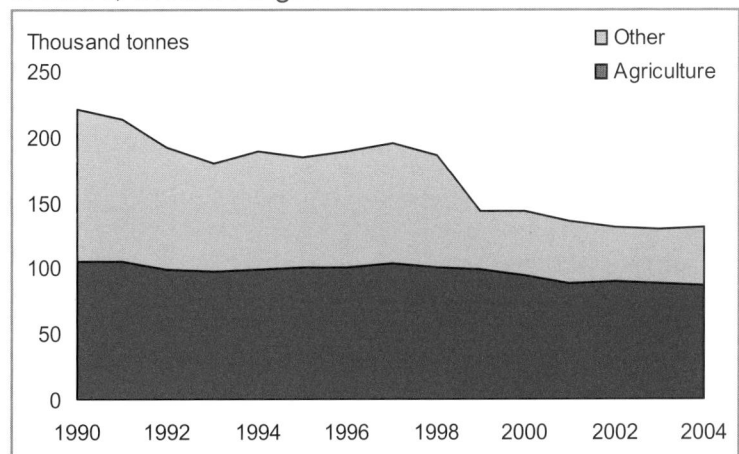

Source: Netcen, Defra e-Digest of Environmental Statistics

2006

agriculture. Agricultural emissions of nitrous oxides are produced mainly from the oxidation of the nitrogen in fertilisers and account for 66 per cent of all United Kingdom nitrous oxide emissions. The fall since the late nineties in these emissions reflects a reduction in fertiliser use (see chart 15.12 on fertiliser use).

27 Carbon dioxide (CO_2) is emitted during cultivation of arable land or semi-natural vegetation, when the soil is rotated to the surface and exposed to the air, when peat or fenland is drained and during the combustion of fossil fuels, eg to power tractors and machinery. Agriculture accounts for less than 1 per cent of carbon dioxide emissions in the United Kingdom.

28 Chart 15.11 shows ammonia (NH_3) emissions. Agriculture emissions have reduced by 9 per cent during the last 10 years and now account for 90 per cent of United Kingdom emissions. This is predominately from housing, storing and spreading animal manure particularly that of cattle and pigs. Inorganic fertilisers also produce ammonia as nitrogen reacts with compounds in the soil and air. The effects of ammonia are usually local but it can be deposited further afield by rainfall. The gradual fall is due to a general reduction in fertiliser use and a reduction in livestock numbers over the last few years, though there has been a 3.5 per cent increase in 2004.

Chart 15.11 Ammonia emissions by source 1990 to 2004; United Kingdom

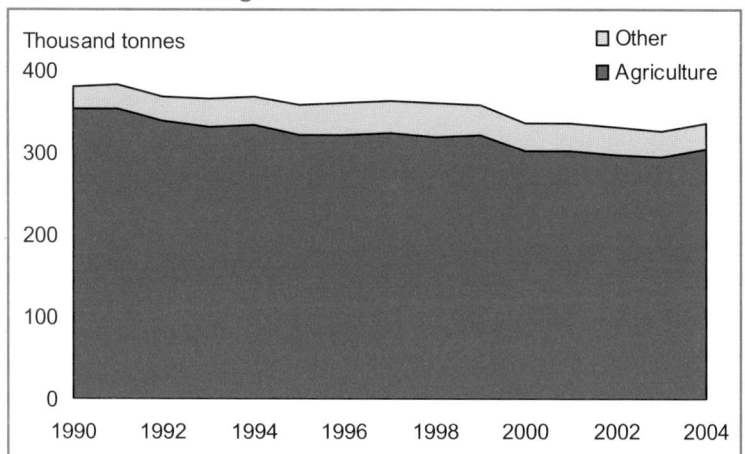

Source: Netcen, Defra e-Digest of Environmental Statistics

29 Many (semi-)natural habitats are naturally nitrogen limited and can be damaged by ammonia (NH_3) emissions, by either, poor air quality locally, or deposited further afield by wind or rain. The nitrogen in the gas can damage sensitive terrestrial and aquatic habitats by enriching the soil or water (with nitrates) and leading to loss of biodiversity. Ammonia also causes acidification which can also affect the aquatic and plant biodiversity. High concentrations of ammonia in the air can damage plants such as lichens, mosses and heathers.

30 Species of plants in naturally nitrogen limited habitats such as moorland, heather, bog and infertile grassland, and upland freshwater lakes and rivers are adapted to low nitrate conditions. Ammonia deposition benefits other species that need more nitrogen, which can then invade the sensitive areas and outnumber the adapted species. Most recent estimates show that there are a significant number of sensitive habitats at risk of damage from air pollution.

31 Around 90 per cent of ammonia emissions are from agriculture, mainly from the breakdown of animal manure. Non-agricultural emissions dominate in areas of large populations.

32 Of the habitats at risk, shown in black on map 15.2, those at greatest risk are likely to receive between 7 to 14kg of ammonia deposition per hectare per year in localised areas where the biodiversity can be damaged. Many of the areas at high risk, are in areas of low ammonia emissions. Further information can be found at: http://www.defra.gov.uk/environment/statistics/index.htm, http://www.naei.org.uk/emissions /emissions_2000.php, http://www.sepa.org.uk/, http://www.doeni.gov.uk.

Map 15.2 Sensitive habitats at risk from ammonia emissions

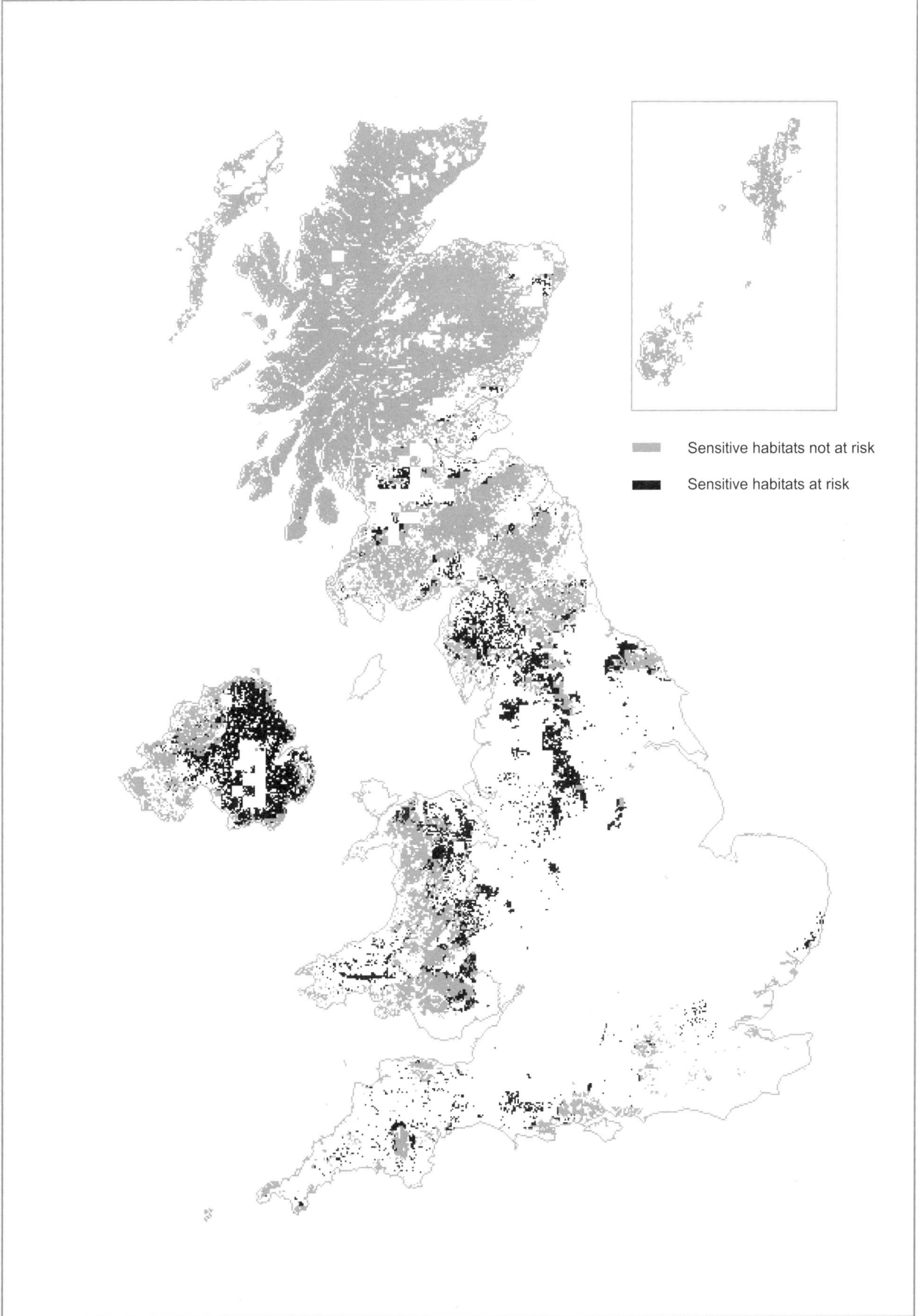

Sensitive habitats not at risk

Sensitive habitats at risk

Source: Centre for Ecology & Hydrology

Soil

33 Soil is one of the fundamental assets of most farms and is essential for food and fibre production, providing support, nutrients and water. However, mismanagement can result in its loss and degradation, which in turn will reduce the ability of soils to perform this service. Soil degradation is both the physical loss (erosion) and the reduction in quality of soil associated with compaction, nutrient decline and contamination.

34 Good soil management and soil quality can increase profitability of farmers. For example, evidence suggests that by improving management of soil organic matter farmers can be better off to the tune of £31 to £66 per hectare (Defra report). While the financial benefits are fairly modest in absolute terms they are often significantly higher than the costs involved in improving the management of soil organic matter.

35 According to the 2006 farm practices survey for England, 53 per cent of farmers had experienced some indicator of soil erosion on their land – indicators included discoloured runoff entering ditches and water courses, sediment deposited in ditches and water courses, sediment deposited on roads and the formation of gullies and rills (Defra Farm Practice Survey 2006): http://statistics.defra.gov.uk/esg /publications/fps/default.asp).

36 Studies have shown that agriculture is the main source of silt in rivers through soil erosion and channel bank erosion. Eroded soil particles carry bound pollutants such as phosphorus, pesticides, heavy metals and micro-organisms; 60 per cent of the phosphorus lost from agriculture is associated with soil erosion (Defra 2003). Soil erosion rates are typically less than 20 tonnes per hectare per year but erosion rates as high as 100 tonnes per hectare have been reported (Environment Agency 2006). Such significant losses of soil can impact on crop production as well as water quality.

37 Although much of the evidence collected suggests that agriculture can have a negative impact on soil, a focus on basic good management of soil to minimise erosion and structural damage and to build up organic matter levels can mitigate many of these negatives over time. Greater emphasis is being given to protecting soil as part of CAP cross compliance, an increase in the incentives to protect soil from erosion (such as under Environmental Stewardship), plus the exploration of a range of soil conservation measures as part of the implementation of the Water Framework Directive. Further information can be found at: http://www.defra.gov.uk/environment/water/wfd/index.htm.

Other resources

38 The power used both directly and indirectly by agriculture comes from mainly finite resources. Table 15.5 shows estimated direct and indirect use expressed as PetaJoules - Joules x 10^{15} (PJ) for purposes of comparison. This is the energy consumed in agricultural production, but not in the processing and distribution of food. It shows that the total energy used in agriculture has fallen by nearly a quarter over 10 years and by nearly 3 per cent in 2005.

39 Energy used directly (for heating, lighting and power) by the agricultural industry is around 0.5 per cent of overall United Kingdom energy use. Although direct energy use has increased in 2005 by 11 per cent, it has fallen by a third over 10 years. Energy used indirectly in the production of agricultural inputs (for the manufacture of fertilisers, pesticides and machinery) is around 1.3 per cent of overall United Kingdom energy demand. The most dominant indirect input of energy, over 50 per cent, arises from the manufacture of fertilisers. Reductions in the use of fertilisers together with efficiency savings during manufacturing have led to a 37 per cent reduction in energy use for fertiliser since the start of 1985. This

Table 15.5 Direct and indirect energy consumption, electricity generation; United Kingdom

Enquiries: Barbara Norton on +44 (0)1904 455577   email: barbara.norton@defra.gsi.gov.uk

units: petajoules PJ = joulesx10^{15}

		Average 1994-96	2001	2002	2003	2004	2005
Total energy consumption		160.9	142.8	141.9	133.2	133.9	130.5
Direct energy		59.0	52.3	47.9	39.5	37.3	41.3
of which:	Natural gas & coal	5.0	8.4	8.7	8.7	8.9	8.2
	Oil products (inc petroleum)	36.9	24.9	21.3	13.3	10.3	15.2
	Electricity	14.0	16.0	14.9	14.5	15.1	14.9
	Biomass	3.1	3.0	3.0	3.0	3.0	3.0
Indirect Inputs		101.9	90.5	94.0	93.7	96.6	89.2
of which:	Fertiliser	58.3	51.0	52.0	49.6	49.5	46.5
	Pesticide	9.5	8.6	9.3	10.4	12.4	10.2
	Tractor purchases	11.3	10.3	12.3	13.4	14.2	12.5
	Animal Feeds	22.7	20.6	20.4	20.3	20.5	20.0
Electricity generation (a)		3.0	11.8	11.5	19.3	12.7	18.2

Source: ADAS, Reports prepared for Defra using : Digest of UK Energy Statistics, Agriculture in the UK, Agricultural Industries Confederation, Agricultural Engineers Association, Crop Protection Association and Department of Trade and Industry.

a)   Includes electricity from farm waste digestion, poultry litter combustion, meat and bone combustion, straw and short rotation coppice.

table also shows electricity production from biomass and farm waste. This is in addition to the energy used on farm that is derived from biomass, which is mainly as heat.

40 Chart 15.12 fertiliser use, shows a gradual decline in fertiliser use in Great Britain. Fertiliser is applied at a higher rate on arable land than on grassland. The fall in fertiliser use is mainly due to a reduction in application rates on grass, where the rate has fallen by a third over 10 years.

Chart 15.12 Nitrogen (N) & Phosphate (P$_2$O$_5$) fertiliser use in Great Britain 1984 to 2004

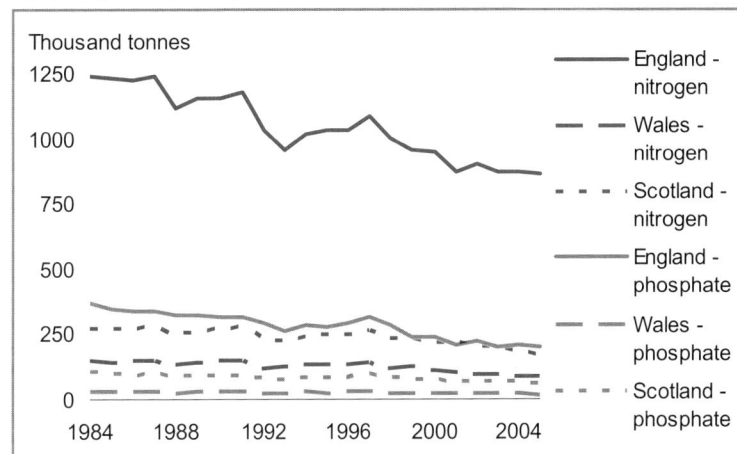

Source: GB Fertiliser practice survey 2003, Defra Census data

Waste

41 An estimated half a million tonnes of waste is produced by agriculture each year, this excludes organic material such as slurry/manure, crop residues, etc., when beneficially re-used on farm. The largest components are animal health products, agrochemicals and plastics.

42 The 2004 report of Defra's Farm Practices Survey (England) shows a general reduction in recycling plastic since the previous survey in 2001. The number of farmers using landfill sites has also fallen and is around 1 to 5 per cent of farmers. Burning continues to be the main way to dispose of waste, especially for plastics and packaging. In many cases nearly 50 per cent of farmers burn these (except plastic crop cover) in the open or use drum incinerators. The full reports can be found on the Defra website at: http://statistics.defra.gov.uk/esg/publications/fps/fpsreport.pdf.

43 In 2005 the Government brought into force Regulations in Scotland to bring agricultural waste within the controls of the EU Waste Framework and Landfill Directives. Similar regulations were made in the rest of the United Kingdom in 2006. The new Regulations make it illegal for the disposal of waste by open burning (unless it is plant tissue) or in farm dumps, i.e. uncontrolled landfills. Further regulations are being consulted on at the end of 2006 to provide three new waste management licensing exemptions for agricultural waste.

44 As well as slurry and manure being used to fertilise the land, other organic material, such as straw and poultry manure, is now being used as a source of energy, both for heat and power on farm and increasingly for electricity generation (see paragraph 38).

Agricultural Change and Environment Observatory

45 The Agricultural Change and Environment Observatory Programme is a major vehicle for identifying environmental risks from a changing agriculture sector. The Government established the Observatory in July 2005 in response to the last major reform of the Common Agricultural Policy (CAP) in 2003. Although the reforms were intended to reduce the environmental impacts of agriculture, it was recognised that not all of the environmental impacts would be easy to predict and might be negative as well as positive. The Observatory was therefore established to provide enhanced monitoring and so pick up early indications of change. Since agriculture is a devolved issue, it focuses on England.

46 Further details on research projects, future work and background information about the Observatory can be found at www.defra.gov.uk/farm/policy/observatory/index.htm.

Valuing environmental impacts of agriculture

47 This chapter presents data on some of the physical impacts of farming on the environment. These impacts can be positive as well as negative and many of the impacts are external to farming so that the costs or benefits are met by other sectors or the general public. By assigning values to these physical impacts they can be compared with each other and aggregated together to give a measure of the overall impact. Bringing together monetised valuations into a coherent framework provides a set of environmental accounts for agriculture.

48 Defra and the devolved administrations commissioned research by Eftec to develop a framework for environmental accounts for agriculture. Published in July 2004, the work proposed a conceptual framework for the accounts. Using benefits transfer, existing data sources were drawn together and weaknesses and gaps in these data sources were identified. The research represented a significant first step in developing environmental accounts although the results should only be considered as indicative.

49 Defra has built on the Eftec study, identifying key gaps and weaknesses in both data and methodology. To take forward this work, a further independent study is being commissioned. The study will aim to refine and develop the accounts, including methods for valuing external impacts with no market value (such as biodiversity) and consider conceptual issues such as the counterfactual; the alternative against which farming's environmental impacts are being compared. As more reliable estimates are developed the environmental accounts will have a valuable role in setting priorities for agricultural policy and as an evidence base for measuring the sustainability of agriculture.

50 For any enquiries on this chapter, please contact Barbara Norton, 01904 455577, Barbara.Norton@defra.gsi.gov.uk.

Chapter **16** Key Statistics for EU Member States

Summary

In 2006:

* income from agricultural activity in the United Kingdom as measured by Indicator A was 24 per cent higher than in 2000, while for the EU15 it was 16 per cent lower;

* the United Kingdom produced the third largest quantity of wheat of the EU25 countries.

In 2005, of the EU25 Member States, the United Kingdom:

* was the third largest producer of cows' milk;

* was the ninth largest producer of pigmeat;

* was the fourth largest producer of beef and veal;

* was the largest producer of sheep and goat meat.

Between 2000 and 2005:

* producer prices for crop products rose by 8.7 per cent in the United Kingdom while rising by 6.4 per cent in the EU15;

* producer prices for animals and animal products rose by 10 per cent in the United Kingdom while rising by 0.9 per cent in the EU15;

* purchase prices for the means of agricultural production rose by 15 per cent in the United Kingdom while rising by 8.6 per cent in the EU15.

Introduction

1 This chapter presents simple analyses of agriculture in the European Union to enable comparison of the United Kingdom with other Member States. The source of the data is the Eurostat website where a range of data is available free of charge. The Eurostat website may be found at http://ec.europa.eu/eurostat.

2 Eurostat is the Statistical Office of the European Communities situated in Luxembourg. Its task is to provide the European Union with statistics at European level that enable comparisons between countries and regions. Eurostat itself does not collect data; this is done in Member States by their statistical authorities who verify and analyse national data and send them to Eurostat. Eurostat's role is to consolidate the data and ensure they are comparable, using harmonized methodology.

Incomes

Indicator A of the income from agricultural activity

3 Chart 16.1 shows Indicator A, a measure of the average income obtained from agriculture, for the United Kingdom and the EU15. An index showing the trend in the euro/sterling exchange rate is also shown.

4 Incomes from agricultural activity in the United Kingdom as measured by Indicator A have risen by 24 per cent since 2000 despite falling in 2004 and 2005 while those in the EU15 have risen by 16 per cent. Incomes in the United Kingdom are influenced by the euro/sterling exchange rate.

Agricultural products

Wheat

5 Chart 16.2 shows the quantities of wheat produced by the top five producing Member States in 2004, 2005 and 2006. This is the production of common wheat and durum wheat.

6 In 2006, the United Kingdom ranked third in the quantity of wheat produced behind France and Germany having produced about 12 per cent of the total for the EU25.

Cows' milk

7 Chart 16.3 shows the proportions of cows' milk collected by the top five producing Member States in 2003, 2004 and 2005. This is cows' milk collected from farms by approved dairies and excludes milk consumed on farm, sold direct to consumers and used for cattle feed.

Chart 16.1 Indicator A of the income from agricultural activity

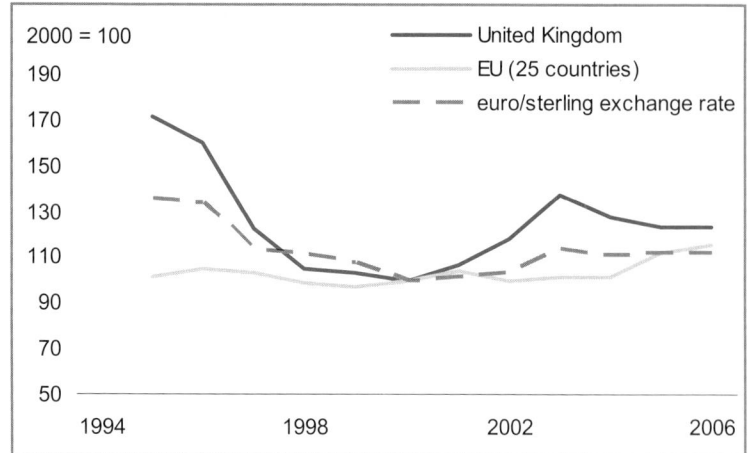

Chart 16.2 Production of wheat

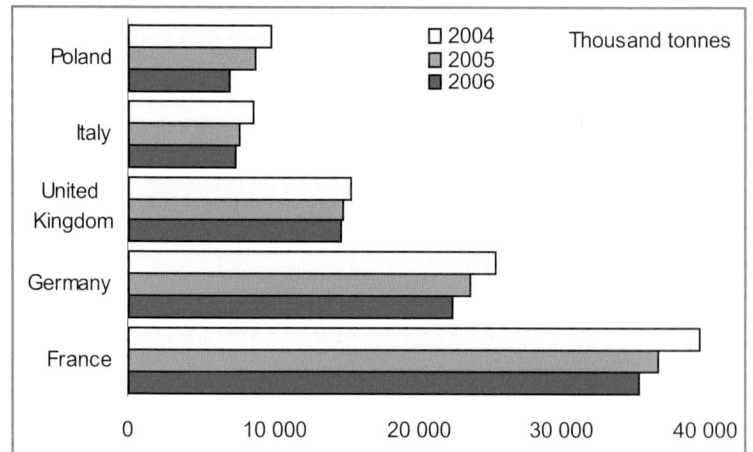

Chart 16.3 Production of cows' milk

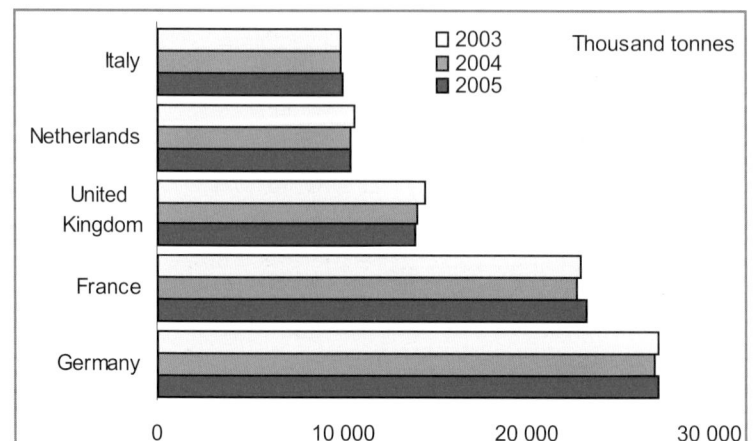

8 In 2005, the United Kingdom ranked third in the quantity of cows' milk collected behind Germany and France having produced about 11 per cent of the total for the EU25.

Pigmeat

9 Chart 16.4 shows the proportions of pigmeat produced in the EU25 countries in 2003, 2004 and 2006. This is the total carcase weight of pigs slaughtered in slaughterhouses and on the farm whose meat is declared fit for human consumption.

10 In 2005, the United Kingdom ranked ninth in the quantity of pigmeat produced with about 3.3 per cent of the total for the EU25.

Beef and veal

11 Chart 16.5 shows the proportions of beef and veal produced in the EU25 countries in 2003, 2004 and 2005. This is the carcase weight of bovine animals (calves, bullocks, bulls, heifers and cows) slaughtered in slaughterhouses and on the farm whose meat is declared fit for human consumption.

12 In 2005, the United Kingdom ranked fourth in the quantity of beef and veal produced behind France, Germany and Italy, having produced about 9.7 per cent of the total for EU25.

Sheep and goat meat

13 Chart 16.6 shows the proportions of sheep and goat meat produced in the EU25 countries in 2003, 2004 and 2005. This is the carcase weight of sheep, including lambs, and goats slaughtered in slaughterhouses or elsewhere whose meat is declared fit for human consumption.

14 In 2005, the United Kingdom was the largest producer of sheep and goat meat in the European Union having produced about 31 per cent of the total for EU25.

Chart 16.4 Production of pigmeat

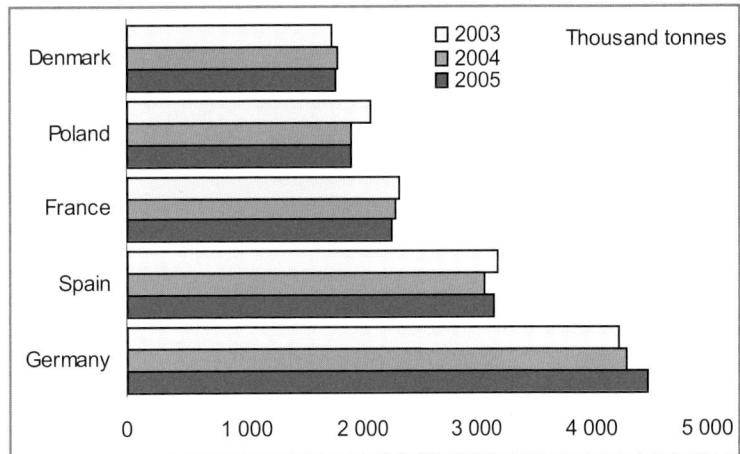

Chart 16.5 Production of beef and veal

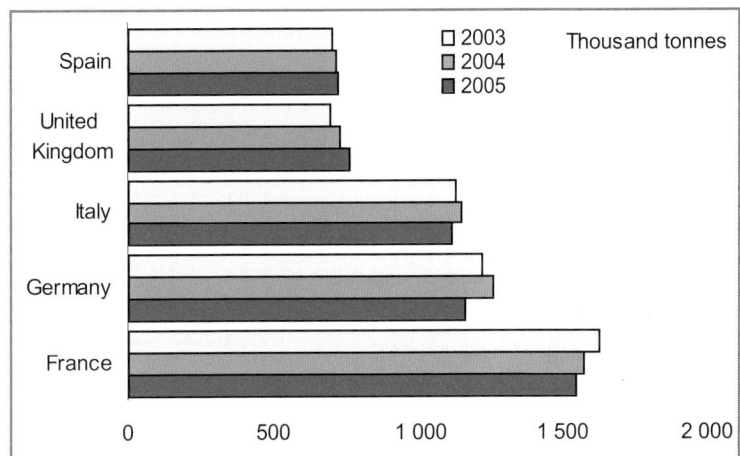

Chart 16.6 Production of sheep and goat meat

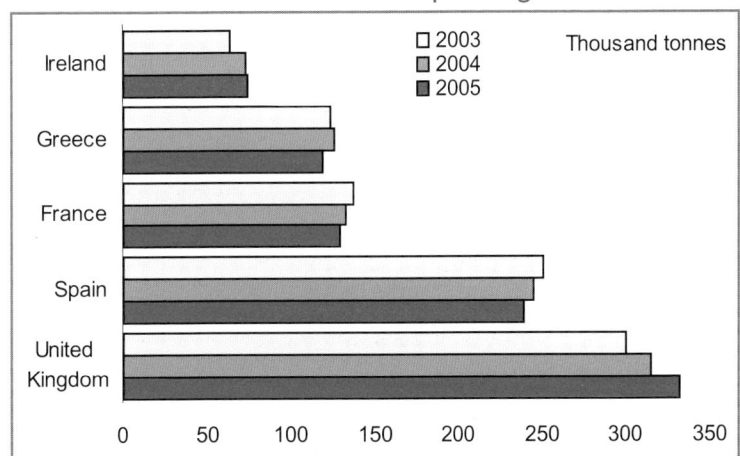

Price indices

Crop products.

15 The indices in Chart 16.7 shows the trends in the nominal producer prices of crop products as a whole. The sub-indices were weighted by the values of sales in 2000. An index showing the trend in the euro/sterling exchange rate is also shown.

16 Crop prices in the United Kingdom rose by 8.4 per cent between 2000 and 2005 while those in the EU15 rose by 6.4 per cent. Producer prices in the United Kingdom are influenced by the euro/sterling exchange rate.

Animals and animal products.

17 The indices in Chart 16.8 shows the trends in the nominal producer prices of animal and animal products as a whole and in the euro/sterling exchange rate.

18 Animal and animal products prices in the United Kingdom rose by 10 per cent between 2000 and 2005 while those in the EU15 have risen by 0.9 per cent. Producer prices in the United Kingdom are heavily influenced by the euro/sterling exchange rate.

Total means of agricultural production.

19 The indices in Chart 16.9 shows the trends in nominal purchase prices of the means of agricultural production as a whole and in the euro/sterling exchange rate.

20 Purchase prices of the means of agricultural production in the United Kingdom have risen by 13 per cent between 2000 and 2005 while those in the EU15 have risen by 8.6 per cent. Purchase prices of the means of agricultural production in the United Kingdom are less heavily influenced by the euro/sterling exchange rate.

Chart 16.7 Producer Price Indices: Crop products

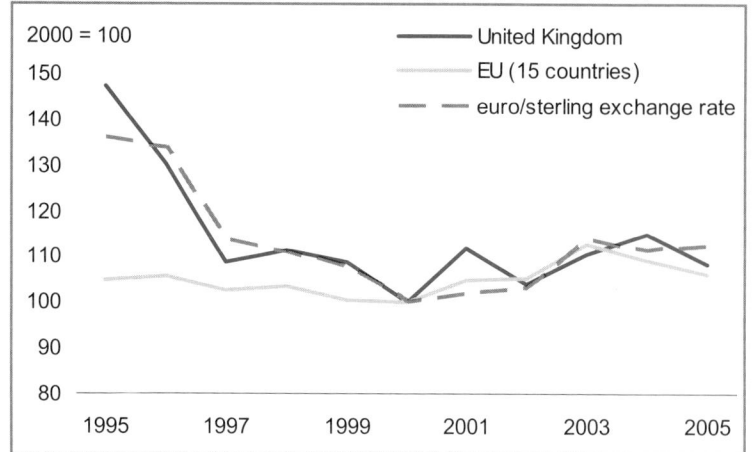

Chart 16.8 Producer Price Indices: Animals and animal products

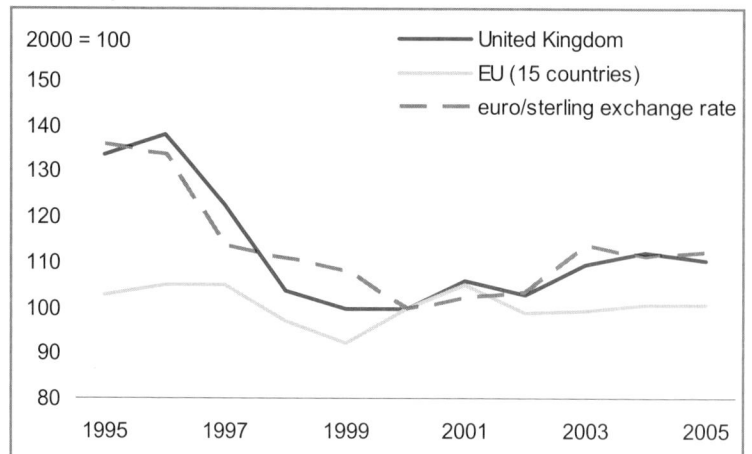

Chart 16.9 Purchase Price Indices: Total means of agricultural production

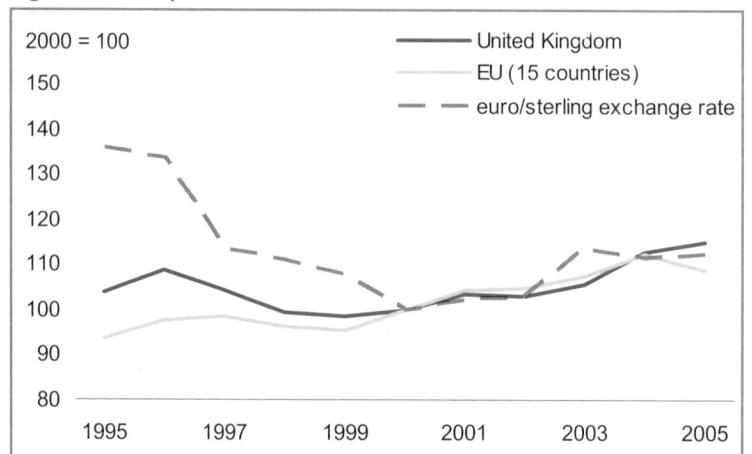